stitch | craft
create
business

THE CRAFT SELLER'S COMPANION

stitch | craft
create
business

THE CRAFT SELLER'S COMPANION

THE CRAFTY ENTREPRENEUR'S ESSENTIAL DIRECTORY
SUPPLIERS, RESOURCES AND ADVICE

D&C
David and Charles

www.stitchcraftcreate.co.uk/business

CONTENTS

INTRODUCTION

The Craft Seller's Companion is an essential reference for craft entrepreneurs – from those who make a full-time living from their craft, to those selling a small number of makes on marketplace websites but dreaming of the crafting 'big time'. This directory of resources is arranged into ten sections – each with helpful listings and contacts for that area, and an inspiring interview from a craft businessperson with tips and suggestions on how to succeed.

Small Business Essentials – in this section you will find listings for small business advice services and contact details for HMRC that will help you to set up your business and start your venture on the right foot. A motivating interview with top cake businesswoman Lindy Smith gives advice on things to consider when starting and growing your business from home.

Craft Business Resources – this section gives listings for specific craft organizations that can give you advice tailored to your craft niche. An interview with Sue Taylor, managing director of Craftworks Cards, reveals how the advice she received from various craft business resources has helped her build the company into a leading UK craft brand.

Suppliers and Wholesalers – listings for a host of craft suppliers and wholesalers feature in this section, allowing you to get a better deal on your craft supplies and ultimately make more profit on your makes! In this chapter's interview, quilting shop owner Alison Stothard gives her tips for success with suppliers.

Online Marketplaces – this section lists all the marketplaces you've heard of and many that you probably haven't – with advice on selling categories, fees, apps that support your selling and community interaction around selling – so you will learn more about marketplaces and find new sales channels to explore. In the interview, knitwear designer Claire Crompton who sells her patterns online, gives her essential tips for marketplace selling.

E-commerce Platforms – if you want to go further than selling on marketplace sites and create your own online boutique, this section gives you a rundown of many of the different software systems available, and the costs, benefits and drawbacks of each program. In the interview, Emma Curtis and Liz Parnell, founders of the craft brand Hamble & Jemima, talk about how to start an online shop of your own.

INTRODUCTION

Print and Publicity Resources – here you'll find listings for traditional print craft media – magazine editors and book publishers – so you can get your work featured and build your profile. In the interview, prolific craft author and writer Dorothy Wood gives valuable tips on getting your work under the noses of editors.

Internet Marketing Resources – listings for social media channels you can use to promote your business online, along with a rundown of the major platforms you can use to host your craft blog. Plus Lauren O'Farrell reveals how she has used internet marketing to build the UK's biggest online craft community, Stitch London.

Craft Fairs and Shows – whether you are looking to find a craft fair to sell your products at, or just want to go along and check out the competition, this section has listings for national and regional shows in both trade and consumer categories. We also hear from talented textile designer Poppy Treffry on building a business through craft fairs, with tips to help your shows run smoothly.

Bricks and Mortar Stores – this section provides a regional rundown of independent shops selling handmade, where you might be able to sell your craft products to offline customers. An exciting interview with Gillian Harris of Gilliangladrag discusses the challenges of wholesaling your products and getting them into retail outlets.

Grants and Funding – getting a helping hand with start up costs, from investing in equipment to getting business cards and flyers made up, to paying a web developer to build you a site, this section gives details of the different funds available to you with information and advice on how to access them. In the interview, Amanda Waring of Mama Jewels reveals how she got a grant to start her unique jewellery business and how you can do the same!

An essential reference that you will turn to time and time again, *The Craft Seller's Companion* is packed with information to help you start, grow and run your craft business all in one place.

For advice on all aspects of running a craft business, visit www.stitchcraftcreate.co.uk/business and follow us on Twitter @SCCBiz or Facebook www.facebook.com/StitchCraftCreateBusiness

Here's to your continued handmade success!

AMe *Editor, Stitch Craft Create Business*

LINDY SMITH

Lindy Smith runs Lindy's Cakes Ltd (www.lindyscakes.co.uk), selling all you need to bake and decorate unique cakes and cookies. She has written 15 books about cakes and cake decoration and conducts frequent workshops around the world on all aspects of sugarcraft. For the last ten years she has exhibited at the Cake International Show at the NEC in Birmingham and other sugarcraft exhibitions and has won many prestigious awards for her work.

Back in 1991, I was inspired by my own wedding cake to take evening classes in cake decorating. I was hooked right from my very first lesson. I have tried many crafts over the years but sugarcraft is the one that I love the most: it combines my love of baking, art, design and colour – what could be more perfect? Originally I experimented in my own kitchen, using techniques I had picked up along the way. Once I had children I made and decorated their birthday cakes; then a friend asked me if I could teach her; a friend of hers asked me to make something for her… after that, it took off by word of mouth.

> ## Sugarcraft combines my love of baking, art, design and colour – what could be more perfect?

SOLE TRADER VERSUS LIMITED COMPANY

Once I started earning enough, I set myself up as a sole trader. That means I was registered with HMRC, as it now is, as self-employed; I was officially a business, but the business was owned and run by one person – me. When you are a sole trader, there is no legal distinction between you and the business: you own all its assets, acquire all its benefits and take all its risks. As your business grows, it makes sense to become a limited company – the 'limited' means you have limited liability for the company's debts, so you personally don't go bankrupt and lose your house if things go horribly wrong. I've always had an accountant to deal with my business affairs and I became a limited company when he advised me to.

As a limited company you pay corporation tax rather than income tax; when I started this was an advantage, as corporation tax was set at a lower rate than income tax, but that isn't true any more. You also have to have a separate bank account and make sure that you keep all your business dealings separate from personal expenses. I actually think that this simplifies things, as you know where you are with the business. Today I employ a book-keeper as well as my accountant and

VALUE ADDED TAX

The other thing you have to consider when your business expands is VAT. In the UK at the moment, if your turnover is more than £77,000 you are legally obliged to be VAT-registered, which means you charge VAT on your products and claim any VAT that you pay out on your purchases back from the government.

Smaller business may choose to register for VAT even though their turnover is below the threshold: it has the advantage that if you sell zero-rated products such as books and some foods (including cakes), you can still claim back the VAT you spend when you buy, say, cake tins or piping bags. Again, it adds to the book-keeping, but that's an unavoidable part of being in business.

it's in the kitchen, the attic or the spare bedroom. But there comes a time when you simply have to have more space. It's a matter of fine judgement when you take on larger premises, because you almost always have to do it before you can really afford it. Running any business is difficult to start with – you are constantly juggling costs and cash flow, and taking on an office or a workshop when you are used to working at home vastly increases your overheads. It's one of the inevitable growing pains. My advice is that you have to have confidence in yourself and what you are doing, but you also have to be sure you can pay the rent and rates. So do take a risk, but not too much of a risk!

use specialist accounting software. I obviously have to pay for these services, but it's worth every penny as far as I'm concerned: it gives me more time to concentrate on the creative side, which I love.

MOVING OUT OF THE ATTIC

Lots of people start their business working from home, as I did, whether

Be warned, though: most small businesses fail because they run out of money. It really helps to have a sound business plan: people like Business Link, local business advisers and your bank can help with this. You need to have a good, strong, well-thought-out idea before you make any

It's a matter of fine judgement when you take on larger premises, because you almost always have to do it before you can really afford it.

approaches – you can't just say, 'I love decorating cakes and I want to do it for a living.' Research what the different organizations and companies offer and find one that suits you and your budget: some may be free for small or start-up businesses. They will help you develop your idea – and that includes an understanding of managing cash flow.

When I began to expand, the first person I employed was my sister-in-law, who came in once a week to help with the book-keeping and admin. After that I took on friends, or friends of friends – I asked around and found people by word of mouth, or advertised locally. With a small business it's important to find the right 'fit'. You have to have people you get on with and who understand what you are trying to do: people who share your enthusiasm and your business ethos, if you like.

LINDY'S CAKES TODAY

Now I employ two people full-time and nine permanent part-timers, though I'm in the process of recruiting another. When I do workshops I have two more helpers and there are four students who come in during the holidays. The eleven permanent people break down into five dealing with mail order; one who focuses on workshops; three doing stock management; one dealing with the media; and one keeping the books and providing financial support. Because

> With a small business it's important to find the right 'fit'. You have to have people you get on with and who understand what you are trying to do.

our business is so multi-faceted, with sales, workshops, exhibitions and my other teaching and writing commitments, there's no such thing as a typical day for me.

It's my job to oversee everything and I have to make time to do that. Somehow I manage to maintain a balance between the creative side and being bogged down in spreadsheets. I make lots of lists – I love lists! In addition to all my day-to-day tasks, I have to think about the future and where the business is going. I'm almost always working on a book and designing new products for our online shop; I also contribute articles (and new designs for cakes) to a lot of magazines both in print and online, so I'm constantly coming up with new ideas. I run at least one workshop a month, sometimes as many as one a week, and that involves preparation. And of course social media, such as Facebook, Twitter and Pinterest, are very important to us

– they are a fabulous way for us to keep in touch with our customers and to get feedback on what they want from us. What with that and the various exhibitions, you could say it was a much more than full-time job – it's a way of life

IT ISN'T all sugar

I am passionate about sugarcraft and spend as much time as I can inspiring other people with my enthusiasm. I love having new ideas and passing them on. But running a business is hard work. If you aren't prepared to put in the hours – lots and lots of hours – and are expecting to get rich overnight, you are going to be sadly disappointed! Particularly if you are giving up regular employment in order to spend more time on what used to be your hobby, you have to remember that you are no longer going to be paid if you aren't working. No more paid holidays. No paid sick leave. It can be hard, too, to

Somehow I manage to maintain a balance between the creative side and being bogged down in spreadsheets.

lose the status of being employed, not to have an easy answer to the question, 'And what do you do?' You have not only to be utterly committed to what you are doing, you have to have the drive to prove yourself or you'll be lost.

> It can be hard, too, to lose the status of being employed, not to have an easy answer to the question, 'And what do you do?'.

MY TOP TIP

Perhaps the most important thing I would say to anyone starting out in business is 'Learn to say no.' You'll come across a lot of people who want something for nothing, and who are keen to promote their own business rather than yours. Do everything you can to learn about people and recognize whom you can trust.

On a practical level, buy some good business books and read them. You don't need qualifications but you do need knowledge. Go to seminars and training workshops and network at every opportunity. And finally, research things before you throw yourself into them. It's a lot easier to get out of trouble if you haven't gone in too deep!

SMALL BUSINESS ESSENTIALS

BIZ HELP 24

About: A business and finance website featuring articles for new and established small businesses.

Services: Featuring over 1,200 articles on a variety of subjects for small businesses, such as invoicing, marketing, advertising and paperwork. Register to receive free news updates, newsletters and helpful tips.

Address: 1 Westpoint Court, Great Park Road, Almondsbury, Bristol BS32 4PS

Email: Contact submission form available on website.

Website: www.bizhelp24.com

BPLANS.CO.UK

About: Free business plan advice and templates.

Services: Featuring in excess of 500 sample business plan templates, including a simple step-by-step writing guide. Make use of the business calculators and make those cash-flow forecasts easier to manage. The website also provides useful tips on starting a business, finance and legal issues.

Tel: 08453 519924

Email: Contact submission form available on website.

Website: www.bplans.co.uk

BUSINESS LINK

About: A Government-run website providing business advice and key resources for all enterprises.

Services: Business Link provides businesses with all the essential information required to begin your own venture, including a fantastic archive of grants and funding available throughout the UK.

Tel: 08456 009006

Email: Contact submission form available on website.

Website: www.businesslink.gov.uk

BUSINESS MATTERS MAGAZINE

About: A leading small and medium enterprise (SME) magazine, established in 1987. They boast 50,000 current annual subscribers.

Services: The magazine provides in-depth advice, business news, interviews with leading entrepreneurs and various other essential business tips and tricks.

Address: Capital Business Media, Ensign House, Admirals Way, London E14 9XQ

Tel: 020 7148 3861

Email: online@cbmeg.co.uk

Website: www.bmmagazine.co.uk

BUSINESS OPPORTUNITIES AND IDEAS

About: A business ideas and inspiration blog.

Services: This blog has many small and homemade business ideas. It provides financial advice, key information about how to start your business, and book reviews. Register to receive free updates and newsletters.

Email: Contact submission form available on website.

Website: www. businessopportunitiesandideas.com

BUSINESS ZONE

About: News and information for business owners.

Services: Business Zone contains news and information regarding finances, marketing, sales, PR and more. They also have a competition for small businesses called 'The Pitch', in which the winner can win £50,000.

Address: Sift Media, 6th Floor Bridge House, 48–52 Baldwin Street, Bristol BS1 1QB

Tel: 01179 158638

Email: dan.martin@siftmedia.co.uk

Website: www.businesszone.co.uk

BUSINESS WINGS

About: Information for new and established small businesses.

Services: This website provides advice for start-up businesses, including finance, administration, business plans and start-up guides. Also features up-to-date news, articles and podcasts.

Address: Dynamis Limited, Dynamis House, Sycamore Street, London EC1Y 0SW

Email: Contact submission form available on website.

Website: www.businesswings.co.uk

ENTERPRISE FIRST

About: An advice website for new businesses and entrepreneurs.

Services: Featuring free advice for start-up businesses on many key issues, such as finance, tax, law and planning. Available to download are templates for business plans, cash-flow forecasts and profit and loss (P&L) forecasts.

Address: 11 Wellington Street, Aldershot, Hampshire GU11 1DX
Tel: 01252 319272
Email: info@enterprisefirst.co.uk
Website: www.enterprisefirst.co.uk

ENTERPRISE NATION

About: Provides homemade businesses with access to a huge variety of resources.
Services: There are a number of free blogs and guides regarding starting up your own business, web design, marketing and finance.
Address: Redbrick House, 9 Town Walls, Shrewsbury, Shropshire SY1 1TW
Tel: 01743 272555
Email: info@enterprisenation.com
Website: www.enterprisenation.com

FEDERATION OF SMALL BUSINESSES

About: A campaign group established in 1974 to protect small businesses and the self-employed.
Services: Providing a range of legal services and advice, tax protection and legal documents; specifically in relation to employment and business law. There is an initial joining fee which varies depending on your number of employees.
Address: Sir Frank Whittle Way, Blackpool Business Park, Blackpool, Lancashire FY4 2FE
Tel: 08082 020888
Email: customerservices@fsb.org.uk
Website: www.fsb.org.uk

FORUM OF PRIVATE BUSINESS

About: A paid-for advice and support service for business owners. A free introductory membership is available and intermediate membership starts from £175.
Services: Services provided include PR, finance and legal advice, as well as tailor-made, online legal documents and language services.
Address: Ruskin Chambers, Drury Lane, Knutsford, Cheshire WA16 6HA
Tel: 08451 301722
Email: info@fpb.org
Website: www.fpb.org

FREE BUSINESS FORUMS

About: This is a forum specifically for small and medium enterprise (SME) owners to take part in discussions.
Services: There are several advice forums on the subjects of marketing, accounting, employment issues, and advice on running or setting up SMEs.
Email: Contact submission form available on website.
Website: www.freebusinessforums.co.uk

FRESH THINKING BUSINESS

About: A free advice website and resource centre for all types of businesses.
Services: Blogs, book reviews and articles written by industry experts to help your business expand. The website includes a section on start-up businesses, which provides relevant information for setting up a business.
Address: 31–35 Kirby Street, London EC1N 8TE
Tel: 08455 000328

Email: info@freshbusinessthinking.com
Website: www.freshbusinessthinking.com

HMRC (HER MAJESTY'S REVENUE AND CUSTOMS)

About: A broad range of information for those who either run their own business, or are looking to start up a business.
Services: HMRC provides advice on the legalities of running a business, such as self assessment and VAT. All of the necessary official forms can be found on the website.
Address: PO BOX 1970, Liverpool L75 1WX
Tel: 08450 109000
Website: www.hmrc.gov.uk

IS 4 PROFIT

About: This website contains advice for new and established small businesses.
Services: Featuring articles, guides, plans and fact sheets on green business practices, employment and business law; Is 4 Profit also provides relevant news for small businesses.
Address: 10 Shieling House, Invincible Road, Farnborough, Hampshire GU14 7QU
Tel: 01252 376650
Email: info@is4profit.com
Website: www.is4profit.com

MY BUSINESS

About: This is a free resource website purely for small businesses, used by over 10,000 business owners.
Services: My Business contains finance, cash-flow, employment and technology guides. Sign up to a free e-newsletter to be kept informed of all

the latest business news. Also included are informative articles written by Managing Directors, solicitors and specialists.
Address: Westminster House, Kew Road, Richmond, Surrey TW9 2ND
Tel: 020 8334 1600
Email: editor@crimsonpublishing.co.uk
Website: www.mybusiness.co.uk

NEWbUSINESS.CO.UK

About: This website provides advice for small and medium sized businesses.
Services: A source of expert advice on a range of different areas such as, banking, legalities, starting up a business, accountancy, finance and more. All the latest business news is available on the website.
Tel: 020 3086 8400
Email: chris.bradshaw@newbusiness.co.uk
Website: www.newbusiness.co.uk

REAL BUSINESS

About: Targeted at small and medium sized enterprises (SMEs) through a variety of media: magazine, online, newsletter, events and social networking sites.
Services: Real Business provides advice and articles on topics such as HR, management, finance, sales and marketing and technology, as well as the latest business news.
Address: Unit G4 Harbour Yard, Chelsea Harbour, London SW10 0XD
Tel: 020 7045 7591
Email: david.tall@caspianmedia.com
Website: www.realbusiness.co.uk

Sage

About: A software advice service for businesses.
Services: Used by over 800,000 businesses in the UK, Sage supplies all varieties of business with advice, such as suggesting the best payment and accounts software for particular companies.
Address: North Park, Newcastle-upon-Tyne NE13 9AA
Tel: 0800 44 77 77
Email: Contact submission form available on website.
Website: www.sage.co.uk

SHELL LIVEWIRE

About: A guidance website for start-up businesses and entrepreneurs aged 16–30.
Services: Although this is primarily targeted at individuals aged 16–30, there is an abundance of useful advice for new businesses. This website includes a guide for writing a business plan, choosing a legal structure, marketing and networking. Shell LiveWIRE also provides video tutorials and a social network community;

"As your business grows, it makes sense to become a limited company so you personally don't go bankrupt and lose your house if things go horribly wrong."
Lindy Smith

---

allowing entrepreneurs to build a profile and network with others.
Address: Design Works, William Street, Felling, Gateshead NE10 0JP
Tel: 01914 236229
Email: enquiries@shell-livewire.org
Website: www.shell-livewire.org

SIFT MEDIA LTD

About: A leading B2B publisher, focusing on online communities.
Services: Sift Media provides branded content to a wide range of sectors including, HR, sales and marketing and finance, as well as small, start-up businesses.
Address: Sift Media, 6th Floor Bridge House, 48–52 Baldwin Street, Bristol BS1 1QB
Tel: 01179 153344
Email: info@siftmedia.co.uk
Website: www.siftmedia.co.uk

SMALL BUSINESS ADVICE

About: A free and confidential advice website, for start-up and existing small businesses.
Services: This website contains a simple and easy-to-use guide for new businesses, including essential start-up information. It discusses planning, contracts, e-commerce and legal requirements. Available to download are business models and templates.
Website: www.smallbusinessadvice.org.uk

SMALLbUSINESS.CO.UK

About: An advice website for owners of small businesses; this is for both well-established businesses and those that are just starting out.

Services: This website provides blogs, news, tips and resources useful to small businesses; legal advice, finance, marketing and more.

Address: Vitesse Media Plc, Octavia House, 50 Banner Street, London EC1Y 8ST

Tel: 020 7250 7024

Website: www.smallbusiness.co.uk

SMARTA

About: An advice service dedicated to small businesses; this caters for everyone from students with a potential idea, to pre-existing businesses.

Services: Smarta can provide advice on a wide range of business topics in the form of written guides, video tutorials, webinars, diaries, blogs, features and much more.

Address: The Leathermarket 4.1.1, 11–13 Weston Street, London SE1 3ER

Email: feedback@smarta.com

Website: www.smarta.com

STARTUP BRITAIN

About: A national campaign, launched in 2011 by the Prime Minister and supported by HM Government. StartUp Britain aims to encourage young entrepreneurs and assist new and growing businesses.

Services: This organization actively runs and launches a huge number of campaigns all over Britain with the intention to boost the national economy. Recent projects include StartUp Loans, in which any entrepreneur between the ages 18–24 can receive a loan of up to £2500 to invest in starting their own business.

Email: info@startupbritain.org

Website: www.startupbritain.co

START UP DONUT

About: An organization focused on offering free advice to small and medium-sized businesses. There are five different websites: law, marketing, IT, tax and start-up.

Services: The website provides a variety of articles, blogs, briefings and checklists; even advice on business ideas and names.

Address: BHP Information Solutions, 6 Grove Road, Redland, Bristol BS6 6UJ

Tel: 01179 042224

Email: info@startupdonut.co.uk

Website: www.startupdonut.co.uk

START UP TV

About: A unique service exclusively for small and start-up businesses, this website integrates the Internet with video advertising.

Services: This website allows businesses to register for free and upload videos promoting their products. For £495, Start Up TV can offer individuals a branded channel on the website for six months. This website also offers advice to businesses concerning banking and financial issues.

Tel: 02084 399440

Email: simon@the-eba.com

Website: www.startuptv.co.uk

START UPS

About: A helpful website providing advice for starting up your own business.

Services: There is a great deal of information available on this website, consisting of how to set up your own businesses, including a guide specifically for homemade businesses.

They cover everything from designing and creating a logo, finding office premises and meeting the legal requirements.

Address: Westminster House, Kew Road, Richmond, Surrey TW9 2ND

Tel: 020 8334 1600

Email: editor@crimsonpublishing.co.uk

Website: www.startups.co.uk

START YOUR OWN BUSINESS

About: A free advice website for helping new, small, local businesses get off the ground.

Services: Links to regional sites can be found on the homepage. The separate regional pages contain useful information and advice for start-up businesses within that region.

Email: andy@startyobusiness.com

Website: www.syob.co.uk

THE WHOLESALE FORUMS

About: This website is mainly for wholesalers, however it does feature advice forums for small businesses.

Services: A members-only community based website, offering guides and advice on how to start up a business. Providing essential information about the roles of social media, marketing and e-commerce within new businesses.

Address: 1100 Great West Road, Brentford, Middlesex TW8 0GP

Tel: 020 3393 4638

Email: support@thewholesaleforums.co.uk

Website: www.thewholesaleforums.co.uk

SUE TAYLOR

Sue Taylor is the managing director of Craftwork Cards (www.craftworkcards.co.uk), a small Leeds-based manufacturing company making cards and craft kits for the retail trade. Starting in her attic in 1998, she has built the company up into a leading UK craft brand.

I have a background in graphic design and I used to run a print and design company. It folded in the 1990s, so I started working freelance and as a result I had the opportunity to produce handmade cards, which I sold to local businesses. I got more and more orders, but making a lot of finished cards was very time-consuming. I obviously knew how to source all the materials that are used in card-making, in particular I knew a lot of paper suppliers, so I decided to do that as a business: rather than spend all that time making cards myself, I would sell the materials so that other people could make them.

Starting out

At the time – it was 1998 – the only cards that were widely available were white and ivory. But I knew that there were lots of different colours and textures out there that could be used as the basis for a card. The idea of selling materials for card-making was a bit niche and a bit unusual back then, and that's what I explored.

All this was before all the online shops and forums there are now. I started out with a black and white, photocopied catalogue. It was only about six pages, selling what we call 'cut and creased' cards, but it had details of lots of different colours and textures of card. I advertised it in the back of Crafts Beautiful magazine and I got about 50 responses in five days. That was the start of my customer base.

> I started out with a black and white, photocopied catalogue. It was only about six pages, but it had details of lots of different colours and textures of card.

Over the next three or four years, the business steadily expanded and I took on some staff. One of the ways we built up business was to take a stand at consumer exhibitions around the country, from Scotland to the south coast. We did about 26 in a year. This was just at the time the internet was becoming more and more important, so we gathered email addresses from people we met at these shows, and before we knew it we had a database.

Today there are 17 of us here in Leeds: myself and a Business Development Manager, plus designers, admin staff, manufacturing staff and the packing team. Everything we make is manufactured on the premises. We can do anything to a piece of card. We buy it in big sheets – about the size of a dining-room table – and then we cut it, crease it, foil it, emboss it, print on it and sell it!

> We can do anything to a piece of card. We buy it in big sheets and then we cut it, crease it, foil it, emboss it, print on it and sell it!

Business Resources

There's a surprising amount of help out there for people starting up in business. One of the first organizations I joined was the Federation of Small Businesses, which provides legal and financial advice and other support. They put me on to Business Link, the government-funded advice service, who had funding available for websites. They gave me the opportunity to meet an expert in web design and development, so I was able to set up a professional-looking website from an early stage.

I haven't dealt with the Craft Council, because they are more geared towards people who are producing finished crafts, rather than those like us who are on the manufacturing side, but we have had help from CHA UK – the Craft and Hobby Association. This is primarily an American organization with a recent offshoot in the UK. They can advise on all sorts of craft-related business questions, such as finding suppliers, and the regulations surrounding exports; they can arrange preferential credit-card rates and business insurance; and they have a team of legal experts. They provide similar services to the Federation of Small Businesses, but more focused on craft.

Craft Business magazine is also very useful: it's a way of keeping in touch with what the competition's doing. It reviews the trade shows and discusses new products that have appeared there, and it's very good on up-and-coming trends.

As for networking, I use LinkedIn a lot, and I'm a member of the Get Mentoring scheme: it isn't specifically craft-related – any entrepreneur can go onto the website and be matched up with someone who can help them or who needs their help.

EXPORTING AND EXPANDING

We've started exporting in the last twelve months and we've had a lot of help from UK Trade and Investment, a fairly new government department. We enrolled on their one-year 'Passport to Export' programme and as a result one of my staff is about to go to Chicago for a week's course on networking and building your business in the US. The Americans hold the biggest trade show in the world for our industry and we've exhibited there for the last three years. We now have two American distributors, but we're hoping that the UKTI programme will help us move forward.

It's a slow process – we thought it might take off more quickly than it has – but we're gradually getting there.

We're also aiming to expand into Europe. We do a lot of business with the TV shopping channel QVC and we're looking to build up a relationship with their German end. QVC are very open to taking on new businesses, so I'd advise anyone who was interested simply to approach their buying team. They have rigorous quality control, but if they thought your product was saleable and you could meet their quality and price specifications, they would set up a vendor contract with you. They have their own presenting team and at first they present your products alongside lots of others. Then it gradually builds up. We've been with them for three years now and it took two years to get our own slots, but we now have one-hour programmes entirely devoted

We now have two American distributors, but we're hoping that the UKTI programme will help us move forward. It's a slow process but we're gradually getting there.

We've been with [QVC] for three years now and it took two years to get our own slots, but we now have one-hour programmes entirely devoted to our products.

to our products. It's a wonderful form of advertising.

Through our website we sell to individuals and to retailers: we have a trade section so that craft shops can buy materials from us. We've no plans to open a shop of our own. There are just too many overheads and not enough footfall, so we'll just have to keep expanding in other ways.

Be Creative

The first thing I would say to anyone starting out in the craft business is, 'Be as innovative as possible.' When I started, cards were a niche market, so the profit margin was high, but now it's very competitive. Doing something different is vital.

I've learnt the hard way not to give too many of my ideas away. Keep your blueprint to yourself. It's difficult, and expensive, to protect your intellectual property. So if

someone does copy your designs (and I've had that happen), you just have to move on to the next thing. Don't rely too heavily on one product – not just because of the risk of copying, but because the craft industry is very trend-led and everything has a short shelf life. You have to keep reinventing yourself.

The Practical Side

Probably even more important that innovation is quality. I think, whatever you're making, there are two facets to

WHERE DO THE IDEAS COME FROM?

Coming up with new ideas means more than just looking at the trends in crafts. We are looking around us all the time, at fashion, at interior design, at colourways that are used in other fields. We also take on board what our customers are saying and what they are asking for. We run competitions on the website to get customers involved, asking them to suggest their favourite colour combinations or to come up with a new-shaped card – anything to get the creative juices flowing. Then we bounce ideas off each other.

the craft market. People will either pay for quality, or they want something really cheap. So make sure that your quality is 100 per cent. And of course alongside that you have to offer a good service.

It's also vital to know your product inside out. Know your competition. Have a good business plan and stick to it. Get your finances in place, don't go silly with your spending and always make sure you can pay your bills.

There's always going to be a demand for cards. There are lots of websites now where you can build your own and get someone to send it out for you, but I think there will always be people wanting to make cards as a hobby. They might want to use different styles or different materials, but they are always going to need the basic card stock. It's still a growing market.

DON'T be TOO PROUD TO ask FOR HELP

My last piece of advice is 'Be true to yourself.' Don't let other people influence your decisions too much. If you're starting a business up and you've got a great idea, go for it.

But don't think you can do everything yourself. Look for all the help you can get, go to all the seminars and the free courses that are out there. If you can pick up just one little bit of information from each one, it can pay dividends. Spend time doing these things. You might think that you aren't going to learn anything and that you know it all, but you never know it all. There's always something to learn.

CRAFT BUSINESS RESOURCES

ARTISTS IN BUSINESS

About: A blog for artists and crafters who are developing a business or have recently established a new business.

Services: A support network for creative business people, Artists in Business offers free workshops and seminars on key business skills. Free downloadable advice about starting your own business and working from home is also available. The blog offers business tips and advice on many issues, such as promoting your work, advertising, networking and more.

Email: jo.artsbiz@gmail.com

Website: artistsinbusiness.blogspot. co.uk

BEST BRITISH HANDMADE

About: This is the website for the 'Handmade in Britain' craft fair.

Services: The fair is designed for new craft businesses that have been in operation for less than a year. Exhibition stalls include textiles, jewellery, leather, metalwork and ceramics. The organizers also offer business support, such as a two-day course to prepare for the crafts fair. Upon joining the fair, crafters can receive a discount on professional photography, and a special rate on any branding. Application for the craft fair does require an initial fee of £20, a stall will then cost between approximately £550–£830, as well as an additional £50 for catalogues, invites and carrier bags.

Address: 10 Cheshire Street, London E2 6EH

Tel: 020 7729 5704

Email: info@handmadeinbritain.co.uk

Website: www.handmadeinbritain. co.uk

CHA-UK

About: A non-profit craft trade association designed to help support and connect creative businesses.

Services: CHA-UK caters to the needs of UK-based craft industry retailers, buyers and suppliers by hosting networking events at trade shows and offering business guidance and support, as well as free online videos and webinars.

Address: Federation House, 10 Vyse Street, Birmingham, B18 6LT

Tel: 01206 364977

Email: craig@cha-uk.co.uk

Website: www.cha-uk.co.uk

CRAFT BLOG, UK

About: All of the best UK craft blogs on one website.

Services: Blogs are useful both for promoting your own business and for learning from others' experiences. This website contains over 500 blogs from the best UK craft bloggers on a variety of subjects, such as papercraft, knitting, sewing, jewellery making and more. Craft Blog UK contains advice about writing a blog, such as how to get started, ideas for topics and how to use the blog to your advantage to increase revenue.

Email: craftbloguk@ymail.com

Website: www.ukcraftblog.com

CRAFT BUSINESS HOME

About: Free advice for anyone starting a homemade craft business.

Services: This website provides guidance for anyone considering starting a craft business; it provides advice about target markets, online marketplaces and how to write a concise business plan. A useful tool is the step-by-step guide on writing a blog. There are also links to a variety of online marketplaces and suppliers.

Website: www.craftbusinesshome. com

CRAFT BUSINESS MAGAZINE

About: A craft magazine specifically for traders.

Services: *Craft Business* Magazine supplies details about current craft trends and provides inspiration for crafters. The magazine features interviews with craft entrepreneurs and up-to-date craft news.

Address: 25 Phoenix Court, 10 Hawkins Road, Colchester, Essex CO2 8JY

Tel: 01206 505983

Email: emma.cant@aceville.co.uk

Website: www.craftbusiness. com/site

CRAFT FOCUS MAGAZINE

About: A craft magazine, free to all UK traders.

Services: This website features details on events and fairs, product reviews and all the latest craft news, as well as providing an extensive directory of trade suppliers.

Address: Broseley House, Newlands Drive, Witham, Essex CM8 2UL
Tel: 01376 535609
Email: info@craftfocus.com
Website: www.craftfocus.com

CRAFT INSURANCE

About: Business insurance designed specifically for crafts people, craft groups and crafts clubs in the UK.
Services: The Craftsman scheme has been available since 1986 and offers specialist insurance to craft businesses and individuals, underwritten by Aviva.
Address: PO Box 5063, Verwood, BH31 6WB
Email: Contact submission form available on website.
Website: www.craftinsurance.co.uk

CRAFTS FORUM

About: A forum for anyone that has an interest in craft.
Services: Crafters can use this forum to share their ideas and projects with like-minded entrepreneurs. Forums on this website are dedicated to specific crafts, such as woodcraft, gift cards, floristry, knitting, patchwork and more.
Email: Contact submission form available on website.
Website: www.craftsforum.co.uk

CRAFTSELLER MAGAZINE

About: A magazine full of craft ideas.
Services: Consists of projects and ideas to inspire, as well as step-by-step guides on new crafting techniques. Accompanying video tutorials can also be found on the website.
Email: craft@craft-seller.com
Website: www.craft-seller.com

CREATIVE CHOICES

About: Part of Creative & Cultural Skills' careers advice websites, Creative Choices is dedicated to helping you develop your career in the creative and cultural industries.
Services: Provides information, advice and resources to help you build skills, find new opportunities, or get a better idea about a particular creative career path. The resources are aimed at enabling creative sector employers and employees, freelancers and sole traders to access the best tools and training to support their growth.
Address: Lafone House, The Leathermarket, Weston Street, London SE1 3HN
Email: info@ccskills.org.uk
Website: www.creative-choices.co.uk

CREATIVE UNIVERSITY

About: An online education programme from market-leading craft publishers F&W Media International.
Services: Provides excellent flexible learning opportunities for craft business and creative professionals, exploring topics that are key to your career growth and success, or that just help you progress in your chosen hobby.
Email: customerservices@creativeuniversity.co.uk
Website: www.creativeuniversity.co.uk

CULTURAL ENTERPRISE OFFICE

About: A business support organization based in Scotland and dedicated entirely to the creative industries.
Services: Cultural Enterprise Office provides business support and advice for creative entrepreneurs through workshops and networking events. This organization also provides free personal advice and training.
Address: Cultural Enterprise Office, 50 Bell Street, Glasgow G11LQ
Tel: 08445 449990
Email: info@culturalenterpriseoffice.co.uk
Website: www.culturalenterpriseoffice.co.uk

HANDMADE HORIZONS

About: A website offering marketing advice, free training and a regular eCourse for craft businesses.
Services: Features an online training course for crafters who are lookng to expand their creative business, with videos, worksheets and live training calls, and also includes a blog with free marketing tips and advice.
Email: hello@handmadehorizons.com
Website: www.handmadehorizons.com

HANDMADE MARKETING

About: A free website providing essential marketing advice.
Services: A section on the Handmade Marketing website dedicated to 'new sellers' is extremely useful, with important information about how to start a business, branding and other key areas. The website also features tips for creating a blog, and has various other resources, allowing visitors to gain invaluable marketing advice and stay informed on the latest business and craft news.
Email: Admin@HandmadeMarketing.org
Website: www.handmademarketing.org

CRAFT BUSINESS RESOURCES

IDEASTAP

About: IdeasTap is an arts charity and social networking site.

Services: IdeasTap supports young, creative individuals who are looking to develop their work into a career. The website is a social networking site, allowing young artists to come together and discuss projects, exhibit work and discover support, advice and opportunities.

Address: IdeasTap Ltd, Woolyard, 54 Bermondsey Street, London SE1 3UD

Tel: 020 7232 5474

Email: info@ideastap.com

Website: www.ideastap.com

MAKE FOR BUSINESS

About: This free website contains valuable resources for anyone who is interested in starting a craft business.

Services: Make For Business has been designed to encourage entrepreneurial crafters to pursue a craft business. This website features a selection of blog posts and the option to subscribe to an RSS feed. They offer a range of advice on starting your own craft business, including accounting, craft fairs, website design, legal issues and licensing. This website is constantly checked and updated, to ensure that all information is relevant.

Email: Contact submission form available on website.

Website: www.makeforbusiness.com

START A CRAFT BUSINESS

About: A free website containing thorough advice concerning the very first steps to starting a business, expansion, PR and much more.

Services: An in-depth and well-researched website that provides information and expert advice regarding every aspect of developing and running a craft business, such as marketing, finance, PR, networking, contracts, legalities and much more.

Address: Daresbury Point, Green Wood Drive, Manor Park, Cheshire WA7 1UP

Email: janem@startacraftbusiness.com

Website: www.startacraftbusiness.co.uk

STITCH CRAFT CREATE BUSINESS

About: The ultimate resource and online community for embarking upon a crafty enterprise. Advice, interviews, news and reviews to help your creative business grow and blossom.

Services: As well as free information given via an informative blog, paid membership includes a Craft Start-Up Kit and online access to this directory, as well as discounts to online training via the Creative University, and discounts off essential craft supplies from a leading craft retailer.

Address: Brunel House, Forde Close, Newton Abbot, Devon TQ12 4PU

Tel: 01626 323300

Email: Contact submission form available on website.

Website: www.stitchcraftcreate.co.uk/business

T-SHIRTS AND SUITS

About: A social networking site for creative entrepreneurs.

Services: T-Shirts and Suits allows the user to advertise events and products, write blogs, join in with discussions in the forum and generally promote their own craft enterprise.

Address: T-Shirts and Suits Ltd, Baltic Creative, 22 Jordan Street, Liverpool L1 0BP

Tel: 01519 061966

Email: office@davidparrish.com

Website: www.creative-enterprise-network.com/page/tshirts-and-suits

THE CRAFTS COUNCIL

About: The Crafts Council are a large, well-established development agency, promoting UK craft, and striving to expand its popularity.

Services: Dedicated to makers, collectors and general enthusiasts of craft, The Crafts Council provides workshops, training, professional development and advice to anybody interested in advancing their skills.

Address: 44a Pentonville Road, Islington, London N1 9BY

Tel: 02078 062500

Email: makerdev@craftscouncil.org.uk

Website: www.craftscouncil.org.uk

THE DESIGN TRUST

About: A members only, online business information and advice service purely for designers and crafters.

Services: The Design Trust aims to help small craft businesses expand. For a fee of £8 per month, crafters can expect unlimited support, advice concerning business plans, expenditure, social media, networking and much more. A useful feature of the website is the 'opportunities' page which consists of advertisements for events with available exhibition space, competitions and other various opportunities.

Address: 12 Reservoir Road, London N14 4BL

Email: info@thedesigntrust.co.uk
Website: www.thedesigntrust.co.uk

THE REFECTORY TABLE

About: The Refectory Table offers various courses for businesses within the creative sector.

Services: All courses are appropriate for new and established businesses and are organized by two entrepreneurs with many years experience in consulting, editing and coaching businesses. Courses include creative business strategy, internet strategy, coaching skills and sales. Courses cost approximately £95 for one day or £160 for two days.

Email: Contact submission form available on website.

Website: www.therefectorytable.com

THE SEWING DIRECTORY

About: A resource for sewing and business-related information.

Services: The Sewing Directory has many useful business articles relating to how to establish a new business, promoting, marketing and website construction. The site also features many interesting sewing related articles, guides and interviews with designers. All advice on this website is free, however becoming a member does provide the opportunity to advertise products on the website.

Address: 41 Robert Street, Cathays, Cardiff CF24 4PD

Tel: 02920 252237

Email: fiona@thesewingdirectory.co.uk

Website: www.thesewingdirectory.co.uk

UK CRAFT FAIRS

About: Aimed exclusively at the UK Craft Community. Members contribute unique, up-to-date content relating to their events, products and or services.

Services: Details upcoming craft fairs, shows, workshops and exhibitions. It provides a directory of craft material suppliers, craft groups and publications, and also lists venues seeking craft event organisers. Members have the opportunity to promote their crafts and attract event organisers.

Email: Contact submission form available on website.

Website: www.ukcraftfairs.com

UK CRAFTS WEBSITES

About: Aims to supply information on the best UK craft websites, news, events and exhibitions.

Services: Online directory listing UK craft businesses (by category), resources, courses, events and exhibitions. You can list details of your events for free, and can also list your business for a fee. Includes a forum and articles section.

Email: Contact submission form available on website.

Website: www.ukcraftwebsites.co.uk

UK HANDMADE

About: UK Handmade is a website and online magazine dedicated to all things handmade, it aims to showcase creativity.

Services: UK Handmade supports designers through their 'Buy Handmade' campaign, which encourages shoppers to purchase handmade products rather than mass-produced, high-street products. This is reinforced through the free magazine, which and informs the reader about the crafter who made it. The website regularly runs showcases: 50–200 products are featured for two week periods, providing an excellent advertising opportunity.

Email: info@ukhandmade.co.uk
Website: www.ukhandmade.co.uk

WALKABOUT CRAFTS

About: A website containing free advice for craft-related businesses.

Services: Walkabout Crafts provides advice on promoting and advertising, insurance, trading standards regulations and web designs. Visitors also have the opportunity to sell products via the website.

Address: 2 South Port, Scottish Borders, Scotland TD7 4AR

Tel: 07733 284443

Email: walkaboutcrafts@tiscali.co.uk

Website: www.walkaboutcrafts.com

ALISON STOTHARD

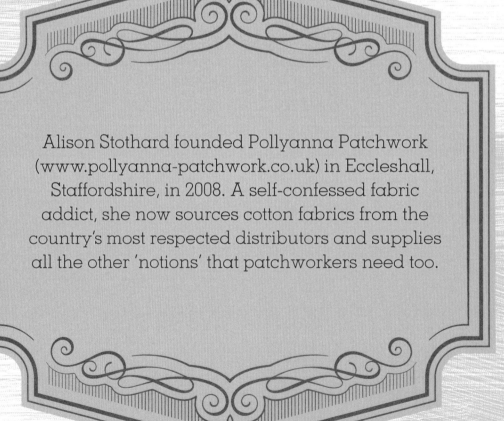

Alison Stothard founded Pollyanna Patchwork (www.pollyanna-patchwork.co.uk) in Eccleshall, Staffordshire, in 2008. A self-confessed fabric addict, she now sources cotton fabrics from the country's most respected distributors and supplies all the other 'notions' that patchworkers need too.

I started my business when my first child was only a few months old. I was a hobby quiltmaker and there was nobody locally selling fabric, so I used to go quite a long way to quilt shows to buy materials. The first time I went to a show after William was born I took him with me and had a terrible time, with people banging into his pushchair and reaching over him. I thought, 'Well, I can't do that any more', went home, had a cry and decided I had to open my own business and sell fabrics myself.

My husband was very supportive. Or at least he humoured me when I came home from a baby yoga class in the village hall and said I'd like to hold a fabric sale there. I got in touch with a distributor, went to visit them and came away with 300 bolts of fabric. I had nowhere to store it – I had to take over the spare bedroom – but I hired the village hall and had my first sale.

> I got in touch with a distributor, went to visit them and came away with 300 bolts of fabric.

ONE THING LED TO ANOTHER

I held three or four fabric sales and people always asked me if I had a shop. Of course I didn't, but I was acquiring and storing more and more products. I set out to rent a self-storage unit – I was expecting my second child by this time and we were going to need that spare room! Then I found that for what it would cost to hire the space I needed, I could have a shop in the High Street. My husband and I had been saving up for a deposit on a house, so with his agreement, I took our life savings and ploughed them into a fabric shop. It meant we carried on renting for a couple more years, but we do have our own home now.

It was quite a mindshift from running a home to running a business: emotionally and mentally it's quite draining. I find it difficult to switch off – I really am living and breathing patchwork. Which is nice: it's wonderful to be able to earn your living from your hobby. But I do much less sewing for myself now. I used to occasionally take on commissions, but I didn't enjoy making things to order. It turned my passion into a job, so I stopped doing it.

I find it difficult to switch off – I really am living and breathing patchwork.

ONLINE PRESENCE

An online presence has been important from the word go. I went to a company that offers a 'hosted cart', and they handled the check-out process for me. All I had to do was put my products up there. It was the easiest and cheapest way to get started. I still have that, but I have my own website too. A domain name, something ending in .co.uk, costs only about £5 for two years and it's a really worthwhile investment. It gives your brand gravitas – makes it look professional.

PROMOTION

For my first fabric sale, I sent 50 letters to local Women's Institutes and got a great response. When I was just quilting for myself I'd been very private about it, hardly ever showing my work to anyone. But now I started to join local quilt groups and once people found out I had a business, they flocked to my sales. I became aware of this whole underworld of quilters that existed in my area. So word of mouth has been really important. I don't do any print advertising – it's all social media, which of course is free.

FINDING STOCK

I deal only with patchwork and quilting, but in addition to fabric I sell thread and all the various 'notions', as we call them, that a quilter might need: scissors, books, patterns, wadding and so on.

I do most of my research online. I tend to look for the manufacturers of fabric that I like and see if they have a local distributor. The best fabrics come from Japan and Korea, but they are imported into the US, where patchwork and quilting are big business, and I buy either from there or from a UK distributor for the American company.

When I started buying fabric, all I had to do was ring up a distributor or send a query through their website, asking to see their products: most companies are happy to send a representative out with armfuls of fabric for you to look at. Some insist on a minimum order; others ask for proof that you are a business rather than a private customer. I've

> I always have in the back of my mind how much I'd be prepared to pay for fabric, but for my business, quality is more important.

sometimes had to send out a photo of my shop to prove that I'm 'real'.

PRICES AND QUANTITIES

I'm less concerned about price than a lot of people: as a quilter myself, I always have in the back of my mind how much I'd be prepared to pay for fabric, but for my business, quality is more important. So is the company's ability to deliver. I'm aware that as a small customer I may not take priority, so I have to be confident that if they do have the fabric, they can ship it to me within a reasonable time. Also, of course, I'm at a disadvantage when it comes to negotiating on price: some companies charge a premium on small quantities, so I may have buy a larger quantity to get the normal, lower price.

But I do find that my customers understand quality and are willing to pay for it. I'm gradually educating them as well! It's all part of the service.

And how do I judge how much to buy? To be perfectly honest, I still haven't figured that one out. I always buy what I like. The shop is a reflection of me. It's my stash – it's just that my stash has overflowed into a retail store.

> I do find that my customers understand quality and are willing to pay for it.

SELLING ONLINE VERSUS IN THE SHOP

There's an interesting difference here. Most people, when they come into the shop, are looking for something to match a fabric they already have. They're not too bothered about the brand as long as the quality and the colour are right. But online, they tend to go for a brand they know and trust.

For example, when I was looking for a range of solids – fabrics in a single colour rather than a pattern – for the shop, I discovered the Kona Cotton Solids range. They're excellent quality, so I decided to take them and now I am one of their biggest stockists: there are over 225 colours available and I usually stock about a hundred at any one time. It wasn't until I started to get lots of orders online that I realised what a following the Kona name already had.

INSIST ON QUALITY

Another important piece of advice is 'Always buy your stock from the physical product.' I was caught out one time when I bought a known brand from a photograph of the fabric, not the fabric itself. When the order arrived, I really wasn't happy with the quality. In hindsight, I should have sent it straight back, but I didn't: I felt obliged to keep it because I had ordered it. It was in my very early days and finding the money to pay for something I didn't want to put on my shelves was difficult. It taught me a lesson. I now have a rule that I never buy fabric, or ribbon, or anything else that has a 'feel' to it, without feeling it myself.

> I now have a rule that I never buy fabric, or ribbon, or anything else that has a 'feel' to it, without feeling it myself.

CUSTOMER SERVICE

With a business like mine, you have to remember that you're not selling a product, you're solving a problem. I email my customers four or five times a week, because I've come to realise that although I have 500 or 600 fabrics to choose from, unless I am fresh in their minds, I won't be the first person they contact when they have a problem. When I am buying stock, I always ask myself, 'What problem is this going to solve for my customers?' You may think that a ruler is just a ruler, for example, but to a customer it's a way of helping them cut out a fabric safely and accurately.

When I email I send hints, tips, news of something that's been happening in the quilting world. That way I establish a

> My focus is on doing what I do as well as I can and doing the very best for my customers.

relationship, particularly with my online customers, that I wouldn't otherwise have. It makes them more likely to buy from me rather than anyone else.

My focus is not on doing better than any of my competitors, but on doing what I do as well as I can and doing the very best for my customers. I could waste a lot of time trying to copy what other people are doing, but that wouldn't be helpful for anybody.

> With a business like mine, you have to remember that you're not selling a product, you're solving a problem.

MY TOP TIP

The first thing I would say to anyone starting up a business like mine is that managing your cash flow is absolutely paramount. Certainly at the beginning, it's much more important than making a profit: you have to be able to pay your suppliers.

SUPPLIERS AND WHOLESALERS

BAKING AND SUGARCRAFT

ALMOND ART
Product: Decorations, cases, icing, toppings, cutters, stands, confectionary supplies, tins, trays and equipment.
Address: 15–16 Faraday Close, Gorse Lane Industrial Estate, Clacton-on-Sea, Essex CO15 4TR
Tel: 01255 223322
Email: sales@almondart.com
Website: www.almondart.com

BLOSSOM SUGAR ART LTD
Product: Cookie cutters, stamps, moulds and equipment.
Terms: £100 minimum order on wholesale.
Address: Dalton House, 60 Windsor Avenue, London SW19 2RR
Tel: 08445 610736
Email: sales@blossomsugarart.com
Website: www.blossomsugarart.com

BLUE RIBBONS SUGARCRAFT CENTRE
Product: Decorations, boards, cases, stands, trays, icing, flavourings, colourings, tins, books and equipment.
Address: 29 Walton Road, East Molesey, Surrey KT8 0DH
Tel: 020 8941 1591
Email: info@blueribbons.co.uk
Website: www.blueribbons.co.uk

BUY 'N' BAKE
Product: Cake decorations, boxes, cupcake cases, toppings, colourings, boards, stands, equipment and more.
Address: Suite 108 Gunnels Wood Road, Stevenage, Hertfordshire SG1 2GR
Tel: 01438 870373
Email: info@buynbake.com
Website: www.buynbake.com

CAKE CRAFT WORLD
Product: Cake decorations, toppings, cupcake cases, boards, stands, colourings, icing, ingredients, equipment and books.
Address: Unit 8 North Downs Business Park, Pilgrims Way, Sevenoaks, Kent TN13 2TL
Tel: 01732 463573
Email: louise@cakecraftworld.com
Website: www.cakecraftworld.co.uk

CAKE DECORATING STORE
Product: Cake decorations, boards, colourings, cupcake cases, cutters, moulds, icing, sugarpaste and equipment.
Terms: No minimum order.
Address: Unit C4 Burley Hill Trading Estate, Burley Road, Leeds LS4 2PU
Tel: 08456 525357
Email: sales@cakedecoratingstore.co.uk
Website: www.cakedecoratingstore.co.uk

CAKE STUFF
Product: Sugarpaste, icing, boxes, colourings, ingredients, boards, tins, cutters, stands, bases, decorations, moulds and equipment.
Terms: No minimum order.
Address: Units 1–5 Gateside Industrial Estate, Lesmahagow, Lanarkshire ML11 0JR
Tel: 01555 890333
Website: www.cake-stuff.com

CAKE TOOL BOX
Product: Cake decorations, cutters, stands, toppings, equipment and more.
Address: 27 Churchill Road, Wellington, Telford, Shropshire TF1 2JB
Tel: 07401 003327
Email: sales@CakeToolbox.co.uk
Website: www.caketoolbox.co.uk

CAKE-LINKS LTD
Product: Cake decorations, tins, boards, stands, cutters, moulds, cupcake cases, books, magazines and equipment.
Terms: No minimum order.
Address: 95 Bargates, Christchurch, Dorset BH23 1QQ
Tel: 01202 496249
Email: info@cake-links.com
Website: www.cake-links.com

CAKES AND FAVOURS
Product: Decorations, boxes, tins, cutters, cases, stands, icing, toppings, moulds, books and equipment.

Address: 8 Town End, Ossett, West Yorkshire WF5 8BJ
Tel: 01924 270063
Email: cakesandfavours@btconnect.com
Website: www.cakesandfavours.co.uk

CAKES, COOKIES & CRAFTS SHOP

Product: Cake decorations, moulds, cutters, piping bags, cupcake cases, stands, boxes, sugarpaste, icing, colourings, flavourings, toppings, tins, equipment, kits and books.
Terms: No minimum order.
Address: Unit 2 Francis Business Park, White Lund Industrial Estate, Morecambe, Lancashire LA3 3PT
Tel: 01524 389684
Email: info@cakescookiesandcraftsshop.co.uk
Website: www.cakescookiesandcraftsshop.co.uk

CELCAKES & CELCRAFTS

Product: Cutters, moulds, stands and equipment.
Terms: £75 minimum order on wholesale.
Address: Springfield House, Gate Helmsley, York YO14 1NF
Tel: 01759 371447
Email: sales@celcrafts.com
Website: www.celcrafts.com

CLUB GREEN

Product: Cake decorations.
Terms: No minimum order.
Address: The Tyrrell Building, Long Reach, Ockham, Surrey GU23 6PG
Tel: 01483 281313
Email: sales@clubgreen.com
Website: www.clubgreen.com

CRAFT SUPERSTORE

Product: Decorations, tins, boards, cutters, equipment, tools and books.
Terms: No minimum order.
Address: Unit 5 Cedar Trade Park, Cobham Road, Dorset, Wimborne BH21 7SD
Tel: 08454 097595
Email: info@craftsuperstore.co.uk
Website: www.craftsuperstore.co.uk

CREATE A CAKE

Product: Decorations, tins, colourings, toppings, cases, icing, cutters, moulds, books and equipment.
Address: 94 Page Moss Lane, Huyton, Liverpool L14 0LX
Tel: 01513 450331
Email: createacake2010@hotmail.co.uk
Website: www.createacakeonline.co.uk

CULPITT

Product: Boards, cases, decorations, toppings, sugarpaste, stands, books, food colourings, equipment and more.
Terms: £50 minimum order.
Address: Jubilee Industrial Estate, Ashington, Northumberland, NE63 8UQ
Tel: 01670 814545
Email: info@culpitt.com
Website: www.culpitt.com

EPE INTERNATIONAL

Product: Appliances, accessories and equipment.
Address: Belfry House, Roydsdale Way, Euroway Industrial Estate, Bradford BD4 6SU
Tel: 01484 429880
Email: sales@epeinternational.com
Website: www.epeinternational.com

GUY PAUL

Product: Cake decorations, boards, boxes, stands, cutters, moulds, piping bags and equipment.
Address: Unit 10 The Business Centre, Corinium Industrial Estate, Raans Road, Amersham HP6 6FB
Tel: 01494 432121
Email: sales@guypaul.co.uk
Website: www.guypaul.co.uk

HAVE YOUR CAKE AND EAT IT

Product: Decorations, tins, boards, cases, icing, colourings, toppings, sugarpaste, cutters and equipment.
Address: 356–358 Spendmore Lane, Coppull, Chorely PR7 5DH
Tel: 01257 795969
Email: info@haveyourcakeandeatit.org
Website: shop.haveyourcakeandeatit.org

HOBBYCRAFT

Product: Cake decorations, icing, cupcake cases, cutters, stands, bakeware, books and equipment.
Address: 7 Enterprise Way, Aviation Park, Bournemouth International Airport, Christchurch BH23 6HG
Tel: 01202 596100
Email: onlinecustomerserices@hobbycraft.co.uk
Website: www.hobbycraft.co.uk

KAREN DAVIES CAKES

Product: Moulds, equipment, books.
Address: Unit 4 Royal Standard House, 330–334 New Chester Road, Birkenhead, Merseyside CH42 1LE
Tel: 01516 430055
Email: Karen@karendaviescakes.co.uk
Website: www.karendaviescakes.co.uk

SUPPLIERS AND WHOLESALERS – BAKING AND SUGARCRAFT

KIT BOX

Product: Templates, cutters, sugarpaste, books and equipment.
Terms: No minimum order.
Address: Unit 3 Neads Court, Knowles Road, Clevedon, North Somerset BS21 7XS
Tel: 01275 879030
Email: support@kitbox.info
Website: www.kitbox.co.uk

KNIGHTSBRIDGE PME

Product: Cutters, cake decorations, cupcake cases, bakeware, boards, crimpers, piping bags, cutters and equipment.
Terms: Trade customers must be/ provide: a business trading from a shop or business unit, company registered, VAT registered, photographic evidence of the shop or unit and spend a minimum of £150.
Address: Unit 21 Riverwalk Road, Enfield, Greater London EN3 7QN
Tel: 020 3234 0049
Email: sales@cakedecoration.co.uk
Website: www.cakedecoration.co.uk

LINDY'S CAKES LTD

Product: Decorations, boards, boxes, cutters, moulds, cases and equipment.
Address: Unit 2 Station Approach, Wendover, Aylesbury, Buckinghamshire HP22 6BN
Tel: 01296 622418
Email: enquiries@lindycakes.co.uk
Website: www.lindyscakes.co.uk

MAKEBAKE

Product: Cake decorations, cutters, boards, trays, tins, stands, flavourings, colourings, moulds, toppings, edible prints, edible ink, ingredients, equipment and books.
Address: Pyramid Court, Unit 2, Nottingham, Nottinghamshire NG5 1DT
Tel: 01159 699848
Email: info@MakeBake.co.uk
Website: www.makebake.co.uk

PATCHWORK CUTTERS

Product: Cutters and embossers.
Address: Unit 12 Arrowe Commercial Park, Arrowe Brook Road, Upton, Wirral CH49 1AB
Tel: 01516 785053
Email: info@patchworkcutters.com
Website: www.patchworkcutters.co.uk

PIPEDREAMS

Product: Cake decorations, sugarpaste, cutters, cupcake cases, boards, stands, colourings, tins, books, magazines and equipment.
Terms: No minimum order.
Address: 2 Bell Lane, Eton Wick, Windsor, Berkshire SL4 6JP
Tel: 01753 865682
Email: pipedreaming@btinternet.com
Website: www.pipedreams-sugarcraft.co.uk

PURE INVITATION

Product: Cake boxes, toppings, decorations, cases and stands.
Address: 15 Lythalls Lane Industrial Estate, Lythalls Lane, Foleshill, Coventry CV6 6FL
Tel: 02476 688692
Email: sales@pureinvitation.co.uk
Website: www.pureinvitation.co.uk

SQUIRES KITCHEN

Product: Decorations, moulds, cutters, sugarpaste, icing, colourings, boxes, boards, bakeware, equipment.
Terms: Trade customers are advised to contact the company for details.
Address: 3 Waverley Lane, Farnham, Surrey GU9 8BB
Tel: 08456 171810
Email: customer@squires-shop.com
Website: www.squires-shop.com

STITCH CRAFT CREATE

Product: Cake decorations, colourings, flavourings, sugarpaste, icing, stands, cases, tins, boxes, toppings, books and equipment.
Terms: No minimum order.
Address: Brunel House, Newton Abbot, Devon TQ12 4PU
Tel: 08448 805852
Email: customerservices@stitchcraftcreate.co.uk
Website: www.stitchcraftcreate.co.uk

SUGAR DADDY'S

Product: Decorations, sugarpaste, colourings, flavourings, cases, cutters, moulds, toppings and equipment.
Terms: No minimum order.
Address: 1 Fisher's Yard, Market Square, St Neots, Cambridgeshire PE19 2AF
Tel: 01480 471200
Email: enquiries@sugar-daddys.co.uk
Website: www.sugar-daddys.co.uk

SUGARCRAFT EMPORIUM

Product: Cake decorations, sugarpaste, icing, colourings, toppings, cutters, boards, stands and equipment.
Address: 56 Worcester Road, Bromsgrove, Worcestershire B61 7AE
Tel: 01527 576703
Email: barbara@sugarcraftemporium.com
Website: www.sugarcraftemporium.com

SUGARCRAFT SUPPLIES

Product: Cake decorations, toppings, cases, boards, stands, colourings, icing, ingredients and equipment.
Address: Unit 1 Sycamore Court, Lotherton Way, Garforth, Leeds LS25 2JY
Tel: 08717 895595
Email: sales@sugarcraft-supplies.co.uk
Website: www.sugarcraft-supplies.co.uk

SUGARCRAFT SHOP

Product: Cake decorations, boards, toppings, cutters, ingredients, sugarpaste, tins, cupcake cases and equipment.
Address: 194 Mosspark Drive, Mosspark, Glasgow G52 1JS
Tel: 01414 272777
Email: shop@sugarcraftshop.co.uk
Website: www.sugarcraftshop.co.uk

SUGARSHACK

Product: Cake boxes, cupcake cases, boards, stands, icing, sugarpaste and equipment.
Terms: No minimum order.
Address: Unit 12 Bowmans Trading Estate, Westmoreland Road, London NW9 9RL
Tel: 020 8204 2994
Email: info@sugarshack.co.uk
Website: www.sugarshack.co.uk

THE BAKER SHOP

Product: Cake decorations, toppings, boards, icing, stands and equipment.
Terms: No minimum order.
Address: Unit 2, 181a Verulam Road, St Albans, Hertfordshire AL3 4DR
Tel: 01727 832091
Email: info@thebakershop.co.uk
Website: www.thebakershop.co.uk

THE CAKE DECORATING COMPANY

Product: Cake decorations, boards, cupcake cases, toppings, icing, sugarpaste, trays, bakeware, stands and equipment.
Terms: No minimum order.
Address: Unit 2B Triumph Road, Nottingham, Nottinghamshire NG7 2GA
Tel: 01159 699800
Email: info@thecakedecoratingcompany.co.uk
Website: www.thecakedecoratingcompany.co.uk

THE FINISHING TOUCH

Product: Cake decorations, icing, sugarpaste, stands, boxes, boards, moulds, cutters and equipment.
Address: 42 Main Road, Gedling, Nottingham, Nottinghamshire NG4 3HL
Tel: 01159 403762
Email: info@tftcakes.co.uk
Website: www.tftcakes.co.uk

THE GOURMET CUPCAKE COMPANY

Product: Cupcake and baking supplies and equipment.
Address: Unit 4 Eckersley Road, Chelmsford, Essex CM1 1SL
Tel: 01245 283986
Email: info@gourmetcupcakes.co.uk
Website: www.gourmetcupcakes.co.uk

THE GREAT CAKE WAREHOUSE

Product: Cake decorations, tins, trays, boxes, cupcake cases, sugarpaste, colourings, flavourings, stands, moulds and equipment.
Address: 23 High Street, Hemel Hempstead, Hertfordshire HP1 3AA
Tel: 07887 421218
Email: thegreatcakewarehouse@yahoo.co.uk
Website: www.thegreatcakewarehouse.co.uk

THE LITTLE CAKE SHOP

Product: Cake decorations, toppings, colourings, sugarpaste, cupcake cases, stands, boards, boxes, cutters, books and equipment.
Address: 6 Bolmere Road, Boldmere, Sutton Coldfield, West Midlands B73 5TD
Tel: 01213 545296
Email: info@thelittlecakeshop.co.uk
Website: www.thelittlecakeshop.co.uk

THE PINK WHISK SHOP

Product: Cake decorations, sugarpaste, cupcake cases, icing, colourings, toppings, cutters, boards, stands, books and equipment.
Address: Brunel House, Newton Abbot, Devon TQ12 4PU
Tel: 08448 805852
Email: Contact submission form available on website.
Website: www.thepinkwhiskshop.com

THE SUGAR SHOP

Product: Cake decorations, boards, boxes, stands, books and equipment.
Address: 57 Lowther Road, Dunstable, Bedfordshire LU6 3NL
Tel: 01582 699807
Email: sales@anniesweddingcakes.co.uk
Website: www.anniesweddingcakes.co.uk

THE SUGARSMITH

Product: Cake decorations, icing, sugarpaste, colourings, boards, stands, cutters, moulds, ingredients and equipment.
Address: Unit 1 & 4 Howitts Aquatic Centre, 291 Rockingham Road, Corby, Northamptonshire NN17 2AE
Tel: 01536 407846
Email: enquiries@thesugarsmith.co.uk
Website: www.thesugarsmith.co.uk

WEDDING ACRYLICS

Product: Cake decorations, stands, cutters, boards, toppings, cupcake cases and equipment.
Address: Unit 21A Garth Works Industrial Estate, Taffs Well, Cardiff CF15 7RN
Tel: 08009 171419
Email: Support@weddingacrylics.co.uk
Website: www.weddingacrylics.co.uk

WINDSOR CAKE CRAFT

Product: Cake decorations, cutters, tins, boards, boxes, cupcake cases, toppings, sugarpaste, moulds, piping bags, kits, stands, books and equipment.
Address: 211 Europa Boulevard, Gemini Business Park, Warrington WA5 7TN
Tel: 01925 444590
Email: Contact submission form available on website.
Website: www.windsorcakecraft.co.uk

BEADING AND JEWELLERY

21ST CENTURY BEADS

Product: Beads: Swarovski crystal, glass, pearl, metal, gemstone, bone, porcelain, wood, plastic and acrylic; charms, findings, kits and equipment.
Terms: No minimum order.
Address: PO Box 644, Wakefield, West Yorkshire WF1 9HL
Tel: 01924 240947
Email: sales@beadmaster.com
Website: www.beadmaster.com

ABAKHAN FABRICS

Product: Beads: acrylic, pearl, bugle, lampwork, glass, wood, shell, metal and seed; pendants, findings, thread, wire and equipment.
Terms: No minimum order.
Address: Coast Road, Llanerch-y-Mor, Mostyn CH8 9DX
Tel: 01745 562100
Email: enquiries@abakhan.co.uk
Website: www.abakhanfabrics.co.uk

ACADEMY ART & CRAFTS

Product: Beads: glass and wood; wire, thread, elastic, books and equipment.
Address: Winton Road, Petersfield, Hampshire GU32 3HA
Tel: 01730 261624
Email: academyartandcrafts@hotmail.co.uk
Website: www.academyartandcrafts.com

BAKER ROSS

Product: Beads: Plastic, wood and shell; wire, thread and equipment.
Terms: No minimum order.
Address: 2–3 Forest Works, Forest Road, London E17 6JF
Tel: 08445 768922
Email: enquiry@bakerross.co.uk
Website: www.bakerross.co.uk

BEAD AURA

Product: Beads: bone, clay, gemstone, shell, crystal, glass, metal, plastic and wood; chains, thread, findings, pendants and equipment.
Terms: £10 minimum order.
Address: 3 Neal's Yard, Covent Garden, London WC2H 9DP
Tel: 020 7836 3002
Email: beadaura@gmail.com
Website: www.beadaura.co.uk

BEAD CRAZY

Product: Beads: acrylic, clay, glass, metal, wood and shell; chains, findings, pendants, thread and kits.
Address: 55 George Street, Perth PH1 5LB
Tel: 01738 442288
Email: info@beadcrazy.co.uk
Website: www.beadcrazy.co.uk

BEAD SISTERS

Product: Beads: Swarovski crystal, glass, acrylic, resin, metal, ceramic, porcelain, silver, bugle, seed, metal and gemstone: chains, thread, findings, charms, pendants, kits and equipment.
Terms: No minimum order.
Address: Mid Cairngarroch Croft, Stoneykirk, Stranraer, Wigtownshire DG9 9EH
Tel: 01776 830352

Email: sales@beadsisters.co.uk
Website: www.beadsisters.co.uk

BEADAHOLICS

Product: Beads: ceramic, acrylic, glass, metal, gemstone, wood, seed, pearl, shell and crystal; pendants, findings and kits.
Tel: 01216 860591
Email: calljan100@hotmail.com
Website: www.beadaholics.co.uk

BEADALICIOUS BEADS

Product: Glass, metal, gemstone and Bali Silver beads.
Terms: No minimum order.
Address: 50 Appleton Road, Eltham, London SE9 6NS
Tel: 07830 995550
Website: www.beadaliciousbeads. co.uk

BEADS & CRYSTALS

Product: Swarovski crystal beads, findings, pendants and equipment.
Address: Unit 1 Holly House, Queensway, Leamington Spa CV31 3LT
Tel: 01926 889966
Email: sales@beadsandcrystals.co.uk
Website: www.beadsandcrystals. co.uk

BEADS 4 CRAFTS

Product: Beads: acrylic, ceramic, crystal, glass, lampwork, metal, millefiori, gemstone, seed, wood and shell; wire, thread, charms, pendants, findings and equipment.
Terms: No minimum order.
Address: Unit 7B Milltown Industrial Estate, Warrenpoint, County Down BT34 3FN
Tel: 02841 753039

Email: sales@beads4crafts.co.uk
Website: www.beads4crafts.co.uk

BEADS DIRECT

Product: Beads: Swarovski crystal, clay, glass, metal, pearl, gemstone, seed, shell, silver and wood; clasps, charms, pendants, chains, wires, thread, kits and equipment.
Terms: No minimum order.
Address: 10 Duke Street, Loughborough, Leicestershire LE11 1ED
Tel: 01509 218028
Email: service@beadsdirect.co.uk
Website: www.beadsdirect.co.uk

BEADS FOR BEADERS

Product: Beads: glass, seed and crystal; wire, thread, findings, kits and equipment.
Terms: No minimum order.
Address: The Coach House, Ryton, Shrewsbury, Shropshire SY5 7LY
Tel: 07868 755569
Email: beadsforbeaders@gmail.com
Website: www.beadsforbeaders.com

BEADS UNLIMITED

Product: Beads: Swarovski crystal, bone, ceramic, glass, metal, plastic and wood; thread, wire, findings, pendants, charms and books.
Terms: £5 minimum order.
Address: 21 Sydney Street, Brighton BN1 4EN
Tel: 01273 740777
Email: mailbox@beadsunlimited.co.uk
Website: www.beadsunlimited.co.uk

BEADSTONE

Product: Beads: glass, gemstone and pearl; clasps and thread.
Terms: £50 minimum order on wholesale.

Address: 4 West Avenue, Lancing, West Sussex BN15 8ND
Tel: 01903 411459
Email: sales@beadstone.co.uk
Website: www.beadstone.co.uk

BEADTIME

Product: Beads: glass, metal, acrylic, ceramic, seed, bugle, lampwork, resin and shell; chains, thread, clasps, findings, kits, books and equipment.
Address: Unit 16 Shepperton Business Park, Govett Avenue, Shepperton TW17 8BA
Tel: 01932 244700
Website: www.beadtime.co.uk

BIJOUX BEADS

Product: Beads: shell, wood, seed, ceramic, metal, pearl, acrylic and terracotta; wire, thread, charms, kits and equipment.
Address: Elton House, 2 Abbey Street, Bath BA1 1NN
Tel: 01225 482024
Email: info@bijouxbeads.co.uk
Website: www.bijouxbeads.co.uk

BLUESTREAK BEADS

Product: Beads: Swarovski crystal, clay, lampwork, gemstone, pearl, glass, acrylic, metal, and shell; chains, findings, pendants, charms, kits and equipment.
Terms: £5 minimum order.
Address: 15 Ronald Rolph Court, Wadloes Road, Cambridge CB5 8PX
Tel: 01223 510757
Email: sales@bluestreakbeads.co.uk
Website: www.bluestreakbeads.co.uk

SUPPLIERS AND WHOLESALERS – BEADING AND JEWELLERY

BOJANGLE BEADS

Product: Beads: acrylic, seed, glass, metal, gemstone, pearl and wood; charms, pendants, wire, thread, findings and kits.
Terms: No minimum order.
Address: 50 Church Gate, Loughborough, Leicestershire LE11 1UE
Tel: 01509 211974
Email: sales@bojanglebeads.co.uk
Website: www.bojanglebeads.co.uk

BURHOUSE BEADS

Product: Beads: ceramic, pearl, gemstone, glass, gold, shambella, shell and silver; thread, wire, pendants, charms, findings, kits and equipment.
Terms: £100 minimum order, £500 annually for new traders.
Address: Quarmby Mills, Tanyard Road, Oakes, Huddersfield HD3 4YP
Tel: 01484 485100
Email: sales@burhousebeads.com
Website: www.burhousebeads.com

CJ BEADERS

Product: Beads: ceramic, crystal, glass, metal, seed, acrylic, pearl, lampwork, wood, resin and shell; wire, chains, pendants, findings, kits and equipment.
Terms: £50 minimum order.
Address: 15 Lakewood Road, Highcliffe, Dorset BH23 5NX
Tel: 01425 279992
Email: admin@cjbeaders.com
Website: www.cjbeaders.co.uk

CRAFTIME

Product: Beads: seed, bugle, resin, pearl, glass and rhinestone; crimps, spacers, charms, pendants, clasps, wire, chains, findings and equipment.
Terms: No minimum order.

Address: Unit 1 Apollo Business Park, Charles Way, Bulwell, Nottingham NG6 8RF
Tel: 01159 519827
Email: sales@craftime.co.uk
Website: www.craftime.com

CRAFTING TIME

Product: Beads: glass, seed and acrylic; charms, findings, thread and equipment.
Terms: No minimum order.
Address: Unit 8 Dunsbridge Business Park, A10 Road, Sherpreth, Cambridgeshire SG8 6RA
Tel: 01763 262417
Email: nina@itscraftingtime.com
Website: www.itscraftingtime.co.uk

CRAFTS TOO LTD

Product: Beads: acrylic, glass and seed; kits, charms, pendants, clasps, crimps, wire, findings and equipment.
Terms: £150 minimum first order, £100 thereafter.
Address: Unit 2 Kingston's Industrial Estate, Eastern Road, Aldershot GU12 4YA
Tel: 01252 330024
Email: peter@crafts-too.com
Website: www.crafts-too.com

CRAFTSCRAFTS

Product: Glass beads, findings, wire, thread, pendants and accessories.
Terms: £50 minimum order.
Address: Block B Parkwood Business Park, Parkwood Road, Sheffield S3 8AL
Tel: 01142 729165
Website: www.ancientwisdom.biz

CREATIVE BEADCRAFT

Product: Beads: Swarovski crystal, acrylic, bone, shell, ceramic, glass, metal, seed, bugle, gemstone and wood; thread, wire, charms, pendants, books, kits and equipment.
Terms: £100 minimum order.
Address: Unit 2 Asheridge Business Centre, Asheridge Road, Chesham, Buckinghamshire HP5 2PT
Tel: 01494 778818
Email: beads@creativebeadcraft. co.uk
Website: www.creativebeadcraft. co.uk

EMERALD CRAFTS

Product: Beads: acrylic, glass, wood, metal, seed and bugle; clasps, wire, thread, kits and equipment.
Terms: No minimum order.
Address: 14 High Street, Lyndhurst, Hampshire SO43 7BD
Tel: 02380 283199
Email: info@emeraldcrafts.co.uk
Website: www.emeraldcrafts.com

EMPIRICAL PRAXIS LTD

Product: Beads: Swarovski crystal, ceramic, glass, seed, shell and wood; wire, thread, pendants, findings and equipment.
Terms: £67 minimum wholesale order.
Address: 27 Abbeyhill, Ashgate, Chesterfield, Derbyshire S43 7JL
Tel: 01246 229208
Email: contact@empirical-praxis.co.uk
Website: www.epbeads.co.uk

FROGWILL.COM

Product: Beads: glass, lampwork, coral, pearl, shell, clay, gemstone, metal, acrylic and millefiori; wire, pendants, charms and findings.

Terms: €100 minimum order.
Address: 3/34 Lencewicza, Warsaw, Poland 01-493
Tel: 0048 506 307545
Website: www.frogwill.com

GLOSSOP CRAFT CENTRE

Product: Beads: glass, wood and seed; thread, findings and equipment.
Terms: No minimum order.
Address: Smith Fold Barn, Glossop, Derbyshire SK13 8DD
Tel: 01457 863559
Email: sales@glossopmaycrafts.co.uk
Website: www.glossopmaycrafts.co.uk

HERITAGE CREATIVE PRODUCTS

Product: Bead kits, thread and equipment.
Terms: £50 minimum order.
Address: 5–6 Haywood House, Hydra Business Park, Nether Lane, Ecclesfield S35 9ZX
Tel: 01142 459777
Email: enquiries@heritagecreativeproducts.com
Website: www.heritagecreativeproducts.co.uk

HOBBYCRAFT

Product: Beads: Swarovski crystal, glass, wood, metal and resin; thread, wire, pendants, clasps, crimps, kits, books and equipment.
Address: 7 Enterprise Way, Aviation Park, Bournemouth International Airport, Christchurch BH23 6HG
Tel: 01202 596100
Email: onlinecustomerserices@hobbycraft.co.uk
Website: www.hobbycraft.co.uk

JILLY BEADS

Product: Beads: Swarovski crystal, wood, shell, clay, metal, gemstones and pearl; thread, clasps, findings and kits.
Terms: No minimum order.
Address: 1 Anstable Road, Morecambe LA4 6TG
Tel: 01524 412728
Email: info@jillybeads.co.uk
Website: www.jillybeads.co.uk

KERNOWCRAFT

Product: Metal and gemstone beads, findings, charms, clasps, thread, wire, kits and equipment.
Terms: No minimum order.
Address: Bolingey, Perranporth, Cornwall TR6 0DH
Tel: 01872 573888
Email: info@kernowcraft.com
Website: www.kernowcraft.com

MOUNTAIN ASH CRAFTS

Product: Beads: seed, gemstone, metal, wood and crystal; clasps, wire, thread, kits and equipment.
Terms: No minimum order.
Address: Halfpenny Green Vineyards, Tom Lane, Bobbington, West Midlands DY7 5EP
Tel: 01384 221554
Email: sales@macrafts.co.uk
Website: www.macrafts.com

MR BEAD

Product: Beads: Swarovski crystal, gemstone, metal, wood, seed, porcelain and acrylic.
Terms: £100 minimum order on wholesale.
Address: 1 The Firs, Wigmore Lane, Luton LU2 8AA
Email: help@mrbead.com
Website: www.mrbead.co.uk

PANDA HALL

Product: Beads: Swarovski crystal, glass, resin, acrylic, clay, wood, metal, lampwork, millefiori, pearl, seed, shell and silver; clasps, chains, pendants, charms, findings, wire and equipment.
Terms: No minimum order.
Address: 287 Whippendell Road, Watford WD18 7NN
Tel: 01923 245104
Email: sales@pandahall.co.uk
Website: www.pandahall.co.uk

PRECIOUS SPARKLE BEADS

Product: Beads: gemstone, pearl, silver, glass and metal: thread, clasps, pendants, findings and equipment.
Address: 8 Bridge Land, Perth PH1 5JJ
Tel: 01738 563264
Email: info@precioussparklebeads.co.uk
Website: www.precioussparklebeads.co.uk

RAINBOW SILKS

Product: Beading and jewellery supplies, books, thread, wire, pendants and findings.
Terms: No minimum order.
Address: 85 High Street, Great Missenden, Buckinghamshire HP16 9EF
Tel: 01494 862111
Email: caroline@rainbowsilks.co.uk
Website: www.rainbowsilks.co.uk

SANDSTONES

Product: Beads: Swarovski crystal, pearl, gemstone, glass, shell, seed and metal; clasps, pendants, findings, thread, books and magazines.
Address: Swiss Cottage, 130 Church Street, Matlock, Derbyshire DE4 3BZ

Tel: 08452 240843
Website: www.sand-stones.co.uk

S.E. SIMONS

Product: Beads: acrylic, crystal, glass, metal, wood, pearl and seed; wire, chains, clasps, findings and equipment.
Terms: £50 minimum order.
Address: Unit 6 Netham Industrial Park, Bristol BS5 9PJ
Tel: 01179 554710
Email: sales@sesimons.co.uk
Website: www.sesimons.co.uk

SIESTA FRAMES LTD

Product: Beading wire, thread, kits and equipment.
Terms: £35 minimum order.
Address: Unit D Longmeadow Industrial Estate, Three Legged Cross, Wimborne, Dorset BH21 6RD
Tel: 01202 813363
Email: sales@siestaframes.com
Website: www.siestaframes.com

STITCH CRAFT CREATE

Product: Beads: Swarovski crystal, wood, glass, metal and gemstone; charms, chains, thread, wire, kits, pendants and equipment.
Terms: No minimum order.
Address: Brunel House, Newton Abbot, Devon TQ12 4PU
Tel: 08448 805852
Email: customerservices@stitchcraftcreate.co.uk
Website: www.stitchcraftcreate.co.uk

TAYLORS SUPPLIES LTD

Product: Beads: acrylic, wood, glass and seed; chains, thread and equipment.
Terms: No minimum order.

Address: Augustus Street, Cheetham Hill, Manchester M3 1HZ
Tel: 01618 340329
Email: info@taylors-supplies.co.uk
Website: www.taylors-supplies.co.uk

THE AFRICAN FABRIC SHOP

Product: Jewellery kits and books.
Address: 19 Hebble Mount, Meltham, Holmfirth, West Yorkshire HD9 4HG
Tel: 01484 850188
Email: info@africanfabric.co.uk
Website: www.africanfabric.co.uk

THE ART OF CRAFT LTD

Product: Beads: glass, acrylic and seed; chains, charms, wire, clasps, crimps, kits, findings and books.
Terms: No minimum order.
Address: 101 Lynchford Road, North Camp, Farnborough, Hampshire GU14 6ET
Tel: 01252 377677
Email: info@art-of-craft.co.uk
Website: www.art-of-craft.co.uk

THE BEAD SHOP HADDINGTON

Product: Beads: Swarovski crystal, Swarovski pearl, bugle, wood, glass, clay, leather, acrylic, metal, porcelain and gemstone; thread, findings, pendants and equipment.
Terms: No minimum order.
Address: 29 Court Street, Haddington, East Lothian EH41 3AE
Tel: 01620 822886
Email: info@beadshophaddington.co.uk
Website: www.beadshopscotland.co.uk

THE BEAD SHOP MANCHESTER

Product: Beads: Swarovski crystal, glass, pearl, seed, resin, clay, gemstone, shell, metal, acrylic, ceramic, porcelain and wood; jewellery findings, thread, wire, pendants and equipment.
Terms: No minimum order.
Address: Afflecks, 52 Church Street, Manchester M4 1PW
Tel: 01612 744040
Email: sales@the-beadshop.co.uk
Website: www.the-beadshop.co.uk

THE BEAD WHOLESALER

Product: Beads: Swarovski crystal, glass, seed, acrylic, resin, clay, shell, millefiori, lampwork and metal; thread, wire, books and equipment.
Terms: No minimum order.
Address: Unit 2 Limavady Business Park, 89b Dowland Road, Limavady BT49 0HR
Tel: 02877 722522
Email: info@thebeadwholesaler.co.uk
Website: www.thebeadwholesaler.co.uk

THE NUMBER 1 BEAD SHOP

Product: Beads: glass, acrylic, clay and gemstone; chains, charms, pendants, thread, findings, kits and equipment.
Address: Clydeside Antique Centre, 121–127 Lancefield Street, Glasgow G3 8HZ
Tel: 01412 290544
Email: beadshopglasgow@btinternet.com
Website: www.mylerscrystals.com

Wobbly Mog

Product: Beads: seed, pearl, acrylic and glass; clasps, crimps, findings, wire, chains, thread, kits and equipment.
Terms: No minimum order.
Address: Unit 2 Abergarw Enterprise Centre, Abergarw Industrial Estate, Brynmenyn, Bridgend CF32 9LW
Tel: 01656 729002
Email: info@wobblyMog.co.uk
Website: www.wobblymog.co.uk

World of Beads

Product: Beads: Swarovski crystal, lampwork, glass, metal, pearl, gemstone, silver, acrylic, seed, wood and clay; findings, charms, thread and kits.
Address: 1 Stonemasons Court, Parchment Street, Winchester, Hampshire SO23 8AT
Tel: 01962 861255
Email: info@worldofbeads.co.uk
Website: www.worldofbeads.co.uk

"Don't rely too heavily on one product – the craft industry is very trend-led and everything has a short shelf life."
Sue Taylor

KNITTING AND CROCHET

Abakhan Fabrics

Product: Knitting needles, crochet hooks, yarns, felting, patterns, books and equipment.
Terms: No minimum order.
Address: Coast Road, Llanerch-y-Mor, Mostyn CH8 9DX
Tel: 01745 562100
Email: enquiries@abakhan.co.uk
Website: www.abakhanfabrics.co.uk

Affinity Yarns

Product: Knitting needles, crochet hooks, yarns, patterns and equipment.
Terms: No minimum order.
Address: PO Box 972, Whittlesford, Cambridge CB22 4WQ
Tel: 01223 835146
Email: info@affinityyarns.com
Website: www.affinityyarns.com

Alpaca Select

Product: Alpaca yarns, knitting patterns and kits.
Address: 82 Frobisher Road, Coventry, CV3 6NA
Tel: 02476 411776
Email: sales@alpacaselect.co.uk
Website: www.alpaca-select.com

Andee Knits

Product: Needles, crochet hooks, yarns, patterns, books, equipment.
Address: Woodside, Puriton Hill, Puriton, Somerset TA7 8AG
Tel: 01278 684738
Email: facebook@andeeknits.co.uk
Website: www.andeeknits.co.uk

Artesano

Product: Knitting needles, yarns, patterns and equipment.
Terms: No minimum order.
Address: Unit G Lamb's Farm Business Park, Basingstoke Road, Swallowfield, Reading RG7 1PQ
Tel: 01189 503350
Email: jenny@artesanoyarns.co.uk
Website: www.artesanoyarns.co.uk

Artyarn

Product: Knitting needles, yarns, crochet cottons, patterns and kits.
Address: 10 High Street, Pointon, Sleaford, Lincolnshire NG34 0LX
Tel: 01529 240510
Email: info@artyarn.co.uk
Website: www.artyarn.co.uk

Bergere De France

Product: Patterns, books, kits, yarns and equipment.
Terms: No minimum order.
Address: 91 Rue Ernest Bradfer, Bar Le Duc, France 55020
Tel: 0033 329 790101
Email: service.export@bergeredefrance.com
Website: www.bergeredefrance.co.uk

Bicester Wools

Product: Yarns, knitting needles, patterns and books.
Address: 86 Sheep Street, Bicester, Oxon OX26 6LP
Tel: 01869 322966
Email: info@bicesterwools.com
Website: www.bicesterwools.com

SUPPLIERS AND WHOLESALERS – KNITTING AND CROCHET

BLUEBERRY BARN
Product: Wool, yarns and patterns.
Address: Osmaston Pastures Farm, Ashbourne, Derbyshire DE6 1NB
Tel: 07714 342410
Email: orders@blueberrybarn.co.uk
Website: www.blueberrybarn.co.uk

COATS CRAFTS UK
Product: Knitting and crochet yarns, kits, patterns and equipment.
Terms: No minimum order.
Address: Green Lane Mill, Holmfirth, West Yorkshire HD9 2DX
Tel: 01484 681881
Email: consumer.ccuk@coats.com
Website: www.coatscrafts.co.uk

COLINETTE
Product: Knitting needles, crochet hooks, yarns, rovings, patterns and kits.
Terms: No minimum order.
Address: Banwy Workshops, Llanfair, Caereinion SY21 0SG
Tel: 01938 810128
Email: trade@colinette.com
Website: www.woolandyarn.co.uk

CORNISH ORGANIC WOOL
Product: Wool and patterns.
Address: King's Cottage, Boswarthen, Newbridge, Penzance TR28 8PA
Tel: 01736 350905
Email: info@cornishorganicwool.co.uk
Website: www.cornishorganicwool.co.uk

CREATIVE YARNS
Product: Yarns.
Terms: £100 minimum order.
Address: 3 Centre Point, Knights Way, Battlefield Enterprise Park, Shrewsbury SY1 3BF
Tel: 08453 130277
Email: info@creativeyarns.co.uk
Website: www.creativeyarns.co.uk

CYGNET YARNS
Product: Knitting and crochet yarns and patterns.
Terms: Minimum order of 12 units.
Address: 12–14 Adelaide Street, Bradford, West Yorkshire BD5 0EF
Tel: 01274 743374
Email: sales@cygnetyarns.com
Website: www.cygnetyarns.com

DESIGNER YARNS
Product: Knitting yarns and patterns.
Address: Unit 8–10 Newbridge Industrial Estate, Pitt Street, Keighley, West Yorkshire BD21 4PQ
Tel: 01535 664222
Email: enquiries@designeryarns.uk.com
Website: www.designeryarns.uk.com

DEVON FINE FIBRES
Product: Bowmont, cashmere and mohair wool.
Address: Westcott Farm, Oakford, Tiverton, Devon EX16 9EZ
Tel: 01398 351173
Email: info@devonfinefibres.co.uk
Website: www.devonfinefibres.co.uk

DMC CREATIVE WORLD LTD
Product: Crochet patterns, kits, thread and books.
Terms: No minimum order.
Address: Unit 21 Warren Park Way, Warrens Park, Enderby, Leicester LE19 4SA
Tel: 01162 754000
Email: Contact submission form available on website.
Website: www.dmccreative.co.uk

EUROPEAN QUILTING SUPPLIES LTD
Product: Knitting needles, crochet hooks, yarns, kits and equipment.
Address: 11 Iliffe House, Iliffe Avenue, Leicester LE2 5LS
Tel: 01162 710033
Email: sales@eqsuk.com
Website: www.eqsuk.com

FAIRFIELD YARNS
Product: Yarns, knitting patterns and equipment.
Terms: No minimum order.
Address: Co-operative Buildings, 131 Rochdale Road East, Heywood, Lancashire OL10 1QU
Tel: 01706 623808
Email: fairfieldyarns@btconnect.com
Website: www.fairfieldyarns.co.uk

FOREST FIBRES
Product: Fibres, yarns, dyes, knitting needles, spinning wheels, weaving looms, kits and books.
Address: Unit G1 Building 13/2, Vantage Point Business Village, Mitcheldean GL17 0DD
Tel: 01594 546118
Email: forestfibres@btopenworld.com
Website: www.forestfibres.co.uk

GILLIANGLADRAG
Product: Wool tops, fibres, yarns, knitting needles, crochet hooks, books.
Terms: £175 minimum order.
Address: The Fluff-a-torium, 20 West Street, Dorking, Surrey RH4 1BL
Tel: 01306 898144
Email: gill@gilliangladrag.co.uk
Website: www.gilliangladrag.co.uk

GROVES AND BANKS

Product: Knitting needles, crochet hooks, kits and equipment.
Address: Long Crendon Industrial Park, Drakes Drive, Long Crendon, Aylesbury HP18 9BA
Tel: 01844 258100
Email: enquiries@groves-banks.com
Website: www.groves-banks.com

HANTEX

Product: Knitting needles, yarns, patterns, books and accessories.
Terms: £130 minimum order, £350 annually thereafter.
Address: Unit 1 Whitehouse Business Units, Eaudyke Road, Friskney, Lincolnshire PE22 8NL
Tel: 08448 794719
Email: sales@hantex.co.uk
Website: www.hantex.co.uk

HOBBYCRAFT

Product: Crochet hooks, knitting needles, yarns, books, kits, equipment.
Address: 7 Enterprise Way, Aviation Park, Bournemouth International Airport, Christchurch BH23 6HG
Tel: 01202 596100
Email: onlinecustomerserices@hobbycraft.co.uk
Website: www.hobbycraft.co.uk

HOBBYKNIT

Product: Knitting needles, haberdashery, yarns, patterns and kits.
Terms: £50 minimum order.
Address: Unit 22, Baildon Mills, Northgate, Baildon BD17 6JX
Tel: 01274 596315
Email: jacquayroyston@supersew.com
Website: www.hobbyknit.co.uk

HULU

Product: Knitting needles, crochet hooks, patterns, yarns, books and equipment.
Terms: No minimum order.
Address: Sentinel House, Poundwell, Modbury, Devon PL21 0XX
Tel: 01548 831911
Email: sales@hulucrafts.co.uk
Website: www.hulucrafts.co.uk

INTERKNIT CAFÉ

Product: Knitting needles, crochet hooks, patterns, yarns, books and equipment.
Terms: £5 minimum order.
Address: 60 Downing Street, Farnham, Surrey GU9 7PN
Tel: 01525 734666
Email: info@interknitcafe.co.uk
Website: www.interknitcafe.co.uk

J. C. RENNIE & CO

Product: Yarns.
Terms: No minimum order.
Address: Milladen, Mintlaw, Aberdeenshire, AB42 5DF
Tel: 01771 622422
Email: info@jcrennie.com
Website: www.jcrennie.com

KING COLE

Product: Knitting and crochet yarns and patterns.
Address: Merrie Mills, Elliott Street, Silsden, Keighley BD20 0DE
Tel: 01535 650230
Email: lance.martin@kingcole.co.uk
Website: www.kingcole.co.uk

KNOLL YARNS LTD

Product: Yarns.
Address: 1 Wells Road, Ilkley, West Yorkshire LS29 9JB
Tel: 01943 602516
Email: info@knollyarns.com
Website: www.knollyarns.com

MILLAMIA

Product: Knitting needles, yarns, kits and patterns.
Address: Studio 11, 32 Bolton Gardens, London SW5 0AQ
Tel: 08450 177474
Email: info@millamia.com
Website: www.millamia.com

PRESTIGE FIBRES

Product: Mohair, alpaca, merino and British wools.
Address: PO Box 147, Leeds LS21 9BD
Tel: 01138 151125
Email: info@prestigefibres.com
Website: www.prestigefibres.com

R. GLEDHILL LTD

Product: Wool.
Address: Pingle Mill, Pingle Lane, Delph, Saddleworth OL3 5EX
Tel: 01457 874651
Email: general@rgledhill.co.uk
Website: www.rgledhill.co.uk

R.E. DICKIE LTD

Product: Yarns: tops, carded web and flock.
Address: West End Works, Parkinson Lane, Halifax, West Yorkshire HX1 3UW
Tel: 01422 341516
Email: wool@dickie.co.uk
Website: www.britishwool.com

RAINBOW SILKS

Product: Knitting needles, crochet hooks, yarns, books and equipment.
Terms: No minimum order.
Address: 85 High Street, Great

Missenden, Buckinghamshire HP16 9EF
Tel: 01494 862111
Email: caroline@rainbowsilks.co.uk
Website: www.rainbowsilks.co.uk

ROWAN

Product: Knitting yarns and patterns.
Address: Green Lane Mill, Holmfirth, West Yorkshire HD9 2DX
Tel: 01484 681881
Email: mail@knitrowan.com
Website: www.knitrowan.com

S.E. SIMONS

Product: Knitting needles, crochet hooks, yarns, patterns, books and equipment.
Terms: £50 minimum order.
Address: Unit 6 Netham Industrial Park, Bristol BS5 9PJ
Tel: 01179 554710
Email: sales@sesimons.co.uk
Website: www.sesimons.co.uk

SIESTA FRAMES LTD

Product: Knitting needles, crochet hooks, kits and equipment.
Terms: £35 minimum order.
Address: Unit D Longmeadow Industrial Estate, Three Legged Cross, Wimborne, Dorset BH21 6RD
Tel: 01202 813363
Email: sales@siestaframes.com
Website: www.siestaframes.com

SIRDAR SPINNING LTD

Product: Knitting yarns and patterns.
Address: Flanshaw Lane, Wakefield, West Yorkshire WF2 9D
Tel: 01924 231669
Email: enquiries@sirdar.co.uk
Website: www.sirdar.co.uk

SCANDINAVIAN KNITTING DESIGN

Product: Knitting needles, crochet hooks, yarns and patterns.
Address: South Lodge, Wellington Court, Spencers Wood, Berkshire RG7 1BN
Tel: 01189 884226
Email: Sales@ ScandinavianKnittingDesign.com
Website: www. scandinavianknittingdesign.eu

STITCH CRAFT CREATE

Product: Knitting needles, crochet hooks, yarns, patterns and equipment.
Terms: No minimum order.
Address: Brunel House, Newton Abbot, Devon TQ12 4PU
Tel: 08448 805852
Email: customerservices@ stitchcraftcreate.co.uk
Website: www.stitchcraftcreate.co.uk

STYLECRAFT

Product: Knitting patterns.
Address: PO Box 62, Goulbourne Street, Keighley, West Yorkshire BD21 1PP
Tel: 01535 609798
Email: info@stylecraftltd.co.uk
Website: www.stylecraft-yarns.co.uk

TAYLORS SUPPLIES LTD

Product: Knitting needles, crochet hooks, yarns, cotton, kits and patterns.
Terms: No minimum order.
Address: Augustus Street, Cheetham Hill, Manchester M3 1HZ
Tel: 01618 340329
Email: info@taylors-supplies.co.uk
Website: www.taylors-supplies.co.uk

THE ART OF CRAFT LTD

Product: Knitting needles, crochet hooks, yarns, patterns, books and equipment.
Terms: No minimum order.
Address: 101 Lynchford Road, North Camp, Farnborough, Hampshire GU14 6ET
Tel: 01252 377677
Email: info@art-of-craft.co.uk
Website: www.art-of-craft.co.uk

THE BLACK SHEEP

Product: Knitting needles, yarns, patterns, books and equipment.
Terms: No minimum order.
Address: Warehouse Studios, Glaziers Lane, Culcheth, Warrinton WA3 4AQ
Tel: 01925 764231
Email: orders@blacksheepwools.com
Website: www.blacksheepwools.com

THE NATURAL FIBRE COMPANY

Product: Wool, mohair, alpaca, organic and vegetable fibres.
Address: Unit B Pipers Court, Pennygillam Way, Launceston, Cornwall PL15 7PJ
Tel: 01566 777635
Email: enquiries@thenaturalfibre.co.uk
Website: www.thenaturalfibre.co.uk

TRIMCRAFT LTD

Product: Knitting needles, crochet hooks, wools, yarns and patterns.
Terms: £100 minimum order.
Address: Manco House, Bolsover Street, Hucknall, Nottinghamshire NG15 7TY
Tel: 01159 834820
Email: sales@trimcraftdirect.com
Website: www.trimcraftdirect.com

WINGHAM WOOL WORK

Product: Fibres, yarns, dyes, felt, equipment, books and magazines.
Terms: No minimum order.
Address: 70 Main Street, Wentworth, Rotherham, South Yorkshire S62 7TN
Tel: 01226 742926
Email: mail@winghamwoolwork.co.uk
Website: www.winghamwoolwork.co.uk

YEOMAN YARNS

Product: Yarns.
Terms: No minimum order.
Address: 36 Churchill Way, Fleckney, Leicestershire LE8 8UD
Tel: 01162 404464
Email: sales@yeomanyarns.co.uk
Website: www.yeoman-yarns.co.uk

Z. HINCHCLIFFE & SONS LTD

Product: Lambswool, cashmere, camel hair and angora.
Address: Harcliffe Mills, Denby Dale, Huddersfield HD8 8QL
Tel: 01484 862207
Email: office@zhinchliffe.co.uk
Website: www.zhinchliffe.co.uk

PAPERCRAFT

A1 CRAFTS

Product: Paper, card, decoupage, die cuts, embossing, embellishments, ink, pens, punches, stamps, stencils, books and kits.
Address: Unit C/E Eckland Lodge Business Park, Desborough Road, Market Harborough, Leicestershire LE16 8HB
Tel: 07850 015888
Email: contact@a1crafts.co.uk
Website: www.a1crafts.co.uk

ABAKHAN FABRICS

Product: Paper, card, buttons, embellishments, adhesives and kits.
Terms: No minimum order.
Address: Coast Road, Llanerch-y-Mor, Mostyn CH8 9DX
Tel: 01745 562100
Email: enquiries@abakhan.co.uk
Website: www.abakhanfabrics.co.uk

ACADEMY ART & CRAFTS

Product: Paper, card, stencils, punches, adhesives, paints, pens, ink, embossing, books and equipment.
Address: Winton Road, Petersfield, Hampshire GU32 3HA
Tel: 01730 261624
Email: academyartandcrafts@hotmail.co.uk
Website: www.academyartandcrafts.com

ARTIST TRADING POST

Product: Paper, card, stamps, embellishments, adhesives, ink, paints, magazines and equipment.
Address: Cwm Carnedd Isaf, Dolfach, Llanbrynmair, Powys SY19 7AF
Tel: 01650 521549
Email: info@artisttradingpost.com
Website: www.artisttradingpost.com

ARTS AND DESIGNS

Product: Paper, card, adhesives, embellishments, stamps, ink, embossing and more.
Address: 3 Milehouse Crescent, Dumfries DG1 1JZ
Tel: 01387 264252
Website: www.artsanddesigns.com

BAKER ROSS

Product: Paper, card, paints, pens, pencils, stencils, tissue, decoupage, kits, adhesives and equipment.
Terms: No minimum order.
Address: 2–3 Forest Works, Forest Road, London E17 6JF
Tel: 08445 768922
Email: enquiry@bakerross.co.uk
Website: www.bakerross.co.uk

BRUSH STROKES

Product: Paper, card, adhesives, stamps, pens, ink, paint and books.
Terms: No minimum order.
Address: Unit 20 Holme Grange Craft Village, Heathlands Road, Wokingham, Berkshire RG40 3AW
Tel: 01189 894756
Email: info@onestrokeuk.com
Website: www.brushstrokescrafts.co.uk

CIRCA DESIGN

Product: Stamps.
Terms: £10 minimum order.
Address: 43 The Brackens, Westbury Park, Clayton, Newcastle ST5 4JL
Tel: 01782 639855
Email: info@circadesign.co.uk
Website: www.circadesign.co.uk

CRAFT SUPERSTORE

Product: Paper, card, punches, die cuts, decoupage, toppers, embellishments, stamps, embossing, stencils, ink, pens, pencils, paints, chalk, stickers, adhesives, kits, equipment, CD Roms, DVDs and magazines.
Terms: No minimum order.
Address: Unit 5 Cedar Trade Park, Cobham Road, Dorset, Wimborne BH21 7SD
Tel: 08454 097595
Email: info@craftsuperstore.co.uk
Website: www.craftsuperstore.co.uk

CRAFTERS COMPANION

Product: Accessories, adhesives, decoupage, pens, paints, glitter, ink, embossing, punches, books, stamps, paper, card and equipment.
Terms: No minimum order.
Address: Collingwood House, Collingwood Street, Coundon, Bishop Auckland DL14 8LG
Tel: 08452 960042
Email: info@crafterscompanion.co.uk
Website: www.crafterscompanion. co.uk

CRAFTIME

Product: Paper, embellishments, ribbons, stencils, pens, accessories and equipment.
Terms: No minimum order.
Address: Unit 1 Apollo Business Park, Charles Way, Bulwell, Nottingham NG6 8RF
Tel: 01159 519827
Email: sales@craftime.co.uk
Website: www.craftime.com

CRAFTING, TIME

Product: Paper, card, adhesives, ink, die cuts, embossing, embellishments, glitter, stencils, punches, stamps, kits and equipment.
Terms: No minimum order.
Address: Unit 8 Dunsbridge Business Park, A10 Road, Sherpreth, Cambridgeshire SG8 6RA
Tel: 01763 262417
Email: nina@itscraftingtime.com
Website: www.itscraftingtime.co.uk

CRAFTSCRAFTS

Product: Paper, glitter, embellishments and equipment.
Terms: £50 minimum order.
Address: Block B Parkwood Business Park, Parkwood Road, Sheffield S3 8AL
Tel: 01142 729165
Email: Sharka@ancientwisdom.biz
Website: www.ancientwisdom.biz

CRAFTY ARTS

Product: Paper, card, punches, embellishments, adhesives, decoupage, die cuts, ink, paints, glitter, stamps, toppers, pens, stickers, kits, equipment.
Terms: No minimum order.
Address: Unit 4 Brooklands Approach, North Street, Romford, Essex RM1 1DX
Tel: 020 7993 5479
Email: sales@craftyarts.co.uk
Website: www.craftyarts.co.uk

CRAFTY DEVILS

Product: Paper, card, decoupage, paints, pens, ink, adhesives, embossing tools, stamps, kits and equipment.
Terms: No minimum order
Address: Unit 22–23 Howard Avenue, Barnstaple, Devon, EX32 8QA
Tel: 01271 326777

Email: enquiries@ craftydevilspapercraft.co.uk
Website: www.craftydevilspapercraft. co.uk

CRAFTY QUILLING

Product: Quilling supplies and kits.
Terms: No minimum order.
Address: 91 Blackpool Road, Carleton, Lancashire, FY6 7QH
Tel: 01253 884242
Email: marjorie@craftyquilling.co.uk
Website: www.craftyquilling.co.uk

CREATIVITY INTERNATIONAL LTD

Product: Paper, adhesives, sequins, glitter, foam, paints, chalk, stamps.
Terms: No minimum order.
Address: 16 Narrowboat Way, Hurst Business Park, Brierley Hill, West Midlands DY5 1UF
Tel: 01384 485550
Email: sales@cilimited.co.uk
Website: www.cilimited.co.uk

DAISY'S JEWELS & CRAFTS

Product: Paper, card, stamps, decoupage, stencils, embossing, adhesives, pens, ink, punches, books and equipment.
Terms: No minimum order.
Address: Unit A Bryant Road, Exhall, Coventry CV7 9EN
Tel: 07779 110813
Email: daisysjewelscrafts@yahoo. co.uk
Website: www. daisysjewelsandcrafts.co.uk

DESIGN OBJECTIVES LTD

Product: Paper, card, adhesives, embellishments, decoupage, stamps, embossing powder, stencils, glitter, paints, brushes, palettes, kits, accessories and equipment.
Terms: No minimum order.
Address: Unit 90 Woolsbridge Industrial Park, Three Legged Cross, Wimborne, Dorset BH21 6SP
Tel: 01202 811000
Email: customerservices@docrafts.com
Website: www.docrafts.biz

ELLISON (SIZZIX)

Product: Paper, card, embossing, die cuts, kits, patterns and equipment.
Terms: No minimum order.
Address: Unit 3 Whitegate Industrial Estate, Wrexham, Wales LL13 8UG
Tel: 08444 998181
Email: europecustomerservices@ellison.com
Website: www.sizzix.co.uk

EMERALD CRAFTS

Product: Paper, card, adhesives, decoupage, die cuts, embellishments, embossing, glitter, ink, pens, paints, punches, quilling, stamps, stickers, kits and equipment.
Terms: No minimum order.
Address: 14 High Street, Lyndhurst, Hampshire SO43 7BD
Tel: 02380 283199
Email: info@emeraldcrafts.co.uk
Website: www.emeraldcrafts.com

EXQUISITE CRAFTS

Product: Paper, card, chalk, decoupage, embellishments, embossing, adhesives, ink, paints, pens, punches, stamps, stickers, stencils, kits and equipment.
Address: 68 Parkway, Westhoughton, Bolton, Greater Manchester BL5 2RY
Tel: 01942 813991
Email: ales@exquisitecrafts.co.uk
Website: www.exquisitecrafts.co.uk

FLUTTERBY CRAFTS

Product: Paper, card, stamps, ink, embossing, embellishments, punches, glitter, decoupage, stickers, pens, paints, adhesives, kits and equipment.
Terms: No minimum order.
Address: The Barns, Lower Henwick Farm, Turnpike Road, Thatcham RG18 3AP
Tel: 01635 860900
Email: lynn@flutterbycrafts.co.uk
Website: www.flutterbycrafts.co.uk

HANDY HIPPO CRAFTS

Product: Paper, card, toppers, decoupage, embellishments, stickers, die cuts, stamps, embossing, punches, pens, paints, adhesives, glitter, kits and equipment.
Address: Crossbow House, 40 Liverpool Road, Slough, Berkshire SL1 4QZ
Tel: 01753 539222
Email: customerservice@handyhippo.co.uk
Website: www.handyhippo.co.uk

HERITAGE CREATIVE PRODUCTS

Product: Paper, card, stencils, embossing, punches, stickers, stencils, adhesives, ink, stamps, kits, equipment.
Terms: £50 minimum order.
Address: 5–6 Haywood House, Hydra Business Park, Nether Lane, Ecclesfield S35 9ZX
Tel: 01142 459777
Email: enquiries@heritagecreativeproducts.com
Website: www.heritagecreativeproducts.co.uk

HOBBYCRAFT

Product: Paper, card, die cuts, decoupage, toppers, punches, stamps, stickers, ink, embossing, quilling, pens, adhesives, kits and equipment.
Address: 7 Enterprise Way, Aviation Park, Bournemouth International Airport, Christchurch BH23 6HG
Tel: 01202 596100
Email: onlinecustomerserices@hobbycraft.co.uk
Website: www.hobbycraft.co.uk

JGD CRAFTS

Product: Paper, card, embossing, adhesives, toppers, stamps, punches, decoupage, die cuts, glitter, paints, pens, pencils, stencils, kits and equipment.
Address: 108 Outram Street, Sutton, Ashfield, Nottingham NG17 4FS
Tel: 01623 557567
Email: enquiries@jgdcrafts.com
Website: www.jgdcrafts.com

KANBAN CRAFTS LTD

Product: Paper, card, stamps and accessories.
Address: 109 Dockfield Road, Shipley, West Yorkshire BD17 7SX
Tel: 01274 582415
Email: Sales@KanbanCrafts.com
Website: www.kanbancrafts.com

KARS UK

Product: Paper, tissue, decoupage, glitter, pens, card, stencils and equipment.
Terms: No minimum order.
Address: PO Box 97, Ochten, Netherlands 4050 EB
Tel: 08702 407993
Email: salesuk@kars.eu
Website: www.kars.nl/uk

MOUNTAIN ASH CRAFTS

Product: Paper, card, adhesives, stickers, stamps, glitter, pens, paints, punches, decoupage, embellishments, die cuts, kits and equipment.
Terms: No minimum order.
Address: Halfpenny Green Vineyards, Tom Lane, Bobbington, West Midlands DY7 5EP
Tel: 01384 221554
Email: sales@macrafts.co.uk
Website: www.macrafts.com

NICKYNACKYNOO

Product: Paper, card, decoupage, die cuts, embossing, embellishments, glitter, ink, paints, pens, chalk, punches, stamps, kits and equipment.
Address: 138 Jefferys Crescent, Huyton, Liverpool, Merseyside L36 4JU
Email: sales@nickynackynoo.co.uk
Website: www.nickynackynoo.co.uk

PAPER ARTS

Product: Paper, card, adhesives, punches, die cuts, embellishments, paints, pens, ink, pencils, stamps, stickers, kits and equipment.
Address: Toadsmoor Road, Brimscombe, Stroud, Gloucestershire GL5 2TB
Tel: 01453 886038
Website: www.paperarts.co.uk

PAPER CELLAR

Product: Paper, card and kits.
Terms: No minimum order.
Address: 41 The Metro Centre, Dwight Road, Watford, Hertfordshire WD18 9SB
Tel: 08718 713711
Email: contact@papercellar.com
Website: www.papercellar.com

PERSONAL IMPRESSIONS

Product: Adhesives, paper, card, decoupage, stickers, embellishments, sequins, glitter, stamps, punches, pens, stencils, kits and equipment.
Address: Curzon Road, Chilton Industrial Estate, Sudbury, Suffolk CO10 2XW
Tel: 01787 375241
Email: customerservices@personalimpressions.com
Website: www.personalimpressions.com

PURE INVITATION

Product: Paper, card, adhesives, ribbons, embellishments and equipment.
Address: 15 Lythalls Lane Industrial Estate, Lythalls Lane, Foleshill, Coventry CV6 6FL
Tel: 02476 688692
Email: sales@pureinvitation.co.uk
Website: www.pureinvitation.co.uk

RAINBOW SILK

Product: Paper, card, embellishments, books and equipment.
Terms: No minimum order.
Address: 85 High Street, Great Missenden, Buckinghamshire HP16 9EF
Tel: 01494 862111
Email: caroline@rainbowsilks.co.uk
Website: www.rainbowsilks.co.uk

S.E. SIMONS

Product: Paper, card, punches, stickers, pens, quilling, stamps, embossing, paints, pens, adhesives, glitter, kits and equipment.
Terms: £50 minimum order.
Address: Unit 6 Netham Industrial Park, Bristol BS5 9PJ
Tel: 01179 554710
Email: sales@sesimons.co.uk
Website: www.sesimons.co.uk

SIESTA FRAMES LTD

Product: Paper, card, adhesives, chalk, embellishments, glitter, kits and equipment.
Terms: £35 minimum order.
Address: Unit D Longmeadow Industrial Estate, Three Legged Cross, Wimborne, Dorset BH21 6RD
Tel: 01202 813363
Email: sales@siestaframes.com
Website: www.siestaframes.com

STITCH CRAFT CREATE

Product: Paper, card, embellishments, stamps, decoupage, quilling, books, kits and equipment.
Terms: No minimum order.
Address: Brunel House, Newton Abbot, Devon TQ12 4PU
Tel: 08448 805852
Email: customerservices@stitchcraftcreate.co.uk
Website: www.stitchcraftcreate.co.uk

STUDIO LIGHT CRAFTS UK

Product: Paper, card, punches, decoupage, stamps, stickers and kits.
Terms: €50 minimum order.
Address: Achterdorpstraat 12, Barneveld, Netherlands 3772 BV
Tel: 0031 342422911
Website: www.studiolightcrafts.co.uk

SUNRISE CRAFTS LTD

Product: Paper, card, die cuts, adhesives, embossing powders, glitter, stickers, toppers, embellishments, stamps, ink, pens, punches, kits and equipment.
Address: Wombourne Garden Centre, Pool House Road, Wombourne, Wolverhampton WV5 8AZ
Tel: 01902 897096
Email: sales@sunrisecrafts.co.uk
Website: www.sunrisecrafts.co.uk

TAYLORS SUPPLIES LTD

Product: Paper, card, adhesives, glitter, embellishments, kits and equipment.
Terms: No minimum order.
Address: Augustus Street, Cheetham Hill, Manchester M3 1HZ
Tel: 01618 340329
Email: info@taylors-supplies.co.uk
Website: www.taylors-supplies.co.uk

THAT'S REALLY CRAFTY

Product: Paper, card, die cuts, decoupage, embossing, embellishments, adhesives, glitter, ink, pens, punches, stamps, kits and equipment.
Terms: £75 minimum order.
Address: 2nd Floor Teddy Bear Hollow, 2 Churgate Mews, Loughborough, Leicestershire LE11 1TZ
Tel: 08453 883569
Email: chris@christianspencerart.com
Website: www.thatsreallycrafty.com

THE ART OF CRAFT LTD

Product: Paper, card, adhesives, embossing, glitter, embellishments, die cuts, punches, stamps, stickers, stencils, kits, books and equipment.
Terms: No minimum order.
Address: 101 Lynchford Road, North Camp, Farnborough, Hampshire GU14 6ET
Tel: 01252 377677
Email: info@art-of-craft.co.uk
Website: www.art-of-craft.co.uk

THE TREASURY

Product: Paper, card, adhesives, glitter, toppers, decoupage, die cuts, embellishments, ink, stamps, paints, chalk, pens, stencils, kits and equipment.
Address: 200 Park Lane, Kidderminster, Worcestershire DY11 6TQ
Tel: 01562 510203
Email: sales@treasurycrafts.com
Website: www.treasurycrafts.com

TONIC STUDIOS LTD

Product: Punches, adhesives, stamps, scissors and tools.
Address: PO Box 302, Bridgend CF31 9HZ
Tel: 01656 749152
Email: info@tonic-studios.co.uk
Website: www.tonic-studios.co.uk

TRIMCRAFT LTD

Product: Paper, card, decoupage, glitter, adhesives, pens, embossing, embellishments, die cuts, stickers, stamps, punches, kits and equipment.
Terms: £100 minimum order.
Address: Manco House, Bolsover Street, Hucknall, Nottinghamshire NG15 7TY
Tel: 01159 834820
Email: sales@trimcraftdirect.com
Website: www.trimcraftdirect.com

VESEY GALLERY

Product: Paper, card, adhesives, paints, pencils, kits and equipment.
Address: 48–50 Chester Road, Sutton, Coldfield, Birmingham B73 5DA
Tel: 01213 552363
Email: sales@veseyartsandcrafts.co.uk
Website: www.veseygallery.co.uk

WOBBLY MOG

Product: Paper, card, quilling, decoupage, stencils, paints, pens, ink, stencils, stamps, punches, stickers, glitter, adhesives, kits and accessories.
Terms: No minimum order.
Address: Unit 2 Abergarw Enterprise Centre, Abergarw Industrial Estate, Brynmenyn, Bridgend CF32 9LW
Tel: 01656 729002
Email: info@wobblyMog.co.uk
Website: www.wobblymog.co.uk

WOLFS HEAD CRAFTS

Product: Paper, card, adhesives, chalk, decoupage, die cuts, embossing, glitter, ink, paints, pens, pencils, stickers, stamps, kits and equipment.
Address: 10S Hildas Close, Chorley, Lancashire PR7 3NU
Tel: 01257 230893
Email: sales@wolfsheadcrafts.co.uk
Website: www.wolfsheadcrafts.co.uk

SEWING AND QUILTING

ABAKHAN FABRICS
Product: Fat quarter fabrics, felt, wadding, patterns, kits, thread, haberdashery and equipment.
Terms: No minimum order.
Address: Coast Road, Llanerch-y-Mor, Mostyn CH8 9DX
Tel: 01745 562100
Email: enquiries@abakhan.co.uk
Website: www.abakhanfabrics.co.uk

ANBO TEXTILES
Product: Fabrics: fat quarters, jelly rolls and charm squares; kits and equipment.
Terms: £500 minimum order or full or half bolts of fabric.
Address: Unit 8–9, Dashwood Industrial Estate, Dashwood Avenue, High Wycombe HP12 3ED
Tel: 01494 450155
Email: sales@anbo.co.uk
Website: www.anbo.co.uk

ANTIQUE ANGEL
Product: Fabrics, patterns, kits and wadding.
Address: 36 Denham Lane, Chalfont St Peter, Gerrard Cross SL9 0ET
Tel: 07765 888136
Email: orders@antiqueangel.co.uk
Website: www.antiqueangel.co.uk

ARTS AND DESIGNS
Product: Cross stitch and needlecraft kits, patterns, charts, thread, needles, hoops, frames and books.
Address: 3 Milehouse Crescent, Dumfries DG1 1JZ
Tel: 01387 264252
Website: www.artsanddesigns.com

ASDING
Product: Fabrics, wadding, thread, patterns and equipment.
Address: 6 The Glebe, Holt End, Beoley, Redditch B98 9AW
Tel: 01572 584486
Website: www.asding.com

ATLAS CRAFT LTD
Product: Needles, hoops, frames, long hook and cross stitch kits.
Address: 1 The Hall Coppice, Egerton, Bolton, Lancashire BL7 9UE
Tel: 01204 591584
Email: atlascraftltd@gmail.com
Website: www.atlascraft.co.uk

BAKER ROSS
Product: Fabrics, embroidery thread, felt, kits and equipment.
Address: 2–3 Forest Works, Forest Road, London E17 6JF
Tel: 08445 768922
Email: enquiry@bakerross.co.uk
Website: www.bakerross.co.uk

BEYOND FABRICS
Product: Fabrics, kits, books, patterns, sewing machines and equipment.
Terms: No minimum order.
Address: 67 Columbia Road, London, E2 7RG
Tel: 020 7729 5449
Email: info@beyond-fabrics.com
Website: www.beyond-fabrics.co.uk

BICESTER WOOLS
Product: Charm squares, jelly rolls, layer cakes, books and kits.
Address: 86 Sheep Street, Bicester, Oxon OX26 6LP
Tel: 01869 322966
Email: info@bicesterwools.com
Website: www.bicesterwools.com

BOGOD & CO LTD
Product: Sewing machines.
Address: 91 Goswell Road, London EC1V 7EX
Tel: 020 7336 7986

CAMELOT CRAFTS
Product: Fabrics: jelly rolls and layer cakes; cross stitch, embroidery and tapestry kits; thread, patterns, haberdashery and equipment.
Terms: No minimum order.
Address: Bransby House, Eaudyke Road, Friskney, Boston PE22 8NL
Tel: 01754 820139
Email: info@camelotcrafts.co.uk
Website: www.camelotcrafts.co.uk

CASTLE COURT QUILTER
Product: Fabrics, thread, equipment.
Address: Castle Court, Castle Street, Whittington, Oswestry SY11 4DF
Tel: 01691 654862
Website: www.castlecourtquilter.co.uk

COAST CRAFTS UK
Product: Thread, fabrics and equipment.
Terms: No minimum order.
Address: Green Lane Mill, Holmfirth, West Yorkshire HD9 2DX
Tel: 01484 681881
Email: consumer.ccuk@coats.com
Website: www.coatscrafts.co.uk

COTTON DREAMS
Product: Fabrics, patterns, needles, pins and equipment.
Address: 28 Oak Drive, Messingham, Scunthorpe, Lincolnshire DN17 3US

Tel: 01724 764014
Website: www.cottondreams.co.uk

CRAFTS AND QUILTS

Product: Fabrics, needles, pins, patterns, thread, wadding, kits, haberdashery and equipment.
Terms: £10 minimum order.
Address: 118–120 Marshside Road, Southport, Merseyside PR9 9SX
Tel: 01704 212257
Email: craftsandquilts@gmail.com
Website: www.craftsandquilts.net

CRAFTY DEVILS

Product: Quilting die cuts.
Terms: No minimum order.
Address: Unit 22–23 Howard Avenue, Barnstaple, Devon EX32 8QA
Tel: 01271 326777
Email: enquiries@ craftydevilspapercraft.co.uk
Website: www.craftydevilspapercraft. co.uk

DEMPSEY DESIGNS

Product: Soft toy kits.
Terms: Minimum order £150 with £15 P&P or £250 with free P&P.
Address: The Long Barn, Duns Tew Road, Hempton, Oxfordshire OX15 0QZ
Tel: 01869 337948
Email: info@dempseydesigns.co.uk
Website: www.dempseydesigns.com

DEVERE YARNS

Product: Embroidery thread, worsted wool and silk.
Address: Weavers House, Hyde Wood Road, Little Yeldham, Halstead CO9 4QX
Tel: 01787 237237
Email: sales@devereyarns.co.uk
Website: www.devereyarns.co.uk

DMC CREATIVE WORLD LTD

Product: Thread, fabrics, hoops, frames and equipment.
Terms: No minimum order.
Address: Unit 21 Warren Park Way, Warrens Park, Enderby, Leicester LE19 4SA
Tel: 01162 754000
Email: Contact submission form available on website.
Website: www.dmccreative.co.uk

ELLISON (SIZZIX)

Product: Quilting patterns, fabric, die cuts, appliqué and equipment.
Terms: No minimum order.
Address: Unit 3 Whitegate Industrial Estate, Wrexham, Wales LL13 8UG
Tel: 08444 998181
Email: europecustomerservices@ ellison.com
Website: www.sizzix.co.uk

EUROPEAN QUILTING SUPPLIES LTD

Product: Fabrics, wadding, needles, pins, thread, patterns, kits, equipment.
Terms: No minimum order.
Address: 11 Iliffe House, Iliffe Avenue, Leicester LE2 5LS
Tel: 01162 710033
Email: sales@eqsuk.com
Website: www.eqsuk.com

FABRIC INSPIRATIONS

Product: Fabrics.
Terms: No minimum order.
Address: Unit 3, The Glade Business Centre, Forum Road, Nottingham NG5 9RW
Email: shop@fabricinspirations.co.uk
Website: www.fabricinspirations. co.uk

FABRICS PLUS

Product: Fabrics, wadding, thread, patterns, needles, pins, books and equipment.
Terms: No minimum order.
Address: 19 Badminton Road, Downend, Bristol BS16 6BB
Tel: 01173 293857
Email: enquiries@fabricsplus.co.uk
Website: www.fabricsplus.co.uk

FIRESIDE FABRICS

Product: Fabrics, wadding, thread, patterns, kits and equipment.
Address: 71 Broadclyst Gardens, Thorpe Bay, Essex SS1 3QS
Tel: 07765 232492
Email: sales@firesidefabrics.co.uk
Website: www.firesidefabrics.co.uk

FISKARS UK LTD

Product: Sewing and patchwork equipment.
Terms: No minimum order.
Address: Bennerley Road, Bulwell, Nottingham NG6 8PE
Tel: 01159 277335
Email: UKinfo@fiskars.com
Website: www.fiskarscraft.co.uk

GILLIANGLADRAG LTD

Product: Felts, fabrics, haberdashery, sewing and tapestry kits, equipment.
Terms: £175 minimum order.
Address: The Fluff-a-torium, 20 West Street, Dorking, Surrey RH4 1BL
Tel: 01306 898144
Email: gill@gilliangladrag.co.uk
Website: www.gilliangladrag.co.uk

GLOSSOP CRAFT CENTRE

Product: Cross stitch, tapestry, kits; cottons, threads, felt, haberdashery, fabrics, patterns and equipment.

Address: Smith Fold Barn, Glossop, Derbyshire SK13 8DD
Tel: 01457 863559
Email: sales@glossopmaycrafts.co.uk
Website: www.glossopmaycrafts.co.uk

GROVES AND BANKS

Product: Wadding, batting, thread, needles, kits, accessories, equipment.
Address: Long Crendon Industrial Park, Drakes Drive, Long Crendon, Aylesbury HP18 9BA
Tel: 01844 258100
Email: enquiries@groves-banks.com
Website: www.groves-banks.com

HANTEX

Product: Fabrics, patterns, ribbons, buttons, felt, thread and kits.
Address: Unit 1 Whitehouse Business Units, Eaudyke Road, Friskney, Boston, PE22 8NL
Tel: 08448 794719
Email: sales@hantex.co.uk
Website: www.hantex.co.uk

HERITAGE CRAFTS

Product: Cross stitch kits, patterns, designs and equipment.
Address: Nathan Court, Redbrook Lane, Brereton, Staffordshire WS15 1QU
Tel: 01889 575328
Email: enquiries@hcrafts.com
Website: www.hcrafts.com

HISTORICAL SAMPLER COMPANY

Product: Cross stitch and tapestry kits and charts.
Terms: £100 minimum order.
Address: PO Box 6740, Billericay, Essex CM11 1ZY

Tel: 01268 711918
Email: joannestellig@btinternet.com
Website: www.historicalsamplercompany.co.uk

HULU

Product: Fabrics, patterns, thread, kits and equipment.
Terms: No minimum order.
Address: Sentinel House, Poundwell, Modbury, Devon PL21 0XX
Tel: 01548 831911
Email: sales@hulucrafts.co.uk
Website: www.hulucrafts.co.uk

JANOME

Product: Sewing machines.
Address: Janome Centre, Southside, Stockport, Cheshire SK6 2SP
Tel: 01616 666011
Email: info@janome.co.uk
Website: www.janome.co.uk

LADY SEW AND SEW

Product: Fabrics, sewing machines, wadding, thread, haberdashery, kits, patterns, books and equipment.
Terms: No minimum order.
Address: Moy House, 57 Institute Road, Marlow, Buckinghamshire SL7 1BN
Tel: 01628 890532
Email: mailorder@ladysewandsew.co.uk
Website: www.lady-sew-and-sew.co.uk

LAUGHING HEDGEHOG

Product: Fabrics: jelly rolls, layer cakes, charm packs, fat quarters; patterns and books.
Terms: No minimum order.
Address: 60 High Road, Buckhurst Hill, Essex IG9 5RW

Tel: 020 8504 8648
Email: sales@laughinghedgehog.com
Website: www.laughinghedgehog.com

MAKOWER UK

Product: Fabrics.
Address: 118 Greys Road, Henley-on-Thomas, Oxfordshire RG9 1QW
Tel: 01491 579727
Email: info@makoweruk.com
Website: www.makoweruk.com

QUILT DIRECT

Product: Fabrics, patterns, sewing machines, felt, wadding, stencils, threads, kits and equipment.
Terms: £5 minimum order.
Address: Peter Tavvy, Tavistock, Devon PL19 9NA
Tel: 01822 810877
Email: info@quiltdirect.co.uk
Website: www.quiltdirect.co.uk

RAINBOW SILK

Product: Fabrics, haberdashery, thread, kits, books and equipment.
Terms: No minimum order.
Address: 85 High Street, Great Missenden, Buckinghamshire HP16 9EF
Tel: 01494 862111
Email: caroline@rainbowsilks.co.uk
Website: www.rainbowsilks.co.uk

S.E. SIMONS

Product: Haberdashery, felt, thread, cotton, ribbons, kits and equipment.
Terms: £50 minimum order.
Address: Unit 6 Netham Industrial Park, Bristol BS5 9PJ
Tel: 01179 554710
Email: sales@sesimons.co.uk
Website: www.sesimons.co.uk

SIESTA FRAMES LTD

Product: Needles, scissors, haberdashery, thread, tapestry frames; embroidery, tapestry, cross stitch and quilting hoops and equipment.
Terms: £35 minimum order.
Address: Unit D Longmeadow Industrial Estate, Three Legged Cross, Wimborne, Dorset BH21 6RD
Tel: 01202 813363
Email: sales@siestaframes.com
Website: www.siestaframes.com

SILKEN STRANDS

Product: Machine and hand embroidery thread, needles, hooks, books and equipment.
Terms: No minimum order.
Address: 20 Y Rhos, Bangor, Gwynedd LL57 2LT
Tel: 01248 362361
Email: sales@silkenstrands.co.uk
Website: www.silkenstrands.co.uk

STITCH CRAFT CREATE

Product: Fabrics, haberdashery, patterns, sewing machines, felt, wadding, needles, frames, hoops, books, kits and equipment.
Terms: No minimum order.
Address: Brunel House, Newton Abbot, Devon TQ12 4PU
Tel: 08448 805852
Email: customerservices@stitchcraftcreate.co.uk
Website: www.stitchcraftcreate.co.uk

T C THREADS

Product: Embroidery thread, fabrics.
Terms: No minimum order.
Address: Edward House, King Edward Street, Hucknall, Nottingham NG15 7JR
Tel: 01159 680089
Email: sales@tcthreads.ltd.uk
Website: www.tcthreads.ltd.uk

TAYLORS SUPPLIES LTD

Product: Fabrics, buttons, haberdashery, needles, hoops, tapestry, embossing, thread, kits and equipment.
Terms: No minimum order.
Address: Augustus Street, Cheetham Hill, Manchester M3 1HZ
Tel: 01618 340329
Email: info@taylors-supplies.co.uk
Website: www.taylors-supplies.co.uk

THE AFRICAN FABRIC SHOP

Product: African fabrics and quilt kits.
Address: 19 Hebble Mount, Meltham, Holmfirth, West Yorkshire HD9 4HG
Tel: 01484 850188
Email: info@africanfabric.co.uk
Website: www.africanfabric.co.uk

THE BUTTON COMPANY

Product: Buttons, ribbons, thread, patterns, kits and equipment.
Terms: £100 minimum order.
Address: 41 Terminus Road, Chichester, West Sussex PO19 8TX
Tel: 01243 775462
Email: sales@buttoncompany.co.uk
Website: www.buttoncompany.co.uk

THE COTTON PATCH

Product: Fabrics, frames, hoops, sewing machines, wadding, thread, haberdashery, books, magazines, kits and equipment.
Terms: No minimum order.
Address: 1283–1285 Stratford Road, Hall Green, Birmingham, B28 9AJ
Tel: 01217 022840
Email: mailorder@cottonpatch.co.uk
Website: www.cottonpatch.co.uk

THE CROSS STITCH GUILD

Product: Charts, patterns, fabrics, thread, accessories, books, equipment.
Terms: No minimum order.
Address: Pinks Barn, London Road, Fairford, Gloucestershire GL7 4AR
Tel: 0800 3289750
Email: jane@thecrossstitchguild.com
Website: www.thecrossstitchguild.com

THE FAT QUARTERS

Product: Fabrics: fat quarters and fat eighths; patterns, quilt and embroidery hoops, sewing machines, thread, wadding and equipment.
Terms: No minimum order.
Address: 5 Chopwell Road, Blackhall Mill, Newcastle upon Tyne NE17 7TN
Tel: 01207 565728
Email: sales@thefatquarters.co.uk
Website: www.thefatquarters.co.uk

THE QUILT ROOM

Product: Fabrics: jelly rolls, dessert rolls, pre-cuts; haberdashery, patterns, books, sewing machines and equipment.
Terms: No minimum order.
Address: 37–39 High Street, Dorking, Surrey RH4 1AR
Tel: 01306 877307
Email: sales@quiltroom.co.uk
Website: www.quiltroom.co.uk

WOBBLY MOG

Product: Cross stitch kits, thread, felt, buttons, ribbons and equipment.
Terms: No minimum order.
Address: Unit 2 Abergarw Enterprise Centre, Abergarw Industrial Estate, Brynmenyn, Bridgend CF32 9LW
Tel: 01656 729002
Email: info@wobblyMog.co.uk
Website: www.wobblymog.co.uk

CLAIRE CROMPTON

Claire Crompton is a cross-stitch and knitwear designer (www.clairecrompton.co.uk) and author of numerous books on both subjects. She has online shops selling her patterns on Etsy, Folksy and Ravelry. She also runs workshops on knitting and crochet.

ONLINE MARKETPLACES

I worked in the knitwear industry for a few years, then went freelance because the time felt right. Online stores were just starting up, so they weren't part of my business to start with, but as they grew I began to put my patterns online and sell them.

If you were starting out now, when there are so many online outlets, I'd advise doing plenty of research. All these sites are very easy to use: they're designed to encourage people to place their products on there. But you need to decide what is best for you. Working as I do in knitting and crochet, Ravelry is the biggest site for me: everyone who's on Ravelry is interested in using yarn in some way. Etsy has a very good reputation for original craft work and Folksy is the up-and-coming UK version.

Check what your competitors are doing on each site, how they are displaying their products and what their photography and their prices are like. Also read the terms and conditions and the policies of the site, to make sure they fit with your ethos and how you want to promote yourself.

> All these sites are very easy to use: they're designed to encourage people to place their products on there.

MAKING YOURSELF STAND OUT

Once you're on a site, raising and maintaining your profile does take a lot of work. It's easy just to put products up and think, 'Well, people will find me eventually'. But you need to keep promoting yourself.

One way to do that is to keep 'renewing' your products. On Etsy, for example, there are a lot of people selling knitting patterns and if you search for 'knitting patterns' the newer ones are listed first. So every day you should go into your shop, add new things if you can, renew others and constantly remind people that you are there.

It's also important to put personality into your shop. A blog is a good way of doing this; or you can link your online shop to your Facebook page. That way, every time you put a new product on, it shows up on Facebook too.

The sites I'm talking about aren't curated – you just register and put up what you like. But you then have to do

quality control on yourself, ask yourself what you want people to see.

There are a number of curated sites, where you have to apply and meet their standards, but I haven't used them so far. I need a bigger range of products before I go on to something like that – they're the next level up, if you like, so I want to establish myself on the non-curated sites first.

Whatever sites you're on, it's good to have a number of different products. People won't engage as much with a shop that has only two or three things as they will with one that has 20 or 25, where they can see that the owner is enthusiastic about their work and their site, and is there putting in the effort. Having said that, you shouldn't put any old thing up just to fill the spaces – remember to think about your quality as well.

THE SECRETS OF A SUCCESSFUL ONLINE SHOP

Photography is very important. Obviously online customers can't pick the thing up and look at it and feel it: they rely on the photos. You can have the best product in the world, but if you don't take a good photo, no one is

going to know that. Look at successful sellers on your site, then look at the style of photograph they use. On Etsy there are tutorials to help you take good photographs. You don't need an expensive camera, but you do need a plain background and a good light source, preferably natural light.

If you're writing something about yourself, try to tell a story. Explain why you're making what you're making and try to convey your enthusiasm. Buying online can be a cold experience – you just click on a product and send your money off. Lots of people like the idea that their money's going to a designer they feel they know.

PRICING YOUR WARES

Research again! When I started selling knitting patterns online, I looked at my

> People won't engage as much with a shop that has only two or three things as they will with one that has 20 or 25.

> You can have the best product in the world, but if you don't take a good photo, no one is going to know that.

competitors. All the yarn companies produce patterns; so do knitting magazines, book publishers, other designers like me. There's also a huge number of free patterns available. I'm competing against all of that. I have to produce a pattern that's unusual, that people can't get for free, and then I have to price it between the yarn companies (who are a lot cheaper than me) and some of the bigger name designers. I settled on a price that covered my costs and gave me a profit, that wasn't so high people wouldn't pay it, but wasn't so low they would think the pattern wasn't worth anything. It took a lot of research to get it right.

When you're making things for sale, you have to look closely at what it has cost you. not just materials, but your time and all your overheads – light, heat, going out in the car to source materials,

everything. Then you add a profit, and remember that you have to pay tax and National Insurance on that profit. If something costs you £4 to make and you sell it for £5, you make £1 profit, but quite a chunk of that will go in tax.

Look at the price of similar products in the marketplace. Don't compare yourself to mass-market producers; look at smaller craftspeople and don't sell your work too cheaply. A lot of craftspeople are hesitant about putting a realistic price on their work. They feel they can't ask £200 for a patchwork quilt, even though they've spent six months making it, so they sell it for £50 and make a loss. But people will pay for beautiful handmade things. If you are producing something they can't find anywhere else, using good-quality materials and very good workmanship, and they can connect to you and see the story behind the product, then they will recognize its value and pay for it.

> Don't compare yourself to mass-market producers; look at smaller craftspeople and don't sell your work too cheaply.

MAKING A LIVING

I'd never advise anyone to look at their craft as a paid hobby. Look at it as part of your work. You can't just put a few things up on Etsy and see what happens: you have to commit to it, but you also have to realise that it isn't going to pay all the bills. Not many people make a good living out of selling crafts: a lot of craft workers have a part-time job and they may run workshops as well, so that the making and selling of products is only a part of their income. It means that if ever one aspect of their work isn't going well, they have something else to fall back on.

RUNNING A BUSINESS

When you start making money from your craft, you have to fill in a self-assessment tax return, so that you pay tax on your extra income. You can also claim tax relief on business expenses such as materials and overheads. Phone your local tax office – hey're always very helpful – and get this sorted out right from the start, because then you can get on with the creative side.

Set up a simple accounting system. From everything I earn I put some aside to cover tax and NI. I make sure that bills are paid on time and I have a credit card

I use only for business expenses. I use an exercise book to list my incomings and outgoings and with any luck at the bottom of the page there is a nice plus sign with my profit at the end of the month.

It really doesn't have to be complicated, but if you're nervous about this sort of thing, you can get help from organizations such as Business Link. Local arts groups often run inexpensive one-day workshops on 'accounting for arts and crafts people' and the HMRC website will give you tips on the basics of accounting. A lot of craft people tend to ignore the business side because they want to concentrate on their craft, but you do have to think, 'I am making these things and selling them to make money.'

UNDER-PROMISE AND OVER-DELIVER

A top tip for any sort of business: don't promise anything you can't deliver. If someone's buying a product that is made to order, don't say you can deliver it in a week if it is going to take you three. Tell them it's going to take four weeks, then when you do it in three they'll think they've got it early and be pleased.

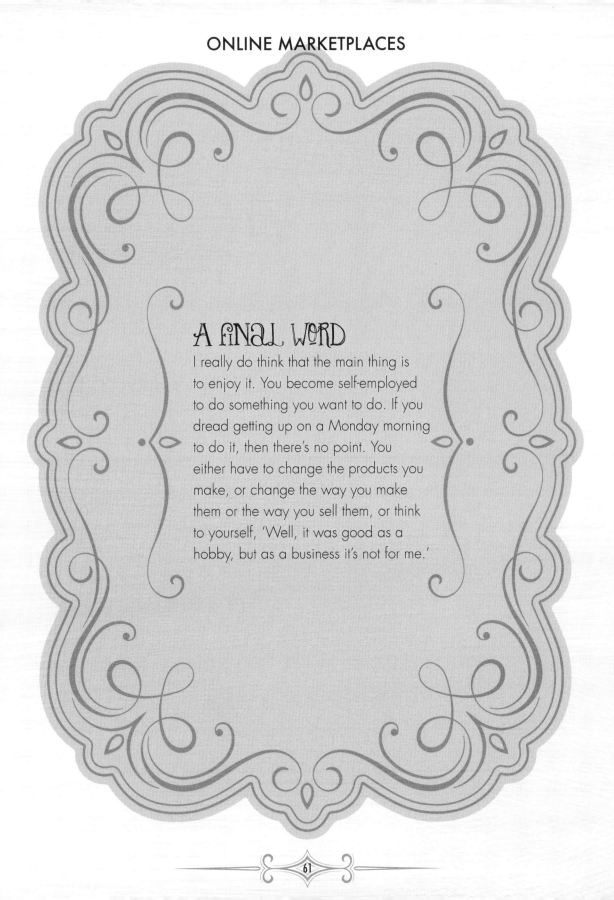

A FINAL WORD

I really do think that the main thing is to enjoy it. You become self-employed to do something you want to do. If you dread getting up on a Monday morning to do it, then there's no point. You either have to change the products you make, or change the way you make them or the way you sell them, or think to yourself, 'Well, it was good as a hobby, but as a business it's not for me.'

ONLINE MARKETPLACES

ARTFIRE

www.artfire.com

Sells: All handmade items.

Fees: 14 day free trial, then a flat fee of $12.95 per month with no additional fees.

About: A small Tucson, AZ based company founded in 2008 with a passion for handmade, art, and indie business. Artfire is an interactive handmade marketplace and craft community that aims to support businesses and brands with innovative features and functions.

Community: Artfire encourages members to interact via Chatterbox forums, Nosh blog and Artfire Guilds on their website. Members can also follow Etsy via their Twitter (@Etsy), Facebook and LinkedIn accounts or through daily emails. Artfire can also be found on Flikr and YouTube.

Shop Personalization: Members can customize their sites to reflect their own unique styles.

Other Tools: Artfire optimize and push items to Google, Bing, Yahoo, TheFind and Google Shopping. Artfire shops are intergrated with the most trusted names in online payments including PayPal and Amazon Payments.

BONANZA

www.bonanzamarket.co.uk

Sells: All handmade items.

Fees: Free listings, 3.5% commission for sales under $500 (varies for higher value items).

About: An online marketplace for buying and selling new or used handmade items. Rated "easiest to use" marketplace in 2012, by Ecommerce Bytes users.

Community: Has busy message forums and a Bonanza Blog, as well as hand-picked lists, community collections and freebies for members.

Shop Personalization: Members can create their own 'booth' with custom banners, badges and profiles. A number of other custom options are available for an additional fee.

Other Tools: Users can import listings from other marketplaces, including eBay and Etsy, and can also push details of ther listings out to their own blogs and Twitter feeds. Google Analytics integration is supported.

CRAFT MARKET CORNER

www.craftmarketcorner.co.uk

Sells: A wide range of handmade products including gifts, crafts and condiments.

Fees: Craft Market Corner allows users to sample a free trial 'stall' prior to registering for a paid market stall.

About: Craft Market Corner was launched to replicate the atmosphere of outdoor craft markets, online; showcasing a huge variety of unique modern and vintage products ranging from jewellery and art to condiments and toys. Craft Market Corner provides an ideal environment for users to connect with their consumers and discuss individual products, simulating the one-on-one advantage of a craft stall with the added benefit of a wider market audience.

Community: Customers can opt to receive a regular newsletter featuring updates and news concerning the online market stalls.

Shop Personalization: Each user can customize their stall, including personal and business information. Users also have the ability to create a custom banner, import company logos and tailor colour themes.

Other Tools: As well as a newsletter, the website also features a blog that provides users with information regarding updates and new features.

CRAFTYBOB

www.craftybob.com

Sells: All handmade items.

Fees: CraftyBob does not charge a fee or commission on handmade cards; all other craft items are subject to a small listing fee of £0.10 for 90 days, plus a fixed sales commission of 10%.

About: Created by craftsuprint.com, CraftyBob is an online marketplace for homemade crafts, artwork and second-hand and up-cycled items. The majority of products featured are gift cards for a variety of occasions including birthdays, weddings, anniversaries, Halloween and Christmas. However, other unique handcrafted items are featured, such as jewellery and gifts. The website is straightforward and simple to navigate, featuring on the Top 50 UK Crafters website: www. top50crafters.co.uk. CraftyBob selects certain shops to feature on the homepage, providing an excellent marketing opportunity for sellers.

Community: CraftyBob has active social media accounts on Twitter (@ craftsuprint) and Facebook; users are able to integrate products for sale with their Facebook accounts. The website also features competitions and games between craft members and a helpful forum on craftsuprint.com, allowing members to discuss issues and share advice.

Shop Personalization: Users can completely customize their online shop, creating banners, avatars and a personal profile.

Other Tools: Users of CraftyBob – buyers and sellers – can create 'Circles' in which favourite members and shops can be added, allowing users to receive updates and view other members' favourites.

DAWANDA

www.en.dawanda.com

Sells: A wide range of products including fashion, jewellery, art, home and garden accessories.

Fees: DaWanda features free registration and free listing with just 5% commission deducted from sales.

About: This vast online marketplace is used worldwide, attracting an estimated 7 million visitors per month. It allows any amateur or professional crafter to showcase and sell their products, featuring unique handmade items, such as jewellery, handbags, stationary and homeware.

Community: DaWanda is socially active on Twitter (@DaWanda_en) and Facebook, keeping members updated of news and features. The DaWanda YouTube channel provides useful

hints and tips, as well as showcasing certain sellers. DaWanda also utilizes a blog to share all the latest news and information with its members, highlighting individual crafters and answering queries.

Shop Personalization: There are many personalization options available with DaWanda, allowing the user to create a personal profile and banner. DaWanda's virtual 'shop window' feature allows users to display up to 16 items on a customized background.

Other Tools: Users are able to create DaWanda widgets to add to their personal websites or blog pages, directing traffic from their own sites to their online marketplace.

DELIGHTED

www.shopdelighted.com

Sells: Handmade goods and supplies.

Fees: Listing fee of $0.20 (for 120 days). 3.5% commission on shippable items; 10% commission for digital downloads.

About: Delighted is a US marketplace and all pricing is in dollars, although UK users are able to set up a store with international shipping. Allows individual sellers and small businesses to earn money by selling their handmade creations or craft supplies.

Community: Has an active forum and 'new listings' section, as well as Facebook, Twitter and Pinterest accounts.

Shop Personalization: Limited customisation allows users to have a custom name for their shop, a banner graphic and social media badges, and shop announcements and messages.

Other Tools: Includes built-in analytics, and also allows users to

import listings form their Etsy accounts. Uses PayPal.

eBay

www.ebay.co.uk

Sells: Any items, except those deemed inappropriate by eBay administrators.

Fees: Insertion fees are dependent upon the initial starting price; eBay also substitutes a commission from any finalized sales.

About: eBay is one of the most well known and trusted websites worldwide. Primarily an auction site; products can also be sold for a fixed 'buy-it-now' price. With over 14 million users, eBay has become a thriving marketplace for individuals and businesses. Users that intend to use eBay as a regular selling platform might prefer to create an eBay Shop; users pay a monthly fee, which varies depending on their monthly turnover. eBay utilizes a feedback system in which buyers and sellers can grade and comment on their buying and selling experiences. Each piece of positive feedback rewards users with a star next to their user names – numbers can reach into the hundreds of thousands for the professional eBay entrepreneur – representing a user's experience and trustworthiness.

Community: eBay's Twitter account (@eBay) and blog (eBay Ink) keep members updated regularly on news, features and products. A dedicated support service is also available for help on an abundance of issues that may occur.

Shop Personalization: eBay shop owners can create logos, customize the colour scheme and font of their page, include product promotions and create

categories for their items. Members who choose not to create a shop can also customize the font, colour and layout of each individual listing uploaded.

Other Tools: Smartphone and Android users can download the eBay app, making creating listings, communicating with buyers/sellers and purchasing items easier.

ETSY

www.etsy.com

Sells: All handmade items.

Fees: Listed items incur a fee of $0.20 for a four month listing; Etsy also substitute a 3.5% commission from any finalized sales.

About: Etsy has become a huge online marketplace dedicate to promoting handmade, vintage and second hand arts and crafts. Creating an Etsy Shop is simple, free and provides instant access to over 15 million buyers.

Community: Etsy's blog (blog. etsy.com) features a variety of topical issues and runs regular features on Etsy shops, as does their YouTube channel. Members can also follow Etsy via their Twitter (@Etsy), Facebook or Tumblr accounts.

Shop Personalization: Members can create a personal profile and a customized shop banner, creating a brand look for their Etsy marketplace.

Other Tools: Etsy features an abundance of apps that customize the client experience, assist in finance management and integrate Etsy with Facebook, Twitter, and LinkedIn. The full range of apps can be viewed at www.etsy.com/apps.

FOLKSY

www.folksy.com

Sells: Handcrafted gifts and supplies.

Fees: Folksy's basic package incurs fees of £0.15 + VAT per item listed and 6% + VAT commission on sales. Folksy Plus requires a fee of £30 per year (inc VAT) and 6% + VAT commission on sales, however listings are free.

About: Featured in national publications, such as The Guardian, Homes and Gardens and Country Living, Folksy has become a widespread and renowned online marketplace for crafters, designers and artists. Products must be able to meet the 'handcrafted' criteria and, unlike many similar websites, Folksy does not accept vintage items. Folksy features a wide selection of handmade gifts, such as bags, belts, bunting and more.

Community: Folksy prioritizes the idea of community and provides regular topics for discussion within their forums, allowing members to interact with one another and share advice. Folksy's blog, titled 'Folksy Makes', invites members to demonstrate their skills and the processes involved in making particular items. Online magazine Frankly is Folksy's own publication, which contains craft-related articles and interviews with their marketplace members in their 'Meet the Maker' feature. Folksy also utilizes social media platforms, such as Twitter (@folksy), Facebook and Instagram (Folksy HQ).

Shop Personalization: Members can create a personal profile, including details about themselves, their craft and inspirations. Folksy marketplaces also features the option to customize the colour theme and shop banner.

Other Tools: Folksy have an active presence on Facebook, Twitter and Pinterest, encouraging users to share their favourite handcrafted products.

ICRAFT

www.icraft.ca

Sells: Handcrafted gifts, jewellery, toys and homeware.

Fees: iCraft requires an initial $25 registration fee and subsequent monthly fees, which vary depending on turnover. iCraft do not take commission on sales.

About: iCraft is an online marketplace dedicated entirely to high quality handmade gifts. Featuring approximately 2000 sellers, iCraft does not exhibit second-hand or vintage products, and maintains strict guidelines for handmade items. Items can only be sold by the makers and designers themselves and not by a third party.

Community: Active users of Facebook and Twitter (@icraft), iCraft also have their own YouTube channel on which they showcase members and provide useful hints and tips. The iCraft website features a regular newsletter,

---

"Every day you should go into your shop, add new things if you can, renew others and constantly remind people that you are there." Claire Crompton

containing interviews with crafting members, and a community forum.

Shop Personalization: iCraft allows members to create a personal profile, customize their shop page and banner and include links to other personal social media websites.

Other Tools: Members can connect their iCraft shop with Google Analytics, allowing them to keep track of traffic and web trends on their shop page.

MISI

www.misi.co.uk

Sells: Handcrafted gifts, craft supplies and vintage items.

Fees: Misi charges £0.20 per item and 3% commission on finalized sales.

About: Established in 2008, Misi (Make It Sell It) is a relatively recent enterprise, yet it is already attracting approximately 7500 visitors per month and has over 3000 sellers. The website specializes in a variety of handmade gifts, such as bridal jewellery, baby accessories, toiletries and vintage items.

Community: Members can connect with Misi on Twitter (@misi_uk) and Facebook, where new products and sellers are regularly promoted. Misi also features a variety of forums to allow users to discuss topics and issues with fellow members.

Shop Personalization: Users have the option of customizing their own Misi websites and banners, however Misi also offer a free custom graphic design service for members.

Other Tools: The Misi widget allows members to integrate their shop on other personal websites and blogs.

NOT MASS PRODUCED

www.notmassproduced.com

Sells: Handmade artisan goods including accessories, art and craft, beauty products, fashion, jewellery, stationery, toys and wedding paraphernalia.

Fees: Details of user fees when using Not Mass Produced are provided upon application.

About: Members of Not Mass Produced are carefully selected and required to meet a range of criteria including using natural, recycled, vintage, sustainable or organic materials. Members are reassured that all administration and marketing will be taken care of by the site, and they will strictly be exhibiting their pieces alongside like-minded artisans, rather than mass produced, cheap products.

Community: Not Mass Produced stays connected with members via Pinterest, Twitter, Facebook, Google+, LinkedIn and their blog.

Shop Personalization: There is little or no personalization option for sellers on Not Mass Produced. Displays are clean, simple and conform within their categories, allowing the items to do the talking.

Other Tools: The Not Mass Produced blog provides a range of useful tutorials.

NOT ON THE HIGH STREET

www.notonthehighstreet.com

Sells: Handmade gifts.

Fees: Upon assessing each application, Not on the High Street offers a fee package that is most suitable for the individual. No fees are incurred for listing products, however Not on the High Street will deduct up to 5% commission on finalized sales.

About: Not on the High Street specializes in high quality and unique handmade items, sourced from small businesses across the UK. Highly regarded in media publications, such as *Country Home*, *Interiors*, *Closer* and *The Independent*, as well as receiving the prestigious 'National Customer Service Award 2010' and the 'Wedding Ideas Award' in 2011 and 2012, Not on the High Street is an influential online marketplace for ambitious makers and designers.

Community: Sellers are kept up-to-date with all the latest news and new features via Not on the High Street's blog, weekly newsletter and email subscriptions. Not on the High Street also features a unique award system for their members called the 'Make Awards', consisting of several categories, such as Best Product, Gift of the Year and Best Customer Service. Buyers nominate and vote for sellers, allowing makers to establish themselves amongst the Not on the High Street community.

Shop Personalization: Upon registering, members are provided with their own URL and page which can be personalized. Each members page can display up to 30 products.

Other Tools: The Not on the High Street production team provide users with advice concerning their page, such as how to maximize sale potential before they are officially launched.

ONLINE MARKETPLACES

RAVELRY

www.ravelry.com

Sells: Knitting and crochet patterns.

Fees: Membership is free.

About: Ravelry allows fibre artists to connect with each other and share patterns, tips and project ideas. The website also supports the emergence of micro-businesses, allowing patterns, products and yarns to be sold on the website, as well as providing users with advertising opportunities.

Community: Ravelry is a community platform for fibre artists in itself, however the website does feature its own blog and extends its community activity through Twitter (@ravelry).

Shop Personalization: Upon registering, members are provided with a virtual 'notebook' page on which current projects can be uploaded and shared with the other 'Ravelers'.

Other Tools: Ravelry is working on a mobile version of their website. There is no official Ravelry app, however others have created several apps to accompany Ravelry. An example is Stitch, which allows users to access Ravelry from a Windows phone.

SEEK & ADORE

www.seekandadore.com

Sells: Handmade clothing, gifts and homeware.

Fees: Membership with Seek & Adore requires an annual fee of £180 which can be spread across monthly payments (£10 for the first 6 months and £20 for the last 6 months) plus a 25% commission on finalized sales.

About: Seek & Adore is a carefully selected group of designers of handmade goods. The website focuses on the designers and their story, encouraging members to actively create blogs and videos revolving around their projects. What sets Seek & Adore apart from other online marketplaces is the level of support that designers receive; an influential PR team continuously promote the website and designers, and advice is readily available in the form of telephone discussions. This prestigious website is ideal for newly emerging designers due to the significant level of support on offer.

Community: As well as maintaining its own regular blog, Seek & Adore encourages designers to create their own blogs - customers prefer to buy from people they feel they know rather than faceless manufacturers. Members can also keep in touch with Seek & Adore via Facebook and Twitter (@seekandadore).

Shop Personalization: Members are provided with an online studio consisting of a selection of pages designed to be filled with personal details, a blog, photographs, interviews and videos.

Other Tools: Seek & Adore is integrated with Facebook and Twitter, allowing buyers to share their purchases and favourite sellers.

THE CRAFTERS BARN

www.thecraftersbarn.co.uk

Sells: Handcrafted gifts and supplies.

Fees: Unlimited listings for £2.30 per month (first 24 hours free). Does not take commission.

About: Aims to offer a retail site for craft sellers at a minimum price, and is one of the only commission-free craft marketplaces in the UK. Sells a diverse range of products including handmade jewellery, fabric crafts, painting, culinary craft and more. Uses PayPal.

Community: Integrated with several social media platforms, including Facebook and Twitter. Includes a 'Sellers Directory' portfolio of each vendor that uses the site.

Shop Personalization: Allows custom banners, but little else at present. They are hoping to add more customisation options in the future.

TOSOUK

www.tosouk.com

Sells: A wide range of handmade, vintage and collectable products and craft supplies.

Fees: ToSouk does not charge fees for listing or deduct commission from sales.

About: A small UK based social marketplace for handcrafted and vintage collectibles, ToSouk was set up purely out of passion for handmade and unique products. Registration is easy and free, allowing newly emerging crafters to enter the world of e-commerce. A 'Souk' is an Arabic market place that sells anything and everything, usually beautiful trinkets and crafts.

Community: The ToSouk website features a variety of community forums, allowing members to discuss ideas, issues and share advice. Members can also connect with ToSouk via Facebook, Twitter (@ToSouk), LinkedIn, Flickr, MySpace and YouTube.

Shop Personalization: There is little or no personalization option for sellers on ToSouk. Displays are clean, simple and conform within their categories, allowing the items to do the talking.

Walkabout Crafts

www.walkaboutcrafts.com

Sells: Art, candles, cross stitch, embroidery, jewellery, patchwork and quilting, soaps, woodcrafts and more.

Fees: Various packages are available based on the size of a business and number of items listed: ranging from the 'Crystal' package with a £10 joining fee and 10 item limit – to the 'Platinum' package which allows users to list up to 200 items at any one time for a cost of £100.

About: Walkabout Crafts is an online community and marketplace for crafters of all abilities and disciplines, providing members with a friendly marketplace to list items for free and reap 100% of the profits. The website features an extensive array of topics for entrepreneurial crafters looking to establish a small business.

Community: Walkabout Crafts welcomes members from across the world and features a 'World Tour' section which invites members to share information about their home countries: history, places to stay, visit, eat and things to do. The website provides an extensive list of social networking sites for members to share their site experiences on, including Facebook, Tumblr, Flickr, LinkedIn and Twitter.

Shop Personalization: Members are able to customize their shop pages, including personal information and photographs of their products on sale.

Other Tools: Walkabout Crafts features a variety of competitions in which members have the chance to win gift vouchers and craft products.

Zibbet

www.zibbet.com

Sells: Handmade goods, fine art, vintage pieces and craft supplies.

Fees: Zibbet offers a basic package which entitles users to free listings – without commission on sales – on up to 50 items. Alternatively, users can opt for the premium package of $9.95 per month or $79 annually, both with unlimited listings.

About: This is a global marketplace for sellers of handmade goods, art, vintage pieces and craft supplies. Premium members benefit from the advantage of randomly featuring on the Zibbet homepage. Zibbet is integrated with shopping websites Google Product Search and TheFind, meaning that every item listed is searchable on these two websites that attract a combined average of 40 million visitors each month.

Community: Zibbet's community hub consists of a range of forums, inviting members to share and discuss issues and advice. Members also have the option to join groups of similar interests, such as 'Teen Crafters', 'Zibbet Graphic Designers' and 'Zibbet Metalworkers' – to name a few. Other community features include instant message chat, Ortist Graphical Scrapbook – an online doodle sharing feature – and a Zibbet blog.

Shop Personalization: Members have a huge variety of personalization options available to them, depending on their package. Premium members are entitled to complete customization, video and image hosting, increased amount of photographs per item and gift certificate and coupon features.

Other Tools: An Etsy importer app allows members to integrate their existing Etsy inventory over to their Zibbet store in minutes. Zibbet is also developing an app which will allow members to sell their items on Facebook.

EMMA CURTIS AND LIZ PARNELL

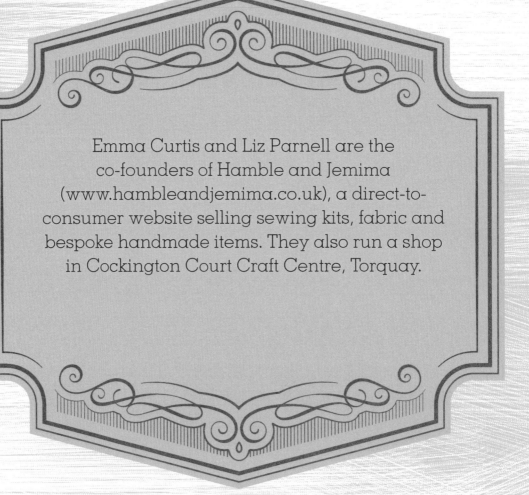

Emma Curtis and Liz Parnell are the co-founders of Hamble and Jemima (www.hambleandjemima.co.uk), a direct-to-consumer website selling sewing kits, fabric and bespoke handmade items. They also run a shop in Cockington Court Craft Centre, Torquay.

We met while we were both working for David & Charles Publishers – Emma as a product manager and Liz as a freelance graphic designer – and one Christmas we decided to make all our own presents, from jams and chutneys to sock puppets and bags. Everyone loved the bags, so we made some more. One thing led to another: we had a market stall for a while but we couldn't keep up with the demand and we decided that instead of producing finished bags, we would put together kits so that people could make their own. Between us, with our different backgrounds, we came up with some really nice designs. One of the reasons our partnership has worked so well is that we have similar ideas, but come at them from different angles.

The craft market has changed enormously in the last few years. Liz has an eleven-year-old daughter and all her friends love our products. Teenage girls also seem much more tuned in to beautiful fabrics and beautiful objects than we ever were. So although our kits have a broad appeal, we certainly have a young following and we give a lot of thought to presentation. Obviously what's inside is important, but we've always looked at the package as a whole.

> **Although our kits have a broad appeal, we certainly have a young following and we give a lot of thought to presentation.**

OUR ONLINE SHOP

From the start, we knew that an online shop was going to be important. Our first website was designed from scratch, but it turned out to be difficult to maintain and to add to. We needed a quick solution (we had a huge order from John Lewis and we were about to send out literally thousands of kits with our web address on). So we went to a website provider, create.net. They supplied the template and then we put our own stamp on it. With Liz and her husband's design skills we were able to make it look very bespoke, even though it isn't a bespoke site. It's worked really well for us.

The most important thing about the site is the shop that came with it: it makes it easy for customers to place an order, the payment is dealt with automatically and we receive a notification. It is as simple as that and it costs us less than £10 a month. Obviously website providers offer

> ## The most important thing about the site is the shop that came with it.

different packages – you don't have to have a shop if you don't need one, but for us it's been crucial.

The other key thing is to be able to log people's interest, so you can build up a database of potential customers. By far the best response we have to any initiative is when we send an email newsletter advertising new products or offering a discount to people who have signed up on the site – it's much more productive than putting an advertisement in a magazine. We have loyal customers who come back again and

again and spend perhaps £50 or £60 at a time on kits.

Once you have your template, you need to make your site look professional and individual. You need a strong home page, the right logo and good images. If you don't have a background in graphic design, it's well worth employing someone who does.

BRIEFING A DESIGNER

To brief a designer effectively, you need to be very clear about what your product is, who your target audience is and what age range you are aiming at. Try pulling pages out of magazines and creating a mood board, to say, 'I like the feel of this.' Look at other websites and find a company that you would like to have a similar feel or image to. Give the designer a tight enough brief that they know what you want, but not so tight that they feel they can't suggest anything – after all, you are employing them for their ideas and, assuming that they are good at their job, you have to trust them.

> ## We have loyal customers who come back again and again and spend perhaps £50 or £60 at a time on kits.

FUNCTIONALITY

In addition to the shop and the data collection, we've found it important to be able to run competitions from the site. People like interaction on websites. They like to be able to express opinions and if there is the possibility of winning something, so much the better. For this we went to wufoo.com: you design a page the way you want it, then Wufoo changes it into Javascript and you drop it into your site. That was very straightforward too.

We also have the facility to offer discounts, so that people can enter a code into a box and get money off. Our handbags and phone cases are probably our best-selling items, but we get a good response on almost anything if we feature it in the newsletter and offer a discount: anything we promote shoots to the top of our best-seller list. We don't hold a huge amount of stock, so any time we find we've got lots of an item, that's what we do: reduce it in price and steer our customers towards it.

INSPIRING PHOTOS

Our gallery is very important to us, too: we have lovely images to inspire people. All our kits are inspirational and that makes us different from a lot of crafts. People do cross stitch because they like cross stitch, for instance, but our products are more about wanting the finished item than they are about the process. Our customers like to think that they are buying individual, unique things: something they buy on the High Street may be cheap, but it's mass-market; whereas with us they feel they're getting something special, something that somebody's put some thought into. It seems wholesome, compared with something you might pay two quid for and then throw away the next day.

> **All our kits are inspirational and that makes us different from a lot of crafts.**

MAINTAINING THE SHOP

Up to a point, our website looks after itself, so it's easy to neglect it when we're busy. But there are always things that can be improved upon; new ideas and things we can add. In an ideal world, we'd be doing this once a week.

The amount of maintenance you need to do depends on the number of products you have and how quickly they turn over. If you have hundreds of products, then obviously you have to spend more time making sure the site's up to date. We have about 20–30 kits, and we also sell fabric, buttons, ribbons and so on separately, so it isn't that hard to maintain. What does take time is advertising a bespoke bag, because we have to take a good photograph and write something about it, just as we do with the other products. Then we sell it and it's gone – so that was quite a lot of work for a one-off piece.

Try not to overload your website with too many products. Some websites are a bit like going to a restaurant where the menu is pages and pages long – it's easy to be overwhelmed and think, 'Oh, I can't be bothered.' But when a menu has a few select, beautiful-sounding things, you're much more likely to pick something you fancy and to enjoy the whole experience. So select the key items for your site carefully, take some lovely photographs and put them on your home page.

BRICKS AND MORTAR

Our shop is really more like a showroom/studio. Because we aren't on a High Street the footfall isn't huge, but we can store a lot of stuff there and we can work on new ideas in a lovely environment. We can sell samples of any finished pieces that we make; we can talk to other craft people and get feedback on products from anyone who comes in. So it's very useful in all sorts of ways, but the vast majority of our business is online.

KEEPING IN TOUCH

The one thing you don't want to do is bombard people with emails and offers – partly because it cheapens your product and partly because no one wants their inbox to be even fuller than it is already. Also, of course, nowadays a lot of people get information from social media, so they don't need many emails. We don't send a newsletter more than once a month, unless we have something genuinely new and interesting to say. It's a fine balance between overkill and making sure our customers remember us and know what's going on.

A FINAL TIP

The whole idea of starting a website can be daunting, because there is so much information out there. People often come up to us and talk about technical things they've done. But it doesn't have to be technical. If you sign up to one of the companies that provide everything built in and give you all the functionality that you need, all you have to do is maintain it: for anything from £2 to £10 a month, that is well worth the moneyAnd whatever else you do, get the look right: get the photography right, get your logo and your home page right. There's nothing more important than that.

E-COMMERCE PLATFORMS

AFCOMMERCE

www.afcommerce.com

Cost: Free.

About: AFCommerce is a well-established e-commerce platform that has spent years steadily developing and is now used by over 250,000 websites. The software is relatively simple and easy to follow, allowing you to create a shopping basket and customize pages within a matter of hours.

Key Features: The design is entirely customizable; from the background, font and border colour to product descriptions, shopping basket styles and page transitions.

Support: Website features a 'Beginners Tutorial', with step-by-step guides on a range of common queries when setting up an online shop, such as categories and product options.

Community: AF Commerce provide the ability create a newsletter which can be emailed to all visitors who make purchases.

APACHE OFBIZ

ofbiz.apache.org

Cost: Free. Extra features available.

About: Apache OFBiz is a community driven project providing templates, designs and several other features from volunteers of the Apache OFBiz community. Templates are available to use, although the option to customize is also available.

Key Features: OFBiz features a web page translation tool, templates and customizable features.

Support: An FAQ wiki section is available to provide support and answer common questions.

Community: A mailing list ensures continuous communication with Apache OFBiz.

BATAVI

www.batavi.org

Cost: Free.

About: Batavi allows the experienced web designer to create a high-end website for their business. The process is rather complex and therefore only recommended for individuals with prior experience in e-commerce platforms.

Key Features: The design can be customized, however there are slight limitations; products are automatically advertised in ICEcat, a free open catalogue. The option to integrate PayPal is a useful advantage.

Support: An 'issue tracker' will direct you to another website (sourceforge.net) to try and resolve your problem.

Community: Sourceforge.net is a forum website that allows interaction with fellow Batavi users.

BIGCARTEL

www.bigcartel.com

Cost: Four pricing levels (the first is free to use) that offer different benefits, customisation and stat tracking. Monthly subscription, no commission.

About: Shopping cart functionality for artists, musicians, crafters and designers, with over 250,000 users.

Key Features: The free 'Gold' level offers only basic features, but premium levels include built-in SEO and analytics support, inventory tracking, full HTML customisation and Facebook store integration.

Support: Extensive help area, plus dedicated support team.

Community: Has a Bigcartel blog, as well as social media feeds.

BROADLEAF COMMERCE

www.broadleafcommerce.org

Cost: Free demo, after which payment is required for support and maintenance costs.

About: An easy-to-navigate website that provides multiple options for web page customization. Support is available from top engineers and fees are not payable straight away.

Key Features: The web page and shopping cart can be customized. Users can create promotions and multiple pictures for each product. Broadleaf is also compatible with mobile devices.

Support: A section of the website consists of step-by-step tutorials on setting up an account and the essentials for operating the website. Training and support programs are also available.

Community: Broadleaf have a blog (www.broadleafcommerce.com) which regularly informs visitors of all the latest news and events. Follow them on Twitter to be kept up-to-date, and join in with discussions on the Broadleaf forums.

E-COMMERCE PLATFORMS

CUBECART
www.cubecart.com

Cost: 14-day free trial, after which there is the option for CubeCart Lite for free, or Pro for a one-time fee of £120. All references to Cube Cart can be removed for a fee of £55.

About: CubeCart is simple and easy to use; featuring numerous plug-ins, such as Paypal, UPS and Google Checkout (only with Pro). Websites can also be integrated with other sites such as Facebook, Pinterest and Twitter.

Key Features: With CubeCart Pro there is no limit to the amount of customers, orders and administrators active on a website. Both options have a logo management scheme and a newsletter tool.

Support: CubeCart offer a lot of help and support: a live, online expert is always available for help as well as a forum and an FAQ's section.

Community: CubeCart have Twitter and Facebook accounts to inform users of the latest e-commerce news.

DRUPAL COMMERCE
www.drupalcommerce.org

Cost: Free.

About: Drupal is a socially integrated e-commerce platform designed to make building a website easy. Setting up an account is quick and free.

Key Features: A unique feature is the ability to completely customize the design of the website. Websites will be compatible with mobile devices and can easily be integrated with Facebook, Twitter and Pinterest.

Support: A video library is available to provide support for any issues that may arise, as well as a FAQ's section and user forum.

Community: Drupal is extremely community-led, featuring a forum for members to discuss issues, as well as a 'How to Contribute' section. Drupal also have a Twitter account (@ DrupalCommerce) and blog (www. drupalcommerce.org/blog) to keep members up-to-date with any news and announcements.

DUKAPRESS
www.dukapress.org

Cost: Free.

About: A free, open-source WordPress e-commerce system.

Key Features: Supports guest checkouts, as well as registered users. Multiple payment modes, including PayPal, vouchers codes and bank transfers.

Support: Limited support through the DukaPress forums and the WordPress Help Center.

Community: Has a blog and a forum.

HIGHWIRE
www.highwire.com

Cost: Starter version is free; Premium version is pay monthly (varies based on sales). No commission.

About: Provides a full multi-channel solution for selling on your own online store, through eBay, Google, Facebook and other sites, and also through mobile devices.

Key Features: Flxible design with full HTML and CSS customisation, plus custom domains, centralised, multi-channel selling, built-in templates for mobile commerce and full SSL security.

Support: Support center available on the website.

Community: Forum integrated with the support center.

INTERCHANGE
www.icdevgroup.org

Cost: Free.

About: A long-running e-commerce platform enabling members to design and create their own website.

Key Features: Websites can be customized to individual taste, as well as providing high security features and a variety of widgets.

Support: Interchange provide a group of support consultants who are contactable through the 'Public Interchange Mailing Lists' and 'Commercial Consultancy Support'.

Community: The 'Public Interchange Mailing List' is a list of discussions and topics.

MAGENTO.GO
www.go.magento.com

Cost: Free 30-day trial, after which £9.99–£79.99 per month with no transaction fees and no contract.

About: Used by 100,000 merchants, Magento.go is the world's fastest growing e-commerce platform. There are various editions, however small businesses are better suited to the hosted edition.

Key Features: Magento.go provides customizable design, unlimited product options, industry leading SEO, loyalty scheme options and customer engagement tools.

Support: The website provides extensive resources to help you build and manage your store, including video tutorials, guides and webinars. Magento U also offers on-demand and live instructor-led training courses.

Community: The Magento.go blog offers great industry insight, news on new features and upgrades, and highlights independent sites using the platform. The support forum allows members to interact with other users and find answers to FAQ's and solutions to common problems.

NOPCOMMERCE

www.nopcommerce.com/default.aspx

Cost: Free.

About: NopCommerce is an easily accessible e-commerce platform that grants the user complete control in relation to customization; ideal for those just starting a business.

Key Features: This platform allows the option to upload an unlimited amount of products, customization, gift cards and one page checkout. Websites can be accessed through mobile devices.

Support: NopCommerce have created a complete user guide and an FAQ's section.

Community: NopCommerce has several community forums for members to discuss issues and to inform its members of news and any announcements. They also have a Facebook page and Twitter account.

OPENCART

www.opencart.com

Cost: Free.

About: A popular, high-end, e-commerce, platform that allows complete control over the design and creation of your online store. This is an easy-to-use website, favoured by many entrepreneurs worldwide.

Key Features: There is no limit on the amount of products or categories that can be listed on a website. Templates and themes are available, as well as complete customization.

Support: Support via community forums, a FAQ's section and video tutorials are all available on the website.

Community: The OpenCart community newsletter covers the latest releases and events, or check out their blog, RSS feed, Facebook page or Twitter account.

OSCMAX

www.oscmax.com

Cost: Free.

About: An ideal e-commerce platform for new and small businesses to develop their online shopping cart. This package is completely free, customizable and easy to use.

Key Features: osCMax allows you to completely customize your shopping cart, or choose from the designed templates available. There are no limitations on the amount of products or categories that can feature on a platform. Also available is the option to include vouchers, coupons, and customer loyalty discounts.

Support: A user manual is available on the website, which supplies information about refunds, terms of use and privacy. osCMax also provide an e-book support section; this is a simple, useful guide, with helpful illustrations guiding users in every aspect of the software.

Community: osCMax have a blog, RSS feed and a forum to notify you of any changes or announcements. Members have the opportunity to subscribe to their newsletter, Facebook page and Twitter account (@oscmax).

OSCOMMERCE

www.oscommerce.com

Cost: Free.

About: osCommerce is a well-established, constantly expanding, e-commerce platform. It is used worldwide on over 12,000 shopping websites, is simple to use and maintain.

Key Features: osCommer is easy to customize and allows easy integration with other existing websites. There are approximately 6,900 free add-ons, such as Facebook integration and optional newsletter facilities.

Support: osCommerce features a 'knowledge base' section on their website to assist members.

Community: Members can subscribe to a mailing list and an e-commerce newsletter to be kept informed of all news and announcements. Frequent interviews with existing members are regularly featured on the website.

PRESTASHOP

www.prestashop.com

Cost: Free. Additional features can be purchased.

About: Prestashop is used by over 100,000 people and is free to join. It is a relatively new, but well-respected site, winning the Open Source Business Application award two years in a row.

Key Features: With over 275 features, unlimited product characteristics and pictures, quantity discounts and translation tools; Prestashop is provides an efficient platform. Customizing an e-commerce platform is simple, with approximately 2,000 modules and templates to choose from.

E-COMMERCE PLATFORMS

Support: Prestashop provide a significant amount of support via a FAQ's section, as well as offering 'Top Tips' and advice on matters such as encrypting cookies. Also available, are a series of 'how to' videos on their YouTube channel, advising you on how to set up and maintain a Prestashop website.

Community: Prestashop features a blog and forum as well as Twitter, Facebook and Pinterest accounts, allowing easy interaction and communication between members.

ROKQUICKCART

www.rockettheme.com/extensions-joomla/rokquickcart

Cost: Free.

About: An extension of Joomla! (an e-commerce platform allowing you to create your own website), RokQuickCart is a customized shopping cart which will integrate directly into an existing Joomla! page. This platform is simple to use and ideal for smaller businesses.

Key Features: Available features include PayPal or Google Checkout, as well as accepting payment in 16 different currencies. RokQuickCart provides two different modes: sandbox (test mode) and production (live mode).

Support: RokQuickCart has a dedicated advice forum to assist with installing the cart.

Community: RokQuickCart is supplied by RocketTheme, which has its own YouTube channel, Facebook, Twitter and Pinterest accounts, as well as an online forum.

SATCHMO

www.satchmoproject.com

Cost: No price stated.

About: Satchmo is a flexible e-commerce platform based on Django. The platform is only compatible if the user has a Python 2.4, or later, database supported by Django.

Key Features: Satchmo allows complete customization of templates, URL and the checkout process.

Support: Extensive support via a wiki page is available, along with an issue tracker on the website.

Community: Satchmo has its own blog and RSS feed to ensure that users are kept up-to-date with any new developments and features.

SHOPABLE

www.shopable.in

Cost: Free. Additional features can be purchased.

About: As well as providing a reliable e-commerce platform, Shopable is passionate about customizing, and offers a range of services such as, marketing, photography and template design.

Key Features: Users can customize their own templates, choose a Shopable template or work with Shopable's top designers for a unique look. Shopping carts can be integrated with other websites, such as Facebook, Twitter, and YouTube.

Support: Support via Shopable's Facebook and Twitter accounts.

Community: All members can sign up to RSS updates and email updates. They also have Facebook and Twitter accounts in which members can discuss their ideas and opinions.

SHOPIFY

www.shopify.co.uk

Cost: Free 30-day trial, after which £19–£115 per month with varying transaction fees (0–2%), and no cancellation fee.

About: Shopify provides a simple platform to create an e-commerce website, offering over 100 professional, stylish templates.

Key Features: There are many key features to Shopify, such as the customizable design, content management system, customer management tools, SEO and analytics, discount code coupon engine, free Google Adwords and Facebook credits and mobile compatibility.

Support: Every Shopify store is assigned a 'Guru'. These on-board coaches help and advise members create and manage their online business. The website also offers support via telephone (to the USA) or email.

Community: The Shopify blog features news and inspiration from other Shopify users; updates, exclusive offers, competitions and wider industry news. The numerous Shopify forums cover everything from design and accounting, to marketing and shipping.

SIMPLECART

simplecartjs.org

Cost: Free.

About: SimpleCart provides as easy way to create an e-commerce site, perfect for basic sites or newly emerging businesses.

Key Features: Easy to customize, with several payment options through PayPal or Amazon, SimpleCart is a fast-running platform.

Support: SimpleCart provide support through their GitHub and Twitter accounts.

Community: Members can interact with one another and with SimpleCart via the GitHub and Twitter accounts.

SPREE

Website: spreecommerce.com

Cost: Free.

About: Spree is an easy-to-use e-commerce platform used by several high profile companies, and starter businesses.

Key Features: Users can customize the e-commerce website and integrate it with other websites and social media pages, such as Facebook, Twitter and Pinterest.

Support: Spree provides extensive support and advice concerning every aspect of using this feature.

Community: Spree utilizes a user-mailing list to keep members updated, as well as connected via their blog, Twitter and Facebook accounts.

STORESPRITE

Website: www.storesprite.com

Cost: Free to download and use. Storesprite logos can be removed for a fee (between £49.99 and £99.99). The option is available to hire an expert to install Storesprite for a charge of £29.99.

About: Storesprite is ideal for novice entrepreneurs who are new to website construction. The service is free, easy-to-use and quick to complete.

Key Features: Storesprite is customizable, allows multiple currency payments and flexible payment platforms, such as PayPal, WorldPay

and Sage Pay and is easy for both businesses and customers to use.

Support: Storesprite provide a unique 'Trouble Ticket' which, for £30, entitles the user to 30 minutes of technical advice. There is, alternatively, an extensive guide and FAQ's section.

Community: Various forums on the Storesprite website are in operation for members to share and discuss issues. Members can also choose to follow Storesprite through Twitter (@ storesprite).

TOMATO CART

www.tomatocart.com

Cost: Free.

About: A fast, efficient, user-friendly platform that provides community and e-commerce platform templates. Tomato Cart is based on a simplified system to give optimum running time.

Key Features: Tomato Cart features efficient administration facilities, simplifying customer management and order management. A range of templates and themes are also available to choose from.

Support: Several 'How To' tutorials are featured on Tomato Cart's blog, as well as an FAQ's section, user and developer guide.

Community: Tomato Cart have utilized social media to enable discussions between members; they have a Twitter account (@tomatocart), a Facebook page, Google+ and LinkedIn profiles, as well as a regularly updated blog and newsletter.

UBERCART

www.ubercart.org

Cost: Free.

About: Based on the award winning Drupal system, Ubercart has all the key Drupal elements, but can be heavily modified to match your own businesses needs.

Key Features: Ubercart allows the user to modify their e-commerce sites with a wide variety of customization options.

Support: Support is available via the FAQ's section, user guide, developer guide, modules and tutorials; all available on the Ubercart website.

Community: Ubercart keeps connected with members through a Google+ account and forums.

VIRTUEMART

www.virtuemart.net

Cost: Free.

About: VirtueMart is a free Joomla! extension, that allows users to create a shopping cart or catalogue of products. It has proven extremely popular with over 2.5 million downloads so far. Users are however required to download Joomla! first to be able to use the VirtueMart extension.

Key Features: You can have multiple images per product, reviews and ratings. There are many different language and currency options. Also you can have coupons and a one-page checkout.

Support: VirtueMart have a knowledge base with several helpful guides for users and developers. There is a FAQ section in which you can quickly receive answers to any questions you may have. Also there are several links to the support section of the Joomla! website.

Community: You can keep in contact with VirtueMart through Facebook and Twitter (@virtuemart).

They have a blog in which members can express their opinions and advice. Others can comment on this and share with their friends. Also there is a forum that has discussions on several key topics.

WORDPRESS E-COMMERCE PLUGIN

www.wordpress.org

Cost: Free.

About: WordPress is a hugely popular platform, used by several online enterprises. With over 60million users, WordPress is a popular choice for developing content management systems, such as websites and blogs. WordPress has been used to create several well known websites such as eBay, the PlayStation blog and The Royal Ballet.

Key Features: WordPress features over 1,000 themes to choose from that are suitable for most businesses; as well as over 20,000 plug-ins, such as Tumblr. WordPress is also compatible with most mobile devices.

Support: A variety of forums discussing specific topics are available, such as installation, using and troubleshooting.

Community: WordPress offer a word camp; this is a conference which explains business and selling specifically in relation to WordPress. You can sign up to their mailing list and follow them on Twitter (@wordpress) for all the latest news and information. WordPress also have a blog, in which they discuss several community issues and recent news.

X-CART

www.x-cart.com

Cost: X-Cart offer a free trial download for either the Gold or Pro package; Gold is recommended for small businesses. Payments are required after the completion of the trial.

About: Relied upon by more than 100 countries, X-Cart is the perfect tool for designing a secure shopping cart. Customer website design services are also available, free-of-charge.

Key Features: Users are able to customize their theme, as well as payment methods and integrate websites, such as Facebook.

Support: 'Chat with us' is a live chat feature that allows the user to discuss any queries with X-Cart directly.

Community: X-Cart has several

"A domain name is a really worthwhile investment. It gives your brand gravitas – makes it look professional."
Alison Stothard

---

community forums to encourage discussion between members. For further contact, users can subscribe to an RSS feed, or follow X-Cart on Twitter (@x_cart) or Facebook.

ZEN CART

www.zen-cart.com

Cost: Free.

About: This software is simple to use and ideal for novices and those who are unfamiliar with e-commerce platforms.

Key Features: Zen Cart is a secure website with many customization options, such multiple currency and language options.

Support: Zen Cart offers support through a range of video tutorials.

Community: Zen Cart offer a free newsletter via email, this is issued every two months and contains news, updates, hints and tips.

ZEUSCART

Website: www.zeuscart.com

Cost: Free.

About: A simple yet richly interfaced shopping cart, this is designed specifically for small- to medium-sized businesses.

Key Features: This cart integrates with the main payment gateways, such as PayPal and Google Checkout; has multi-currency set up, is quick to install and allows users to create an unlimited number of sub-admin accounts.

Support: Zeuscart have their own YouTube channel featuring various guides and tutorials, as well as telephone support.

Community: Members can connect with Zeuscart via Twitter, Facebook and LinkedIn.

DOROTHY WOOD

Dorothy Wood is a craft author and designer (www.dorothywood.co.uk), working mainly for David & Charles Publishers and for many national craft magazines. She has also recently become the first UK Ambassador for Swarovski Elements.

I trained as a dress and design teacher and then did an advanced course in embroidery and textiles, but I never did much with these qualifications until I was in my late thirties. My sister worked in publishing, and one day she phoned and asked if I could make a christening robe for a baby book. That's how I got started. After I'd done that one project, the publisher asked, 'What else can you do?' and it built up from there.

I obviously benefited from a bit of nepotism, but at the beginning it is often a matter of who you know. Otherwise, approaching magazines is a good way to start. Craft editors are always desperate for people to do work for them, as long as those people are good, can move with the times, do something contemporary and stand out just a little bit from the crowd. I'd advise putting together a portfolio to show your style and the range of your work. The words will come later and there are editors to help you, but the craft has to be distinctively your own.

> ## The words will come later and there are editors to help you, but the craft has to be distinctively your own.

I made my first approaches through the Internet, but if you want to meet people, trade fairs and big craft fairs can be a good opportunity to introduce yourself to editors: most of the magazines have stands there. Nowadays you don't even need to carry a physical portfolio, as long as you have good pictures on your smartphone.

I'm lucky in that I am versatile – it's in the genes, all the women in my family have done all sorts of different arts and crafts – so when an editor came to me and said, 'We want to do something about... Can you do...?', I learnt to say yes. If you can only do one thing – particularly if it is something not very mainstream that goes in and out of fashion, like quilling – you're going to have very intermittent work. You have to be adaptable.

> If you can only do one thing you're going to have very intermittent work. You have to be adaptable.

WORKING TO A BRIEF

When you're commissioned by a magazine, you have to do what they ask. When an editor sends you a brief, read it carefully before you start – and then reread it before you send the piece off. Even now, after working in this field for many years, I sometimes find that I've overlooked something basic: I might be making a series of cards and realise that I've ignored the instruction to put 'Greetings' on each one. Checking the brief again at the last minute stops you making this sort of elementary mistake.

I do my best work with a tight brief, because then I have a better chance of producing exactly what the company is looking for. If an editor says something vague like, 'I'm looking for a layered necklace', I do a bit of research and email her perhaps half a dozen photographs to say, 'Is this the sort of thing you're looking for?'. Very often, she'll like one specific picture out of those six. Then I can go ahead and make something that I am confident will please her. Editors do know what they want, but they aren't always able to put it into words. So my job is very much that of a problem solver. I use art to solve editors' problems.

WRITING THE WORDS

In addition to producing the craft work, a magazine will expect you to provide instructions on how to make it and they're likely to ask you for a specific number of 'steps'. Read the individual magazine and study its style. How have they written about other projects? How do they express the measurements? (Some people say 2cm, others 2 centimetres, others might want it in inches as well.) Do they say 'foam pad' or 'sticky fixer'? If you look for this sort of thing, you can gear your writing to their needs.

CARE ABOUT QUALITY

People often think that they can make projects for books and magazines half-heartedly, so the piece arrives not quite stuck together finished. Photographers have a lot of horror stories about projects falling to bits when they're trying to photograph them. I would always advise finishing things to a professional standard. You really don't know if a bag or a necklace or anything else is going to work unless you finish it properly.

BOOK IDEAS

I've rarely taken a book idea to a publisher – they tend to come to me. Craft publishing is very sales led, so publishers come up with ideas they think will sell. If they think that jewellery is going to be the next big thing, they'll go looking for someone who can write a book on jewellery.

But they may ask me to develop their general idea. Initially that might mean a single A4 sheet, just a list of contents, but after they've approved that I bulk it up with images and more detailed suggestions. I'm not making the projects at this stage; I'm doing research and finding ideas and colours that would pull together to make a nice book. I often assemble a mood board of ideas taken from magazines or printed off the internet, to show the publisher what they'll be getting, so that there are no nasty surprises later on.

If you do want to approach a publisher, go to a bookshop and see who is publishing craft books in your field; then visit

> I often assemble a mood board to show the publisher what they'll be getting, so that there are no nasty surprises later on.

their website, get in touch with the Commissioning Editor and ask if you can send them a portfolio – again, with different things you can do, showing that you aren't a one-hit wonder. It's unlikely that they will want to publish a book that you have come up with, but they may be taken by your style and your ideas and ask you to contribute to a book they already have in mind.

THE bOOK-MAKING PROCESS

There's a lot more involved in making a book that many people realise. Not only do you have to produce the work and write the words to go with it, you have to write to a deadline. I remember the first big book I did: I was very pleased because I had nearly all the projects done and my deadline was two weeks away. But I hadn't started writing and I realised that if I wrote 1500 words a day (which is quite a lot), it would take me 42 days to finish and I had 14! That's a common mistake in craft work: it's easy to concentrate on the craft and forget to allocate time for the words.

On the other hand, people are often frightened at the idea of writing, say, 20,000 words, but there's no

> **It's easy to concentrate on the craft and forget to allocate time for the words.**

> Sometimes with step photography two stages can look quite similar, and because you're the author, you're the person who knows which picture should be where.

need to be. Once it's broken down into 300 words of introduction, and a hundred words at the beginning of each chapter and perhaps 50 to introduce each project and then the various steps – before you know it, you'll find that you're nearly there.

Once you've sent everything in to the publisher, the editor may ask you questions to clarify anything that isn't clear. Then you'll see page proofs and you'll be asked to look for specific things. For example, you need to check that all the photographs are in the right order. Sometimes with step photography two stages can look quite similar, and because you're the author, you're the person who knows which picture should be where. You're likely to see several stages of proofs, with the last ones being in colour. The further through the process you get, the more expensive it is to make changes, so you have to take time to check carefully at the appropriate time.

COPYRIGHT

A lot of people are scared of showing other people their designs because they think they're going to be stolen. This would be important if you were working in commercial design, but with books or magazines you're doing it specifically so that other people can copy your designs, or be inspired by them. It's an anxiety that holds a lot of people back and really it shouldn't.

SELF-PROMOTION

I haven't often been interviewed about my books, but I do promote myself as much as possible. I have a website which often brings in work. I have a business Facebook page and I encourage people to 'like' it. I tweet and I use Instagram; and Pinterest is an excellent site for crafters because it's all about creating mood boards and showing people your style. A few years ago I wrote a jewellery book that meant I worked quite closely with Swarovski Elements. I knew they had Ambassadors in the United States who promoted their crystals and I mentioned to their UK sales manager that I liked this idea. Next time I went to see her I took a number of pieces from the book with me. They liked the fact that I had used a range not many people use – so again, I was being a little bit different. A few days later the sales manager phoned me and asked if I would like to become their first UK Ambassador. This didn't come out of the blue – I had been quite proactive, in a quiet way!

CRAFT MAGAZINES

BEADS & BEYOND

About: *Beads & Beyond* is a design-led craft magazine filled with gorgeous jewellery and bead suppliers for designers and crafters who want to learn how to create their own jewellery. This includes both the home hobbyist and the budding entrepreneur.

Publisher: Traplet Publications

Address: Traplet House, Pendragon Close, Malvern WR14 1GA

Tel: 01684 588500

Editor: Michelle Powell

Email: michelle.powell@traplet.com

Website: www.beadsandbeyondmagazine.com

Blog: www.beadsandbeyondmagazine.com/blog

CAKE CRAFT AND DECORATION

About: A monthly publication featuring instructive tutorials on cake decoration and sugarcraft. The vast range of projects and designs provided are suitable for enthusiasts of all abilities, and include useful hints and tips.

Publisher: Anglo American Media

Address: Editorial Office, PO Box 3693, Nuneaton, Warwickshire CV10 8YQ

Tel: 02476 738846

Editor: Julie Askew

Email: editor@cake-craft.com

Website: www.cake-craft.com

CAKE DECORATING

About: A weekly magazine containing helpful hints and tips on how to bake and ice cakes, cookies and biscuits. *Cake Decorating* uses simple, step-by-step instructions accompanied by illustrations; an ideal magazine for beginners.

Publisher: De Agostini UK

Address: Battersea Studios 2, 82 Silverthorne Road, London SW8 3HE

Tel: 08444 935440

Email: customercare@deagostini.co.uk

Website: www.mycakedecorating.co.uk

Blog: www.mycakedecorating.co.uk/blog

CAKES AND SUGARCRAFT

About: A magazine with recipes for both beginners and experienced bakers, providing guides for cakes suitable for all occasions: Christmas, birthdays, weddings, Christenings and more. It examines the latest trends and provides lots of helpful tips.

Publisher: Squires Kitchen

Address: Alfred House, 3 Waverley Lane, Farnham, Surrey GU98BB

Tel: 01252 727572

Editor: Jenny Royle

Email: customer@squires-group.co.uk

Website: www.squires-shop.com

CARDMAKING AND PAPERCRAFT

About: This weekly magazine is full of useful facts and reviews, essential to any keen card-maker. *Cardmaking and Papercraft* features a variety of expert opinions, reviews the latest products and will often include a free sample.

Publisher: Immediate Media

Address: Immediate Media Company Origin Ltd, Tower House, Fairfax Street, Bristol BS1 3BN

Tel: 01179 279009

Editor: Kirstie Sleight

Email: kirstie.sleight@immediate.co.uk

Website: www.cardmakingandpapercraft.com

Blog: www.cardmakingandpapercraft.com/blogs

CLOTH

About: *Cloth* prioritizes sustainability and recycling and champions the make, do, and mend attitude. Featuring useful tips and techniques for updating a tired wardrobe, *Cloth* is perfect for the fashion-forward individual who is conscious of the environment and the purse strings.

Publisher: Real Design and Media

Address: 9th Floor Tower House, Fairfax Street, Bristol BS1 3BN

Tel: 01179 290990

Editor: Scott Purnell

Email: scott@clothmagazine.co.uk

Website: www.clothmagazine.co.uk

CRAFT MAGAZINES

COMPLETE CARDMAKING

About: This bimonthly magazine features a complimentary CD with every issue, sharing the latest templates and designs for your use.
Publisher: Practical Publishing Int. Ltd
Address: Suite G2 St Christopher House, 217 Wellington Road South, Stockport SK2 6NG
Tel: 08445 611202
Editor: Lee Jepson
Email: lee.jepson@practicalpublishing.co.uk
Website: www.practicalpublishing.co.uk/completecardmaking

CRAFT & DESIGN

About: *Craft & Design* is a contemporary well-established, British craft magazine, featuring all the latest craft news, designers and advice. Readers will be kept well informed of all the latest fairs and craft events.
Publisher: PSB Design and Print Consultants Ltd
Address: PO Box 5, Driffield, East Yorkshire YO25 8JD
Tel: 01377 255213
Editor: Angie Boyer
Email: info@craftanddesign.net
Website: www.craftanddesign.net
Blog: www.craftanddesign.net/blog

CRAFT BUSINESS

About: This is a trade publication that is both online and in magazine format. It provides traders with current trends, topical information and retail advice. *Craft Business'* online publication is free for subscribers.
Publisher: Aceville Publications
Address: 21–23 Phoenix Court, Hawkins Road, Colchester, Essex CO2 8JY

Tel: 01206 505900
Editor: Emma Cant
Email: emma.cant@aceville.co.uk
Website: www.craftbusiness.com

CRAFT STAMPER

About: A specialist monthly magazine purely for craft with stamps; *Craft Stamper* contains advice on all the latest stamping techniques, as well as including some challenging designs. Readers will receive a free stamp with each issue.
Publisher: Traplet Publications
Address: Traplet House, Pendragon Close, Malvern WR14 1GA
Tel: 01684 588500
Editor: Katy Fox
Email: cs@traplet.com.
Website: www.craftstamper.com
Blog: www.craftstamper.com/blog

CRAFTS BEAUTIFUL

About: This well-established magazine features tutorials and advice for traditional and contemporary craft making. *Crafts Beautiful* issues 13 publications per year, each with a free gift, a multitude of patterns and templates.
Publisher: Aceville Publications
Address: 21–23 Phoenix Court, Hawkins Road, Colchester, Essex CO2 8JY
Tel: 01206 505900
Editor: Sarah Crosland
Email: sarah@aceville.co.uk
Website: www.crafts-beautiful.com

CRAFTSELLER

About: *CraftSeller* is specifically targeted at crafters and hobbyists who are looking to sell their homemade gifts. This useful magazine features the latest apps, websites and craft techniques to support entrepreneurs.
Publisher: Immediate Media Company Origin Ltd
Address: Tower House, Fairfax Street, Bristol BS1 3BN
Tel: 01179 279009
Editor: Zeena Moolla
Email: craft@craft-seller.com
Website: www.craft-seller.com

CREATIVE CARDMAKING

About: Exclusively available in select craft shops, *Creative Cardmaking* provides tips, guides and advice. The magazine usually includes free papers and designs with each issue.
Publisher: Practical Publishing Int. Ltd
Address: Suite G2 St Christopher House, 217 Wellington Road South, Stockport SK2 6NG
Tel: 08445 611202
Editor: Laura Dougherty
Email: laura.dougherty@practicalpublishing.co.uk
Website: www.practicalpublishing.co.uk/creativecardmaking

CRAFT MAGAZINES

CREATIVE STAMPING

About: For crafters of any level, *Creative Stamping* is ideal for advice and project ideas for all occasions. The magazine usually contains free high quality stamps.
Publisher: Practical Publishing Int. Ltd
Address: Suite G2 St Christopher House, 217 Wellington Road South, Stockport SK2 6NG
Tel: 0844 561 1202
Editor: Laura Dougherty
Email: laura.dougherty@practicalpublishing.co.uk
Website: www.practicalpublishing.co.uk/creativestamping

CROSS STITCH CARD SHOP

About: This well-established magazine is dedicated to cross stitch cards, featuring expert advice and patterns for every occasion. *Cross Stitch Card Shop* issues 13 publications per year, each containing a free cross stitch card kit.
Publisher: Immediate Media Company Origin Ltd
Address: Tower House, Fairfax Street, Bristol BS1 3BN
Tel: 0117 927 9009
Editor: Hannah Bellis
Email: hannah@cross-stitching.com
Website: www.cross-stitching.com

CROSS STITCH COLLECTION

About: Purely for experienced cross-stitchers, *Cross Stitch Collection* presents a range of classic designs, product reviews and competitions.
Publisher: Future PLC
Address: 2 Balcombe Street, London NW1 6NW
Tel: 020 7042 4000
Editor: Catherine Hood

Email: csc@futurenet.co.uk
Website: www.myfavouritemagazines.co.uk

CROSS STITCH CRAZY

About: A fun magazine for people of all ages and abilities. Patterns range in difficulty and include step-by-step guides.
Publisher: Immediate Media Company Origin Ltd
Address: Tower House, Fairfax Street, Bristol BS1 3BN
Tel: 01179 279009
Editor: Sarah Trevor
Email: sarah@cross-stitching.com
Website: www.cross-stitching.com

CROSS STITCH GOLD

About: An ideal magazine for the more experienced cross-stitcher, *Cross Stitch Gold* features eight fairly complex projects created by top designers, in an easy to follow format.
Publisher: Immediate Media Company Origin Ltd
Address: Tower House, Fairfax Street, Bristol BS1 3BN
Tel: 01179 279009
Editor: Hannah Bellis
Email: hannah@cross-stitching.com
Website: www.cross-stitching.com

CROSS STITCHER

About: A magazine for all abilities, *Cross Stitcher* provides designs and project ideas, displayed in an easy-to-follow format.
Publisher: Future PLC
Address: Beauford Court, 30 Monmouth Street, Bath BA1 2BW
Tel: 01225 442244
Editor: Charlie Moorby
Email: charlie.moorby@future.net.com

Website: crossstitcher.themakingspot.com
Blog: crossstitcher.themakingspot.com/blog

FLAIR Magazine

About: The only magazine dedicated to machine embroidery, *Flair Magazine* is a bestseller, publishing four issues per year. Each issue features essential embroidery news and reviews, patterns and step-by-step guides.
Publisher: Flair Magazine
Address: PO Box 544, Exeter EX1 9FD
Tel: 01392 662050
Editor: Liz Keegan
Email: liz@flairmagazine.co.uk
Website: www.flairmagazine.co.uk

FOOD HEAVEN

About: *Food Heaven* is series of magazines which serves to provide the reader with all of their cooking and baking needs. Featuring the popular titles *Cupcake Heaven* and *Baking Heaven*, *Food Heaven* will also include a special magazine on the subjects of cake decorating, cupcakes for kids and much more. It is packed with inspiring recipes and projects, beautiful photography and the chance to learn new techniques.
Publisher: Anthem Publishing
Address: Suite 6MG Piccadilly House, London Road, Bath BR1 6PL
Tel: 01795 414877
Editor: Paul Pettengale
Email: paul.pettengale@anthem-publishing.com
Website: anthem.subscribeonline.co.uk

CRAFT MAGAZINES

KNIT NOW

About: *Knit Now* issues 13 publications per year and features all of the latest knitting news and trends, patterns and ideas.
Publisher: Practical Publishing Int. Ltd
Address: Suite G2 St Christopher House, 217 Wellington Road South, Stockport SK2 6NG
Tel: 0844 561 1202
Editor: Kate Heppell
Email: kate.heppell@ practicalpublishing.co.uk
Website: www.practicalpublishing. co.uk/knitnow

KNIT TODAY

About: *Knit Today* provides reviews on all the latest knitting and crochet accessories and books, as well as supplying the reader with lovely patterns. This magazine features competitions and giveaways, and is suitable for all ages and abilities.
Publisher: Immediate Media Company Origin Ltd
Address: Tower House, Fairfax Street, Bristol BS1 3BN
Tel: 0117 927 9009
Editor: Marie Parry
Email: marie.parry@immediate.co.uk
Website: www.knit-today.com
Blog: www.knit-today.com/ask-expert/blog

KNITTING

About: *Knitting* is a magazine for knitters and crocheters of all abilities. It has a wide choice of exclusive knitting and crochet patterns, interesting articles and the latest news and reviews. Readers can subscribe to a *Knitting* e-book for Androids and Smartphones.
Publisher: Guild of Master

Craftsman Publications Ltd
Address: 166 High Street, Lewes, East Sussex BN7 1XU
Tel: 01273 477374
Editor: Emma Kennedy
Email: emmak@thegmcgroup.com
Website: www.thegmcgroup.com

LET'S GET CRAFTING

About: A perfect magazine for any beginner, *Let's Get Crafting* features bright and colourful designs with easy-to-follow instructions. Each issue features advice from top designers and a free kit. Free patterns are available for download from the *Let's Get Crafting* website.
Publisher: Aceville Publications
Address: 21–23 Phoenix Court, Hawkins Road, Colchester, Essex CO2 8JY
Tel: 01206 505900
Editor: Elizabeth Hudson
Email: elizabeth.hudson@aceville. co.uk
Website: www.letsgetcrafting.com

LET'S KNIT

About: For the fashion-conscious knitter, this magazine is a must. *Let's Knit* is full of easy-to-follow, contemporary patterns and represents the latest knitting trends. Readers can stay updated with all the latest knitting fashions via the *Let's Knit* Twitter account (@letsknitmag).
Publisher: Aceville Publications
Address: 21–23 Phoenix Court, Hawkins Road, Colchester, Essex CO2 8JY
Tel: 01206 505900
Editor: Sarah Neil
Email: sarah.neal@aceville.co.uk
Website: www.letsknit.co.uk

LET'S MAKE CARDS

About: *Let's Make Cards* contains lots of fun cardmaking ideas and inspirations. Each issue comes with a free cardmaking kit to allow readers to practise the current issue's designs.
Publisher: Aceville Publications
Address: 21–23 Phoenix Court, Hawkins Road, Colchester, Essex CO2 8JY
Tel: 01206 505900
Editor: Elizabeth Hudson
Email: elizabeth.hudson@aceville. co.uk
Website: www.letsmakecards.com

MAKE JEWELLERY

About: A magazine devoted entirely to jewellery making, *Make Jewellery* contains advice and designs for creating glamorous pieces on a budget. This monthly magazine caters for a range of abilities.
Publisher: Aceville Publications
Address: 21–23 Phoenix Court, Hawkins Road, Colchester, Essex CO2 8JY
Tel: 01206 505900
Editor: Lorraine Luximon
Email: lorraine.luximon@aceville. co.uk
Website: www. makejewellerymagazine.com

"Read the individual magazine and study its style."
Dorothy Wood

MAKING

About: *Making* is a monthly magazine that focuses on a wide range of crafts. The magazine features sections for each room of the domestic house, tailoring the designs and guides appropriately, for example, recipes for the kitchen, clothes for the bedroom and soaps and toiletries for the bathroom.

Publisher: Guild of Master Craftsman Publications Ltd

Address: 166 High Street, Lewes, East Sussex BN7 1XU

Tel: 01273 477374

Editor: Sian Hamilton

Email: makingeditor@thegmcgroup.com

Website: www.makingmagazine.com

Blog: www.craftsinstitute.com/making/blog

MAKING CAKES AND BAKES

About: This family-orientated magazine features an assortment of tasty recipes for cakes, pastries, savouries and much more. Subscribers can purchase back issues of *Making Cakes and Bakes* on the website.

Publisher: Magmaker Ltd

Address: Cromwell Road, New Road, St Ives, Cambridgeshire PE27 5BF

Tel: 01480 496130

Editor: Leeanne Cooper

Email: liz.purkiss@magmaker.co.uk

Website: www.makingcakesandbakes.co.uk

MAKING CARDS

About: *Making Cards* is a monthly magazine featuring designs suitable for a variety of occasions and abilities. Each issue supplies the readers with guides and a sample of paper.

Publisher: Magmaker Ltd

Address: Cromwell Road, New Road, St Ives, Cambridgeshire PE27 5BF

Tel: 01480 496130

Editor: Sally Jarvis

Email: sally.jarvis@magmaker.co.uk

Website: www.makingcardsmagazine.com

MOLLIE MAKES

About: *Mollie Makes* showcases the latest in contemporary handmade craft from around the world. Each of the 13 annual publications contain design guides and instructions on making the latest craft pieces.

Publisher: Future PLC

Address: Beauford Court, 30 Monmouth Street, Bath BA1 2BW

Tel: 01225 442244

Editor: Jane Toft

Email: molliemakes@myfavouritemagazines.co.uk.

Website: www.molliemakes.com

Blog: www.molliemakes.com/blog

NEW STITCHES

About: A cross stitch magazine suitable for makers of all abilities, featuring the latest designs selected by Mary Hickmott. *New Stitches* provides readers with a selection of traditional and unusual patterns and guides.

Publisher: Creative Crafts Publishing

Address: Well Oast, Brenley Lane, Faversham, Kent ME13 9LY

Tel: 01227 750215

Editor: Janice Broadstocks

Email: janice@ccpuk.co.uk

Website: www.newstitches.co.uk

PAPERCRAFT ESSENTIALS

About: Ideal for budding crafters, *Papercraft Essentials* features card ideas, designs and easy-to-follow guides. The designs are simple and can be completed quickly.

Publisher: Practical Publishing Int. Ltd

Address: Suite G2 St Christopher House, 217 Wellington Road South, Stockport SK2 6NG

Tel: 0844 561 1202

Editor: Melanie Tickle

Email: Melanie.tickle@practicalpublishing.co.uk

Website: www.practicalpublishing.co.uk/papercraftessentials

PAPERCRAFT INSPIRATIONS

About: One of the UK's bestsellers, *Papercraft Inspirations* is perfect for beginners and experts. This magazine is a proven source of inspiration for many crafters, containing ideas, advice and techniques.

Publisher: Future PLC

Address: 2 Balcombe Street, London NW1 6NW

Tel: 020 7042 4000

Editor: Jenny Dixon

Email: jenny.dixon@futurenet.com or papercraft@futurenet.co.uk

Website: papercraftinspirations.themakingspot.com

Blog: papercraftinspirations.themakingspot.com/blog

CRAFT MAGAZINES

PARCHMENT CRAFT

About: A unique magazine dedicated to the use of Parchment, this magazine contains plenty of original projects in each issue. *Parchment Craft* has proven to be extremely popular and is read worldwide.

Publisher: Magmaker Ltd

Address: Cromwell Road, New Road, St Ives, Cambridgeshire PE27 5BF

Tel: 01480 496130

Editor: Carl Golder

Email: carl.golder@magmaker.co.uk

Website: www. parchmentcraftmagazine.com

PATCHWORK & QUILTING

About: *Patchwork & Quilting* is one of the first magazines of its kind, featuring contributions from both established and newly emerging quilters. The magazine is accompanied by a website, where readers can discover a compendium of patterns and patchwork inspiration.

Publisher: Traplet Publications

Address: Traplet House, Pendragon Close, Malvern WR14 1GA

Tel: 01684 588500

Editor: Dianne Huck and Judi Mendelssohn

Email: pq@traplet.com

Website: www.pandqmagazine.com

Blog: www.pandqmagazine.com/blog

POPULAR CRAFTS

About: *Popular Crafts* is the ultimate craft magazine, covering everything from knitting and cardmaking to more unknown practices, such as pyrography.

Publisher: My Hobby Store

Address: 9 High Street, Green Street Green, Orpington, Kent BR6 6BG

Tel: 08448 488822

Editor: Katharine Jewitt

Email: katharine.jewitt@myhobbystore.com

Website: www.popularcrafts.com

POPULAR PATCHWORK

About: *Popular Patchwork* magazine provides readers with the latest sewing and quilting news, reviews and an array of projects, suitable for all abilities and ages.

Publisher: My Hobby Store

Address: 9 High Street, Green Street Green, Orpington, Kent BR6 6BG

Tel: 08448 488822

Editor: Bridget Kenningham

Email: bridget.kenningham@myhobbystore.com

Website: www.popularpatchwork.com

QUICK CARDS MADE EASY

About: From the publishers of *Knit Today* and *Cross-Stitch Card Shop*, *Quick Cards Made Easy* is a well-established magazine for anyone interested in cardmaking. Featuring patterns and projects that are quick and easy to complete, the magazine also contains product reviews, expert advice and news.

Publisher: Immediate Media Company Origin Ltd

Address: Tower House, Fairfax Street, Bristol BS1 3BN

Tel: 01179 279009

Editor: Sarah Bostock

Email: sarah.bostock@immediate.co.uk

Website: www. cardmakingandpapercraft.com

Blog: www. cardmakingandpapercraft.com/blogs

SCRAP 365

About: Scrap 365 is a fresh and innovative scrapbooking magazine, featuring a selection of projects accompanied with informative and simple guides.

Publisher: Traplet Publications

Address: Traplet House, Pendragon Close, Malvern WR14 1GA

Tel: 01684 588500

Editor: Katy Fox

Email: scrap365@traplet.com.

Website: www.scrap365mag.com

Blog: www.scrap365.blogspot.co.uk

SCRAPBOOK MAGAZINE

About: This bimonthly magazine contains helpful suggestions for creating a scrapbook, featuring inspirational interviews with established designers.

Publisher: Practical Publishing Int. Ltd

Address: Suite G2 St Christopher House, 217 Wellington Road South, Stockport SK2 6NG

Tel: 08445 611202

Editor: Lindsey Hopkins

Email: Lindsey.Hopkins@practicalPublishing.co.uk

Website: www.practicalpublishing.co.uk/scrapbookmagazine

CRAFT MAGAZINES

SEW

About: *Sew* magazine is ideal for fashion-forward designers who want to produce in-trend pieces. Each issue features a workbook with a collection of modern templates and designs.
Publisher: Aceville Publications
Address: 21–23 Phoenix Court, Hawkins Road, Colchester, CO2 8JY
Tel: 01206 505420
Editor: Lynn Martin
Email: lynn.martin@aceville.co.uk
Website: www.sewmag.co.uk

SEWING WORLD

About: A monthly magazine with a fresh, colourful style, full of all the latest sewing news and inspiration; *Sewing World* is suitable for levels of ability.
Publisher: Traplet Publications
Address: Traplet House, Pendragon Close, Malvern WR14 1GA
Tel: 01684 588500
Editor: Julie Bonnar & Julie Briggs
Email: sw@traplet.com
Website: www.sewingworldmagazine.com

SIMPLY CARDS AND PAPERCRAFT

About: *Simply Cards and Papercraft* is filled with inspiration and designs for a wide variety of occasions. It features helpful tips and step-by-step guides.
Publisher: Practical Publishing Int. Ltd
Address: Suite G2 St Christopher House, 217 Wellington Road South, Stockport SK2 6NG
Tel: 08445 611202
Editor: Melanie Tickle
Email: melanie.tickle@practicalpublishing.co.uk
Website: www.practicalpublishing.co.uk/simplycards

SIMPLY HOMEMADE

About: This is a magazine for those passionate about homemade products, covering a wide range of crafts, such as knitting, beading and baking. All projects have are accompanied by clear instructions with illustrations – ideal for beginners.
Publisher: Practical Publishing Int. Ltd
Address: Suite G2 St Christopher House, 217 Wellington Road South, Stockport SK2 6NG
Tel: 08445 611202
Editor: Diane Grimshaw
Email: diane.grimshaw@practicalpublishing.co.uk
Website: www.practicalpublishing.co.uk/simplyhomemade

SIMPLY KNITTING

About: *Simply Knitting* is representative of knitting's recent surge in popularity amongst younger generations. This is an ideal magazine for beginners, supplying simple patterns and guides. Mobile compatible issues are available for readers with Smart Phones and Androids.
Publisher: Future PLC
Address: 2 Balcombe Street, London NW1 6NW
Tel: 020 7042 4000
Editor: Debora Bradley
Email: simplyknitting@futurenet.co.uk
Website: simplyknitting.themakingspot.com
Blog: simplyknitting.themakingspot.com/blog

THE KNITTER

About: *The Knitter* is targeted at experienced knitters, featuring challenging, original patterns, intricate techniques and complex projects.
Publisher: Future PLC
Address: 2 Balcombe Street, London NW1 6NW
Tel: 020 7042 4000
Editor: Juliet Bernard
Email: theknitter@futurenet.com
Website: theknitter.themakingspot.com
Blog: www.theknitter.themakingspot.com/blog

THE WORLD OF CROSS STITCHING

About: An extremely popular magazine, *The World of Cross Stitching* is a bestseller with new and experienced crafters. Each issue features new techniques, gift ideas and free samples.
Publisher: Immediate Media Company Origin Ltd
Address: Tower House, Fairfax Street, Bristol BS1 3BN
Tel: 01179 279009
Editor: Ruth Southorn
Email: ruth@cross-stitching.com
Website: www.cross-stitching.com

WEDDING CAKES

About: Dedicated solely to the art of wedding cake baking and decorating, *Wedding Cakes* is a bible for any bride-to-be, aspiring baker or sugarcrafter. Each issue features a vast catalogue of the latest cake trends and designs, as well as extensive directory of suppliers and bakeries.
Publisher: Squires Kitchen
Address: Alfred House, 3 Waverly House, Farnham, Surrey GU98BB
Tel: 01252 727572
Editor: Jenny Stewart
Email: customer@squires-group.co.uk
Website: www.squires-shop.com

CRAFT PUBLISHERS

ACP BOOKS

Publisher: Octopus Publishing Group Ltd

Categories: Cake decorating, baking and sugarcraft.

Submissions Policy: No policy is stated; it is advisable to contact the editorial team.

Address: Faraday Close, Durrington, Worthing, West Sussex BN13 3RB

Tel: 01903 828501

Editorial Contact: Sarah Bailey

Email: publisher@octopus-publishing. co.uk

Website: www.octopusbooks.co.uk

APPLE PRESS PUBLISHING

Publisher: Apple Press

Categories: Knitting, crochet and jewellery.

Submissions Policy: No policy is stated; it is advisable to contact the editorial team.

Address: 7 Greenland Street, London NW1 0ND

Tel: 020 7284 7168

Editorial Contact: Liane Stark

Email: lianes@apple-press.com

Website: www.apple-press.com

BATSFORD

Publisher: Anova Books Group Ltd

Categories: Textiles and embroidery.

Submissions Policy: Anova Books Group Ltd will accept unsolicited manuscripts on the condition that proposals contain an outline, chapter outlines and a sample chapter. All submissions must be typed and double-spaced with pages numbered. Submissions should also include a stamped and self-addressed envelope.

Address: The Old Magistrates Court, 10 Southcombe Street, London W14 0RA

Tel: 020 7605 1400

Editorial Contact: Tina Persaud

Email: customerservice@anovabooks. com

Website: www.anovabooks.com/ imprint-batsford

BLACK DOG PUBLISHING LTD LONDON

Publisher: Black Dog Publishing Ltd London

Categories: Knitting, papercraft and ceramics.

Submissions Policy: No policy is stated; it is advisable to contact the editorial team.

Address: 10A Acton Street, London WC1X 9NG

Tel: 020 7713 5097

Editorial Contact: Phoebe Adler

Email: editorial@blackdogonline.com

Website: www.blackdogonline.com

CASSELL ILLUSTRATED

Publisher: Octopus Publishing Group Ltd

Categories: Knitting, sewing and embroidery.

Submissions Policy: No policy is stated; it is advisable to contact the editorial team.

Address: Endeavour House, 189 Shaftsbury Avenue, London WC2H 8JY

Tel: 020 7632 5400

Editorial Contact: Alison Goff

Email: publisher@octopus-publishing. co.uk

Website: www.octopusbooks.co.uk/ cassell-illustrated

CICO BOOKS

Publisher: Ryland Peters & Small

Categories: Sewing, crochet, cake decorating, jewellery, papercraft, quilting and crafts for children.

Submissions Policy: Submissions must include a detailed proposal, personal statement, relevant experience and contact details.

Address: 20–21 Jockey's Fields, London WC1R 4BW

Tel: 01256 329242

Editorial Contact: Cindy Richards

Email: cindy.richards@cicobooks.co.uk

Website: www.cicobooks.com

CRAFT PUBLISHERS

COLLINS & BROWN

Publisher: Anova Books Group Ltd

Categories: Housekeeping, knitting, sewing, felting and general craft.

Submissions Policy: Anova Books Group Ltd will accept unsolicited manuscripts on the condition that the proposal contains an outline, chapter outlines and a sample chapter. All submissions must be typed and double-spaced and pages numbered. Submissions should also include a stamped and self-addressed envelope.

Address: The Old Magistrates Court, 10 Southcombe Street, London W14 0RA

Tel: 020 7605 1400

Editorial Contact: Katie Cowan

Email: customerservice@anovabooks. com

Website: www.anovabooks.com/ imprint-collins-and-brown

CONRAN OCTOPUS LTD

Publisher: Octopus Publishing Group Ltd

Categories: High-end books on housekeeping, interiors and sewing.

Submissions Policy: No policy is stated; it is advisable to contact the editorial team.

Address: Endeavor House, 189 Shaftsbury Avenue, London WC2H 8JY

Tel: 020 7632 5400

Editorial Contact: Alison Goff

Email: publisher@octopus-publishing. co.uk

Website: www.octopusbooks.co.uk/ conran

DAVID & CHARLES

Publisher: F&W Media International Ltd

Categories: Quilting, sewing, cake decorating and papercraft.

Submissions Policy: Submission must include a covering letter, synopsis and sample material with photographs.

Address: Brunel House, Forde Close, Newton Abbot TQ12 4PU

Tel: 01626 323200

Editorial Contact: Ali Myer

Email: ali.myer@fwmedia.com

Website: www.fwmedia.co.uk

DK BOOKS

Publisher: Dorling Kindersley

Categories: Needlework, sewing, knitting and jewellery.

Submissions Policy: DK Books will not accept unsolicited manuscripts.

Address: 80 Strand, London WC2R 0RL.

Tel: 020 7010 3000

Email: Adulteditorial@uk.dk.com

Website: www.dk.co.uk

EBURY

Publisher: The Random House Group Ltd

Categories: Flower arranging, knitting, baking and cake decorating.

Submissions Policy: Ebury will only accept book proposals from a literary agent; they will not accept unsolicited manuscripts.

Address: 20 Vauxhall Bridge Road, London SW1V 2SA

Tel: 020 7840 8400

Editorial Contact: Jake Lingford

Email: eburyeditorial@randomhouse. co.uk

Website: www.eburypublishing.co.uk

GMC PUBLICATIONS

Publisher: Guild of Master Craftsmen Publications Ltd

Categories: Papercraft, ceramics, jewellery, metalwork, knitting, candle making and sewing.

Submissions Policy: GMC Publications will not accept unsolicited manuscripts.

Address: 166 High Street, Lewes, East Sussex, BN7 1XU

Tel: 01273 477374

Editorial Contact: Dominique Page

Email: pubs@thegmcgroup.com

Website: www.thegmcgroup.com

HAMLYN PUBLISHERS

Publisher: Octopus Publishing Group Ltd

Categories: Cake decorating, papercraft, knitting and cross stitch.

Submissions Policy: Author submissions can be emailed to the editorial team.

Address: Endeavor House, 189 Shaftsbury Avenue, London WC2H 8JY

Tel: 020 7632 5400

Editorial Contact: Alison Goff

Email: publisher@octopus-publishing. co.uk

Website: www.octopusbooks.co.uk/ hamlyn

CRAFT PUBLISHERS

JACQUI SMALL PUBLISHING

Publisher: Aurum Press
Categories: Papercraft, knitting, jewellery, ceramics and sewing.
Submissions Policy: No policy is stated; it is advisable to contact the editorial team.
Address: 7 Greenland Street, London NW1 0ND
Tel: 020 7284 7161
Editorial Contact: Barbara Phelan
Email: sales@jacqismallpub.com
Website: www.aurumpress.co.uk

KYLE BOOKS

Publisher: Kyle Books
Categories: Knitting, sewing and homemade gifts.
Submissions Policy: No policy is stated; it is advisable to contact the editorial team.
Address: 23 Howland Street, London W1T 4AY
Tel: 020 7692 7215
Editorial Contact: Kyle Cathie
Email: kyle.cathie@kylebooks.com
Website: www.kylebooks.com

LAURENCE KING PUBLISHING LTD

Publisher: Laurence King Publishing Ltd
Categories: Textiles, clay and interior design.
Submissions Policy: Submissions require applicants to fill out a book proposal form, found on the website.
Address: 361–373 City Road, London EC1V 1LR
Tel: 020 7841 6900
Editorial Contact: Jo Lightfoot
Email: commissioning@laurenceking.com
Website: www.laurenceking.com

PIATKUS

Publisher: Little Brown Book Group Ltd
Categories: Stitching and sewing.
Submissions Policy: Only proposals sent via a literary agent will be considered.
Address: 100 Victoria Embankment, London, EC4Y 0DY
Tel: 020 7911 8000
Editorial Contact: Tim Whiting
Email: info@littlebrown.co.uk
Website: www.piatkusbooks.net

MITCHELL BEAZLEY

Publisher: Octopus Publishing Group Ltd
Categories: Sewing and crochet guides.
Submissions Policy: No policy is stated; it is advisable to contact the editorial team.
Address: Endeavor House, 189 Shaftsbury Avenue, London WC2H 8JY
Tel: 020 7632 5400
Editorial Contact: Tracy Smith
Email: publisher@octopus-publishing.co.uk
Website: www.octopusbooks.co.uk/mitchell-beazley

NEW HOLLAND PUBLISHERS

Publisher: New Holland Publishers
Categories: Quilting, sewing, woodwork, papercraft and needlecraft.
Submissions Policy: No guidance is given.
Address: 8 The Arena, Mollison Avenue, Enfield, Middlesex EN3 7NL
Tel: 020 8804 0400
Editorial Contact: Fiona Schultz
Email: fiona@newholland.com.au
Website: www.newhollandpublishers.com

POTTAGE PUBLISHING

Publisher: Pottage Publishing
Categories: Crochet.
Submissions Policy: No policy is stated; it is advisable to contact the editorial team.
Address: PO BOX 202, South Okendon, Essex, RM15 6WZ
Email: info@pottagepublishing.co.uk
Website: www.pottagepublishing.co.uk

POTTER CRAFT

Publisher: Random House Inc
Categories: Papercraft, knitting, jewellery, clay and sewing.
Submissions Policy: They have no set policy but recommend that you first go to a literary agent.
Address: 20 Vauxhall Bridge Road, London SW1V 2SA
Tel: 020 8231 6800
Editorial Contact: Caitlin Harpin
Website: www.crownpublishing.com

PR BOOKS

Publisher: PR Books Ltd
Categories: Knitting and sewing.
Submissions Policy: No policy is stated; it is advisable to contact the editorial team.
Address: Mealbank Industrial Estate, Kendal, Cumbria LA8 9DL
Tel: 01539 733332
Website: www.prbooks.co.uk

QUADRILLE PUBLISHING

Publisher: Quadrille Publishing Ltd
Categories: Jewellery making, knitting, crochet, sewing and stitching.
Submissions Policy: No policy is stated; it is advisable to contact the editorial team.
Address: Alhambra House, 27–31 Charing Cross Road, London WC2H 0LS
Tel: 020 7839 7117
Editorial Contact: Jane O'Shea
Email: jane@quadrille.co.uk
Website: www.quadrille.co.uk

READER'S DIGEST

Publisher: Vivat Direct
Categories: Knitting and sewing.
Submissions Policy: No policy is stated; it is advisable to contact the editorial team.
Address: 157 Edgware Road, London W2 2HR
Tel: 0207 053 450
Editorial Contact: Gill Hudson
Email: theeditor@readersdigest.co.uk
Website: www.readersdigest.co.uk

REGENCY HOUSE

Publisher: Regency House Publishing Ltd
Categories: Art and craft books.
Submissions Policy: No policy is stated; it is advisable to contact the editorial team.
Address: Unit P1 Watermill Industrial Estate, Aspenden Road, Buntingford, Hertfordshire SG9 9JS
Tel: 01763 274666
Editorial Contact: Maureen Trodd
Email: regency-house@btconnect.com
Website: www. regencyhousepublishing.com

RYLAND PETERS & SMALL

Publisher: Ryland Peters & Small
Categories: Jewellery, sewing, knitting, quilting, crochet, baking and papercraft.
Submissions Policy: Submissions require a proposal and personal statement.
Address: 20–21 Jockey's Fields, London WC1R 4BW
Tel: 020 7025 2200
Editorial Contact: Cindy Richards
Email: cindy.richards@ rpsandcicobooks.com
Website: www.rylandpeters.com

SEARCH PRESS LTD

Publisher: Search Press Ltd
Categories: Sewing, embroidery, crochet, cake decorating and knitting.
Submissions Policy: Submissions require a proposal and brief synopsis, at least six images intended to be used within the publication and a contents list.
Address: Wellwood, North Farm Road, Tunbridge Wells, Kent TN2 3DR
Tel: 01892 510850
Editorial Contact: Rosalind Dace
Email: enquiries@searchpress.com
Website: www.searchpress.com

TOUCAN BOOKS

Publisher: Toucan Books Ltd
Categories: Dolls houses, household guides and gardening.
Submissions Policy: No policy is stated; it is advisable to contact the editorial team.
Address: 111 Chatterhouse Street, Fourth Floor, London EC1M 6AW
Tel: 020 7250 3388
Editorial Contact: Robert Sackville West
Email: info@toucanbooks.co.uk
Website: www.toucanbooks.co.uk

"Editors do know what they want, but they aren't always able to put it into words."
Dorothy Wood

LAUReN O'FARReLL

Lauren O'Farrell runs Stitch London, the UK's biggest craft community (www.stitchldn.com). She is also an author, fibre artist and graffiti artist under the pseudonym Deadly Knitshade. She tweets under several guises including @deadlyknitshade and @cooeythepigeon (fibre-feathered star of the *Stitch London* book). www.whodunnknit.com

I had never picked up a knitting needle until 2004, when I was diagnosed with Hodgkin's lymphoma. When I started going to hospital for chemotherapy and radiotherapy there was a lot of hanging around; it was all pretty miserable and I needed something to do. I'd seen Debbie Stoller's book *Stitch 'n' Bitch*, where she suggests going to the pub with some friends and knitting. I'd never thought of knitting as something you could be creative with, but Debbie's book had lots of cool items, like covers for your mobile phone. So I asked a couple of friends to teach me to knit, and out we went.

That was effectively the first meeting of Stitch and Bitch London – we were very British and insisted on the 'and' instead of 'n'. Knitting became really meaningful to me because it had nothing to do with my cancer. It was as if I had replaced the needles I was having in the hospital every day with knitting needles. That may sound odd, but it made a huge difference during my treatment.

As my friends and I talked to other people about knitting, more and more wanted to come along, so I started sending out emails saying, 'We're going to such and such a place.' I'd always wanted to be a writer, so the emails quickly turned into a newsletter with information about what was going on in craft in London and links to patterns online. I taught myself about HTML and Photoshop so I could put in illustrations and graphics. Friends forwarded it to friends and it started popping up on online forums with people saying, 'You have to read this.' So the group grew and grew, both in the flesh and online.

OUR FIRST big EVENT

The day I got out of hospital was the day 'graffiti knitting' was born. Deadly Knitshade, my knitting alter ego, appeared in my head and I had the idea of knitting a scarf for one of the lions in Trafalgar Square, as a celebration of my being better. When I mentioned it in the newsletter, so many people wanted to be involved – and knit on behalf of other people they knew who were fighting cancer, or in memory of people who hadn't survived – that we ended up with over 150 metres of scarf and joined all four lions up. I'd thought I would run up in the night, put the scarf round a lion and run away again. Instead I was interviewed by the BBC, and cancer survivors came up to me and said, 'This is wonderful. You've made something funny and lovely out of a horrible thing.' I thought, 'Oh my God. I'm taking over the world. With knitting.' And we raised thousands of pounds for Cancer Research, all thanks to an online newsletter.

It was about this time that we changed the name from Stitch and Bitch to Stitch London, because we had moved such a long way from just knitting in the pub. I felt we could do great things with this.

Oh my God. I'm taking over the world. With knitting.

SOCIAL MEDIA

I've never really seen this side of things as a job, because it just makes sense to me. All the time I've been running Stitch London, I've been talking to people online about it. For me it was never just a knitting group, it was a community:

we all care about each other, support each other, and that for me is every bit as important as the knitting. There are Stitch Londoners in 52 countries now, including someone who joined recently from Ethiopia. Social media means that we can reach out all over the world and we just keep growing. Without that, once all the knitters in London had joined – well, that would have been it!

I find that big businesses don't really understand social media yet. Any Facebook post that I make, or anything I tweet, is going to go out to thousands of people. If I recommend a new yarn, those people will try it because they trust me. A lot of businesses would kill for that sort of direct marketing, but they just can't get there.

I've never advertised, but I have done a lot of press, because people want to talk to me. I've accidentally created this monster – I call it the Woolly Godzilla – and they want to know how it happened. So it's got lots of publicity through its own momentum.

ADVICE FOR BEGINNERS

I'd advise anyone starting a craft business to get online in as many ways as possible. A website is essential, because it allows anyone you talk to to look at what you're doing in more detail and in their own time. If you aren't technologically expert, go and learn. If you do craft, you already know that your brain's capable of learning new things, so look at YouTube – it will teach you how to do almost anything. If you're not very good at writing the copy for your site, find someone who is and get them to do you a favour in return for something you can do for them.

Learning to be a little bit techy really isn't hard. It might look it, but it isn't. All the information is out there, and people will help you: people who are online will help you be online.

ONCE YOU'RE THERE

It's important to talk about what you do. A lot of people seem to think that it's better just to promote the 'brand', that it looks more professional that way. But actually people want to know what's going on behind the scenes, to see that there's a real person there. They are

Learning to be a little bit techy really isn't hard.

more willing to trust and do business with someone they feel they know.

All this breaks down the barrier between you and your customer – although you need to have a dividing line between your online self and the person who actually wanders round your house. That can be quite hard. I have a number of Twitter accounts – a personal one, a Deadly Knitshade

LET THE SITES DO THE MARKETING

Instagram is a brilliant community. It's Twitter for people with cameras. I went on there, looked at how other people were using it successfully and learnt from them how to use it for myself. Now I can put a picture of Cooey, my knitted pigeon, on Facebook and say, 'If you like this, you can find the pattern in my *Stitch London* book.' So Instagram and Facebook are doing marketing for my book, targeting people who I know are interested in what I'm doing, while I'm having fun making a bike out of buttons for my pigeon.

If you aren't having fun with social media, you aren't doing it right, because it is the most fun place in the world: it's like being at a cocktail party all day. There's always something crazy going on.

one, a Stitch London one, and so on. I have different Facebook pages too, and I've had some people who comment on every single thing I write on every single site. I've just had to discourage them gently. On Twitter people often ask me to follow them, but I will only follow people I know: otherwise I would feel that I had 5,000 voices shouting at me all the time. You have to retain some sort of privacy.

MAKING THE MOST OF THE MEDIA

Because all these media change so fast, you have to keep up. If people start talking about the new thing, get on it. The latest for me is Pinterest, which is wonderful for craft because it's so visual,

but no doubt there'll be something else along in a minute.

Anywhere that you post pictures, make sure they are good ones. It's worth investing in a good camera and learning how to use it. I have seen people make amazing stuff and then put up the worst, blurriest photos. Not only does that make your work look bad, it makes you look unprofessional. You need to look at how other people are doing things successfully and do it too.

Twitter is also the best market research tool in the world. You put up a photo and people have to press perhaps five keys to tell you whether they love it or hate it. It's a lot easier than asking anyone to fill in a form.

You need to look at how other people are doing things successfully and do it too.

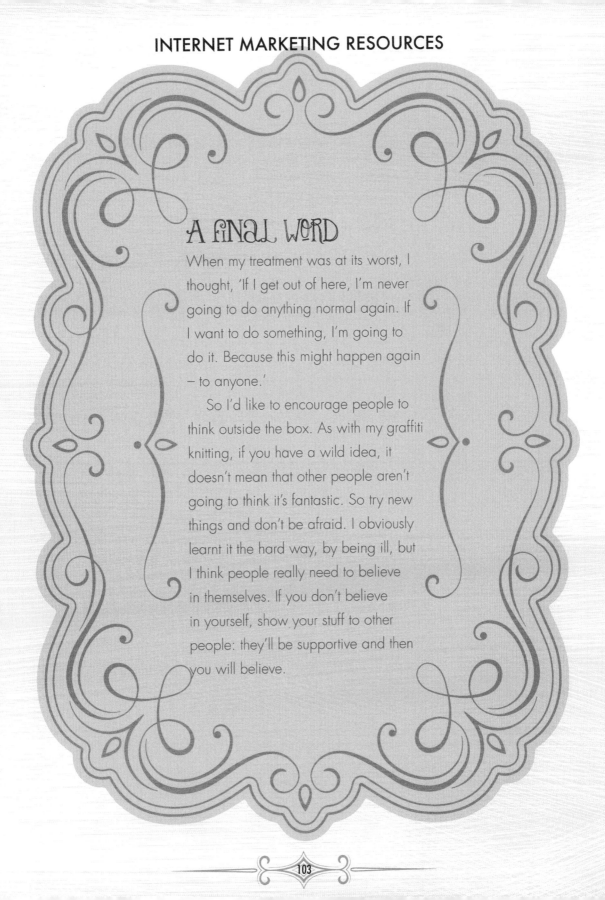

A FINAL WORD

When my treatment was at its worst, I thought, 'If I get out of here, I'm never going to do anything normal again. If I want to do something, I'm going to do it. Because this might happen again – to anyone.'

So I'd like to encourage people to think outside the box. As with my graffiti knitting, if you have a wild idea, it doesn't mean that other people aren't going to think it's fantastic. So try new things and don't be afraid. I obviously learnt it the hard way, by being ill, but I think people really need to believe in themselves. If you don't believe in yourself, show your stuff to other people: they'll be supportive and then you will believe.

SOCIAL MEDIA MARKETING

CARE2

About: Founded in 1998 by Randy Paynter and with over 20 million registered members as of September 2012, Care2 is a social networking website that aims to connect people of similar beliefs and morals; people who care about the environment, natural resources and a greener, balanced life.

Key Features: Members can create personal profiles and connect with like-minded individuals. Key features of Care2 include the ability to create online petitions, fundraisers, purchase e-cards (the proceeds of which are donated to charity), receive relevant newsletters and job advertisements with responsible and progressive companies. Care2 is a community of individuals who are actively leading a healthier, sustainable lifestyle, whilst supporting socially responsible causes.

Website: www.care2.com

DEVIANTART

About: Launched in 2000, DeviantART is one of the largest online communities dedicated entirely to artists. As of September 2012, the site reported to have over 23 million registered members, with over 140,000 submissions of work per day.

Key Features: DeviantART allows members to create a personal profile and upload photographs or videos of their art work. There are a wide variety of categories for artists to submit their work into, such as digital art, photography, artisan crafts, film, literature and many more. Submitted work can then receive comments and feedback from other members. Members can also create and join groups, take part in competitions and access journals and newsletters.

Website: www.deviantart.com

FACEBOOK

About: This internationally famous social networking website launched in 2004, and reached 1 billion members around the world as of 2012. Founded by Mark Zuckerberg, Facebook was initially intended for Harvard students; this soon expanded to surrounding colleges, and rapidly the world.

Key Features: Members can create personal profiles, business profiles, pages, private groups and events. Facebook is continuously evolving and creating new applications every day: members can easily network with each other, upload photographs, videos, documents, music and so much more. Businesses can create their own profiles or 'pages' and encourage users to 'like' these pages, which in turn will automatically notify members of any updates made.

Website: www.facebook.com

"Raising and
maintaining your
profile does take
a lot of work."
Claire Crompton

FLICKR

About: Launched in 2004 by the company Ludicorp, Flickr is a photograph and video hosting, social media website. As of April 2011, Flickr had accumulated over 50 million registered users.

Key Features: Flickr allows members to upload photographs or video content that they have either discovered or taken themselves. Members have the option to share their images and videos privately between friends and family, or publicly. Initially a popular service for bloggers to host images which they had imbedded into blog posts, Flickr is a great way for companies to visually advertise products artistically, reaching a wide audience of like-minded people.

Website: www.flickr.com

GOOGLE+

About: Google+ is an international, social networking website powered by Google. As of September 2012, Google+ reported the site as having over 400 million registered users.

Key Features: Members can create a personal profile, connect with other members, share interests, photographs, videos, thoughts and chat with one another. Google+ allows members to create 'Circles' – groups of people who can share with each other privately. Other features include 'Hangouts' which enables group video messaging and 'Whats Hot', similar to Twitter's 'Trending', in which a live stream displays what Google+ members are

currently discussing and sharing.
Website: www.plus.google.com

INSTAGRAM

About: Instagram is a photograph and video sharing social networking website founded by Kevin Systrom and Mike Krieger. As of 2012, Instagram had over 30 million members.

Key Features: Currently used as an application on Smartphones and Androids, Instagram allows members to take a photograph and apply a choice of filters and effects, creating an extremely professional finish. Members can then upload these photos directly to their Instagram profile, where other members can view, 'like', comment on and share.

Website: www.instagram.com

LINKEDIN

About: LinkedIn is a professional and business social networking website that launched in 2003. The website is effectively a digital, interactive CV, boasting over 175 million registered users as of June 2012.

Key Features: Members can create a professional profile, producing a CV of previous employments, academic achievements, certificates, awards, skills, interests and other relevant information. Businesses can create profiles which employees can link to and members can 'like'. LinkedIn is an innovative social platform that allows members to search for jobs and companies to headhunt prospective employees.

Website: www.uk.linkedin.com

PINTEREST

About: Pinterest is, in effect, a virtual pinboard. Since its initial launch in 2010, Pinterest has soared from 9,000 users to over 11.7 million in 2012, and attracts approximately 11 million visitors every week. The aim of Pinterest is to connect users all over the world through shared interests.

Key Features: Members can create categories, known as 'boards', in which they can then 'pin' images; categories could consist of absolutely anything, such as recipes, fashion, crafts, animals - the options are limitless. Users can connect with one another, 'like' each others pins and 'repin' images to their own 'boards'. Pinterest acts as an interactive mood board, providing inspiration and sharing anything and everything with the world. Businesses can utilize Pinterest as a virtual storefront to drive customers to their ecommerce website; as the platform revolves around visual stimuli, users feel less bombarded by commercial information and promotions.

Website: www.pinterest.com

RAVELRY

About: Ravelry is an online community specifically created for fibre art: knitting, crochet, weaving, spinning, dying and more. Founded by Casey and Jessica Forbes in 2007, Ravelry reached over 2 million registered users as of 2012.

Key Features: Ravelry allows fibre artists to connect with each other and share patterns, tips and project ideas. The website also supports the emergence of micro-businesses,

allowing patterns, products and yarns to be sold on the website, as well as providing users with advertising opportunities.

Website: www.ravelry.com

SQUIDOO

About: Squidoo is a free community platform that allows users to create single pages on the topic of their choice - much like a blog – Squidoo refers to these pages as 'lenses'.

Key Features: Users, termed 'lensmasters', can create a lens on the topic of their choice, be it baking, crafting, grammar, music or photography. Lensmasters can create as many lenses as they wish, with the opportunity to earn royalties on these submissions should they become popular and receive a high rate of interaction on the website.

Website: www.squidoo.com

"Pinterest is an excellent site for crafters because it's all about creating mood boards and showing people your style." Dorothy Wood

---

STUMBLEUPON

About: StumbleUpon, founded in 2001, is a discovery search engine that generates web content for users based on their personal interests.

Key Features: Upon creating a profile, users are asked to tick boxes of generalized categories that interest them, such as classical music, photography, humour, arts and crafts and more. From the selected categories the StumbleUpon search engine generates relevant web pages at the click of a button. A 'thumbs up' or 'thumbs down' button allows the users to tailor the web content that they receive; the more a user 'stumbles' the more StumbleUpon learns what interests the user and what doesn't. For businesses, StumbleUpon provides a feature called 'Paid Discovery', in which the company's URL website will reach target audiences.

Website: www.stumbledupon.com

T-SHIRTS AND SUITS CREATIVE ENTERPRISE NETWORK

About: Created by David Parrish, T-Shirts and Suits is a social networking website specifically catering for individuals and groups working within the creative industries, or looking to establish a new creative business.

Key Features: T-Shirts and Suits allows individuals and groups of crafters, designers and makers to connect with one another, advertise events and products, write blogs, discuss and debate in forums and generally promote their own craft enterprise. Users can provide each other with expert and personal advice concerning all aspects of launching and running their own creative enterprise.

Website: www.creative-enterprise-network.com/

TUMBLR

About: A completely customizable social networking and microblogging platform that enables users to share anything, from photographs and videos to quotes and website links. Tumblr was launched in 2007 by David Karp and had accumulated 75,000 users within its first 2 weeks. As of September 2012, Tumblr boasted over 76 million users.

Key Features: Tumblr allows users to create microblogs, on which they can share content they find interesting: videos, photographs, websites, documents, text and more. Users can create a 'Tumblr' button on their bookmark bar, allowing them to instantly share something found on another website.

Website: www.tumblr.com

TWITTER

About: Created by Jack Dorsey and launched in 2006, Twitter is an international social networking and microblogging website that boasted over 500 million users as of 2012. Twitter is a completely open, social media platform popular with celebrities and businesses as a tool to enhance their PR; members can follow other members and receive a live stream of statuses.

Key Features: Twitter is comprised of a live stream of information; members can upload short statements called 'Tweets' that followers can read and share ('Retweet'). This platform is a great way for individuals and businesses to keep customers constantly updated, as well as creating a friendly and approachable persona. Interestingly, Twitter includes a 'Trending' feature, which reveals what the majority of users are talking about at any one time; it is an impressive feat to cause a subject to start 'Trending'.

Website: www.twitter.com

YOUTUBE

About: Launched in 2005, YouTube is a video hosting platform which allows users to upload video clips. The website reportedly receives, on average, 800 million visitors per month.

Key Features: Visitors are not required to register to YouTube to be able to view videos, allowing videos to reach a much wider audience than some other video hosting websites. YouTube is rapidly evolving and can be utilized for a huge number of uses, such as advertising, video blogging ('vlogging'), video tutorials and even launching aspiring singing careers. Features of YouTube allow users to comment on, like and share videos.

Website: www.youtube.com

"We get a good response on almost anything if we feature it in the newsletter and offer a discount."
Emma Curtis and Liz Parnell

BLOGGING PLATFORMS

Aeonity

About: Aeonity is a basic blog hosting website that is simple to use and ideal for those who are new to blogging.

Key Features: Users can create their own blog page without any technical experience. Aeonity provides numerous themes and templates to assist in the design of the blog. Other advantages to using Aeonity are that it is simple, free from adverts and free to use.

Cost: Free.

Community: Aeonity provides a range of topics to support with the most common of issues: groups in which members can advise each other and contact information to speak to a member of the support team directly.

Website: www.aeonity.com

Blog.com

About: Blog.com is a simple and easy-to-use blogging platform powered by WordPress.

Key Features: Creating an account with Blog.com is free, providing users with a simple domain address, a variety of themes to choose from and the option to upload images, videos, music, documents and more. With a premium account, users have the option to disable adverts from their blog page and host their own adverts instead.

Cost: Free. Additional features and upgrades can be purchased.

Community: Blog.com features a help and support database with a wealth of information concerning common queries and problems.

Website: www.blog.com

Blogger

About: Powered by Google, Blogger is a popular platform amongst new bloggers, with a clear, simple interface.

Key Features: In contrast with other blogging platforms, Blogger offers a variety of free features. Features include: customizable templates, free domain names, image and video hosting, integration with other websites and the opportunity to earn money through AdSense advertisement.

Cost: Free. Additional features and upgrades can be purchased.

Community: Blogger provides an extensive help and support section that provides advice and tackles many common issues.

Website: www.blogger.com

Bravenet

About: A free website builder specifically designed for small businesses and entrepreneurs.

Key Features: Drag and drop website builder with customisable themes. Free email marketing, free stock photos for members, free web applications, plus fee-based custom domain names.

Cost: Free. Custom domains can be purchased.

Community: Support center and various forums available through the website.

Website: www.bravenet.com

Drupal

About: Drupal is an extremely popular CMS (content management system) used for developing websites, forums, social networks, blogs and more.

Key Features: Drupal features an easy-to-use interface with the ability to include text, videos, images, podcasts and polls. Users have the option to custom design their own websites or choose from the available themes and templates.

Cost: Free.

Community: Drupal provides an extensive amount of support, such as forums, live chat and advice documents. A number of books and professional training services are also available.

Website: www.drupal.org.uk

FreeBlogit

About: FreeBlogit is a free and straightforward blogging platform powered by WordPress.

Key Features: A free service that allows users to create multiple websites or blogs with up to 20 megabytes of storage. FreeBlogit is focused on traffic, providing detailed statistics and SEO (search engine optimized) themes. Users can easily access and update blogs via their mobile devices.

Cost: Free.

Community: FreeBlogit features a range of video tutorials to assist in the creation of blogs, design, writing blog posts, managing comments and more. Community forums are also available for members to discuss issues and share advice.

Website: www.freeblogit.com

BLOGGING PLATFORMS

Joomla

About: Joomla is a popular CMS (content management system) used for creating online content, such as websites and blogs.

Key Features: Joomla provides an assortment of themes to choose from to create a professional looking blog, as well as a translation service, plug-ins and an abundance of customizable options.

Cost: Free.

Community: Joomla provides a glossary of terms to assist users with technical jargon, a troubleshooting tool, training, an online helpdesk and more.

Website: www.joomla.co.uk

Jux

About: Jux is an innovative platform that differs slightly to the conventional blogging platforms available. In effect, Jux allows users to create their own microblogging website.

Key Features: Jux allows users to customize their microblog completely, without distracting adverts, side bars, navigation tabs or widgets; Jux provides a clean, high resolution 'edge-to-edge' appearance. Users can upload and present articles elegantly, as well as including images and videos in a clutter-free environment – highly recommended for displaying artwork and craft images.

Cost: Free.

Community: Users can contact Jux via their contact information or by getting in touch with them on their Twitter or Facebook accounts.

Website: www.jux.com

LifeType

About: Launched in 2005, LifeType is a straightforward, open-source, blogging platform.

Key Features: LifeType allows users to create multiple users per blog – perfect for small groups and organizations. Users can easily manage their blogs using the simple administration interface, choose from a range of templates and install plug-ins.

Cost: Free.

Community: An abundance of support is available from the LifeType website, including FAQ's, forums, wiki and a mailing list.

Website: www.lifetype.net

LiveJournal

About: A blogging platform with a social media feature integrated, LiveJournal allows users to create blogs, diary entries and articles, sharing these within their community of friends.

Key Features: As well as creating a blog, LiveJournal allows users to interact and network with other users and leave comments and feedback on blog posts. Users have a variety of templates to choose from, as well as customizable privacy settings and packages to choose from.

Cost: Free. Additional features and upgrades can be purchased.

Community: LiveJournal features an FAQ's sections, providing answers for a multitude of common issues, as well as the option to submit questions to the LiveJournal support team.

Website: www.livejournal.com

Movable Type

About: Popular with some of the worlds largest media companies, small and medium businesses and individual bloggers; Movable Type is an award winning blogging platform.

Key Features: Movable Type provides an efficient solution to creating a webpage and blog. Users can create a personal profile and create multiple websites and blog pages using the templates and themes provided.

Cost: Free. Additional features and upgrades can be purchased.

Community: Movable Type provides a superior support system through their dedicated support teams and forums.

Website: www.moveabletype.org

Posterous

About: Posterous is a simple blogging platform owned by Twitter that has gained widespread recognition as an innovative blogging and 'lifestream' platform.

Key Features: Designed to be used on-the-go with Smartphones and Androids, allowing users to update anything, anywhere. Users are able to create a personalized domain name, synchronize with existing websites and customize their Posterous space from a collection of provided themes and templates.

Cost: Free.

Community: Posterous provides a number of in-depth articles concerning common issues, as well as contact information and a feedback form for users to get in touch with the company.

Website: www.posterous.com

BLOGGING PLATFORMS

SERENDIPITY

About: Ideal for the personal blogger or professional business, Serendipity is flexible and easy to customize.

Key Features: Serendipity is appropriate for use by individuals, small groups and businesses. The default package is relatively straightforward, providing a huge collection of themes to choose from and the ability to install over 120 plug-ins. Other features include anti-spam filters, multiple authors and synchronization with other websites.

Cost: Free.

Community: Users can access support and advice via the FAQ's section or by discussing issues with other users in existing forums.

Website: www.s9y.org

SQUARESPACE

About: SquareSpace is an elegant and uncomplicated website and blogging platform.

Key Features: Themes and templates are created by SquareSpace's top designers, tailored to suit the individual's needs. SquareSpace's features are available to all members regardless of payment package; packages merely represent the volume of memory available.

Cost: SquareSpace offers a 14 day free trial before users must opt for the paid 'standard' or 'unlimited' package.

Community: SquareSpace provides a number of ways to access help and support: a search engine of their knowledge base, step-by-step workshop videos and live chat support with specialists.

Website: www.squarespace.com

TUMBLR

About: As well as functioning as a popular social media platform, Tumblr is also an extremely popular microblogging website that allows users to upload and share almost anything.

Key Features: Tumblr allows users to create microblogs, on which they can share content they find interesting: videos, images, websites, documents, text and more. Users can create a 'Tumblr' button on their bookmark bar, allowing them to instantly share something found on another website.

Cost: Free.

Community: Tumblr provides an extensive help section with, including FAQ's and the ability to submit individual queries.

Website: www.tumblr.com

TYPEPAD

About: Simple to create and easy to navigate, Typepad is popular amongst beginners as well as large media companies, such as Sky News and the BBC.

Key Features: Users can easily create a profile and customize their blog pages using the provided themes and templates, or create a completely unique template from scratch. Typepad consists of a large community of crafters, allowing users to promote their craft businesses as well as sell their products.

Cost: Typepad provides a 14 day free trial of their 'Plus' 'Unlimited' and 'Premium' packages, after which a monthly fee is required should the user wish to continue using the software.

Community: The Typepad community provide a support network for one another; extra support is available via the Typepad support team or the detailed knowledge base.

Website: www.typepad.com

WEEBLY

About: Simple website builder that enables users to create personal sites and blogs or establish web presences for businesses.

Key Features: Simple drag and drop website builder with 100s of themes. Multimedia features include photo slideshows, audio and video support and maps. Fully calibrated for mobile use.

Cost: Free.

Community: Has a support center and blog, plus social media profiles.

Website: www.weebly.com

WORDPRESS

About: WordPress is a particularly popular blogging platform used by a huge number of companies, such as Flickr and CNN.

Key Features: Users are able to create a blog or website for free. Key features of WordPress include traffic statistics, anti-spam filters, SEO (search engine optimization) and a range of themes and layouts to choose from. Created blogs and websites can be synchronized with a number of popular social media websites to allow for automatic updating.

Cost: Free. Additional features and upgrades can be purchased.

Community: WordPress provides a support community through a range of forums, support pages or directly with their 'Happiness Engineer'.

Website: www.wordpress.com

POPPY TREFFRY

Poppy Treffry is a textile designer (www.poppytreffry.co.uk) who produces and sells a range of quirky gifts in her shop in St Ives, Cornwall, through her own online store and around the world. She is the author of two books on freehand machine embroidery, the hallmark of her work.

I've always tried to make high quality products, but when I first started selling them, I was really nervous about asking shops and galleries to stock them. A friend made the initial approaches for me – I think other people had more faith in me than I did. But once I had a positive response, I knew that I was on to something.

I used to make everything myself, but now there are seven of us in the shop and office and I employ three people as stitchers. For every new product, I make the prototype, work out the colours and produce a template. Once I'm happy with that, Sarah cuts out all the base pieces, Freya cuts out the appliqué pieces, and then my stitchers take boxes of fabric home, sew it all up and bring it back finished.

We do three big retail shows each year: the Contemporary Craft Fair in Bovey Tracey, Devon in June, the Cornwall Design Fair in August and the Country Living Show in London in November. We also tend to go to one trade show in the spring and another in the autumn. And of course we have to keep the 'bricks and mortar' shop stocked. We can be thrown a bit off-balance if we get a big order and the customer wants it within a fortnight when we already have a full order book, but most of the time we cope. Me stitching into the night and stitching all weekend, which used to be my life, happens a lot less often now.

FIRST STEPS

My first step towards setting up my own business was to go to a trade show, where I sold to various shops and galleries. In Cornwall there is a lot of support for people starting out in arts and crafts. Thanks to the local Craft Developments Officer I had a loan from the Prince's Trust – it wasn't a huge amount, but it helped me to put a display together for that first show. Through the same Craft Developments Officer, I met a lot of other people in the craft world, so I was able to talk to them and discuss what had worked for them and what hadn't. I also created my first website, which functioned as an online shop.

All these things had come together by the time I did my first show. The fact that I had a website meant that people I saw there were able to go home and look me up, and I had quite a lot of follow-up business afterwards.

FIRST SHOWS

I'd advise anyone starting out and wanting to attend a show to go along to it first and get a feel for it. Have a look at what sort of thing is on offer, what seems to be selling and what the clientele is like. You can read the website, of course, but everything it says is going to be positive: much better to go and see for yourself, chat to other exhibitors and see what they think. You'll also find out things that you wouldn't learn from the website, like the layout of the venue – there may be a front area that gets much more traffic than the back one. So it may be worth negotiating with the organizers, and possibly paying a bit more to get a bigger stall in a better position. You wouldn't know that sort of thing if you didn't go and look.

IS IT WORTH IT?

Before you apply to exhibit at a show, ask other exhibitors what they think works and doesn't work and how much money you can expect to make, so you can decide whether it will be worth your while. After all, the big shows are going to cost quite a lot of money. Not everyone is prepared to share this sort of information, but a lot of people are.

Having decided on a show you'd like to exhibit at, look at the website: it may ask you to contact the organizer or to fill in an application form. You also have to send up to six high quality images of your work. These are the things that will clinch whether you get in or not. The people who are doing the selecting obviously don't have you or your work in front of you, so the quality of the images is really important.

ONCE YOU'RE IN

There are two types of show: trade shows and retail shows. With trade shows, I take only one sample of each item, because we're showing them to

> The people who are doing the selecting obviously don't have you or your work in front of you, so the quality of the images is really important.

people from shops and galleries and hoping that they will want to stock our products. We take orders and supply those orders normally four to six weeks later.

With retail shows, you are selling the products there and then, so the first big decision is how much to take. At first I always took far too much, but now I discipline myself keep a record of how many of each item I sold at a particular show last year and base my decisions on that. In theory everything is priced beforehand, though in practice I always find that I am still putting price tags out as we open on the first day.

As for what's going to sell and what isn't, my experience is absolutely that whatever I take least of, I could have sold most of. My colleague Freya and

I also have a rule of thumb about our products: if we really like it, it won't sell. She and I have quite quirky taste: we both love a badge I made that has an illustration of a pea and the word 'pea' written on it, but we've come to realise that peas just don't sell very well. If I like an idea for an item I tend to make it anyway, but I've learnt not to produce too many.

> If I like an idea for an item I tend to make it anyway, but I've learnt not to produce too many.

> I discipline myself keep a record of how many of each item I sold at a particular show last year and base my decisions on that.

Apart from the products themselves, I keep a check list of what I have to take to each show. For trade shows that means trade price lists, order forms and information about minimum orders and lead time. For retail shows, it's publicity material – leaflets, business cards, postcards, something that people can take away to remind them of me later.

A CAUTIONARY TALE

If I was giving one piece of advice to someone going to shows for the first time, it would be, 'Read all the information you are sent.' I once went to a four-day show that I thought was a three-day show and everything I had done was geared towards my being there for only three days. I'd booked the hotel for three nights instead of four, I'd even bought my assistant's train ticket home for the third day. Nightmare.

PRACTICALITIES

What you need to take in order to set up your stand varies from show to show, because a 'show' can be anything from the huge Country Living Fair at the Business Design Centre in London to a table in a marquee in a field. But they should all send out information about what is included in the price, what else you can have if you pay for it and what you have to bring for yourself. It's important to know this, because you don't want to fill your car up with furniture if you don't have to; on the other hand you don't want to turn up and find a table isn't provided.

I always take a credit card machine, because people expect to be able to pay by card. It's important to make sure it's working – I once had a machine die on me for an hour and I could see that I was losing money with every second that ticked by. I've been to rural shows where there isn't a very good signal and if people see that you are having trouble with your card payments they pass by. They may plan to come back later, but they just don't. Some shows offer a central paying service, so you give your customers a slip which they can take to the till and the payments are credited to your bank account a few weeks later. I've sometimes found that quite useful, although of course it means you have to wait for your money. Another possibility is to rent a terminal for the event; that's quite expensive, but in the beginning it might be worth trying either of these options before you commit yourself to a contract on a machine.

> I once had a machine die on me for an hour and I could see that I was losing money with every second that ticked by.

TOP TIPS

To summarize: the first thing you have to do is get
'out there' and get feedback. Find out if your stuff
is any good and if there is a market for it.
And, from the word go, work out your costs. I've always been
aware of how much materials cost and how long things
took me to make, so when I did start to sell things I already
had a realistic idea of what my costs were. If something is
expensive to make and you aren't pricing it right, you may
be selling lot of them, but in fact you're making a loss.

NATIONAL TRADE SHOWS

ART MATERIALS - LIVE

Categories: Painting, calligraphy and fine art.

About: For beginners and the experienced, this trade show aims to provide all painting enthusiasts with a large variety of supplies, as well as providing workshops and demonstrations to allow individuals to develop themselves as artists.

Location: NEC, Birmingham.

Month: November.

Organizer: International Craft and Hobby Fair Ltd (ICHF).

Address: Dominic House, Seaton Road, Highcliffe, Dorset BH23 5HW

Tel: 01425 272711

Email: info@ichf.co.uk

Website: www.ichf.co.uk

AUTUMN FAIR

Categories: Various arts and crafts.

About: Although this fair is not purely for homemade products, this could work to your advantage by allowing your creations to stand out. The fair is well known, it is the largest of its kind in Europe, and receives approximately 73,000 visitors.

Location: NEC, Birmingham.

Month: August.

Organizer: i2i Events.

Address: Greater London House, Hampstead Road, London NW1 7EJ

Tel: 020 7728 5000

Email: info@bctf.co.uk

Website: www.i2ieventsgroup.com

BEADS UP NORTH

Categories: Beading, jewellery and equipment.

About: Beads Up North is a notable annual beading event, taking place in the North West of England. The shows include numerous trade stalls and a variety of workshops and demonstrations.

Location: Various locations.

Month: Various dates throughout the year.

Organizer: Halfpenney's Mail-Order Beads & Beadwork.

Address: The Beading Room, 26 Melbourne Street, Clayton-Le-Moors, Accrington BB5 5LS

Tel: 01254 236049

Email: gordon@halfpenney.co.uk

Website: www.beadsupnorth.co.uk

BRITISH CRAFT TRADE FAIR

Categories: Various arts and crafts.

About: A strictly handmade, well-established three-day event featuring over 500 crafters. Features a section purely for recently established businesses to meet the industry experts.

Location: Great Yorkshire Showground, Yorkshire.

Month: April.

Organizer: Primary Sport Management Ltd.

Address: Hammonds Barn, London Road, Burgess Hill, West Sussex RH15 9QJ

Tel: 01444 246446

Email: info@ichf.co.uk

Website: www.bctf.co.uk

CAKE INTERNATIONAL

Categories: Sugarcraft, baking and cake decorating.

About: A large, international show featuring a wide variety of workshops, demonstrations and entertainment. Attracting visitors from all over the world, this is a fantastic event to attend to refine skills or learn new techniques.

Location: NEC, Birmingham; Event City, Manchester; ExCel, London.

Month: November, March and April.

Organizer: International Craft and Hobby Fair Ltd (ICHF).

Address: Dominic House, Seaton Road, Highcliffe, Dorset BH23 5HW

Tel: 01425 272711

Email: info@ichf.co.uk

Website: www.ichf.co.uk

CRAFT 4 CRAFTERS

Categories: Papercrafts, stamping, scrapbooking, sewing, cross stitch, embroidery, beading, patchwork, quilting, baking, sugarcraft and more.

About: Craft 4 Crafters provides an enormous variety of supplies for the crafting community, as well as an array of tutorials, workshops and demonstrations.

Location: Westpoint Arena Exeter.

Month: Various dates throughout the year.

Organizer: Craft 4 Crafters.

Tel: 08453 040222

Email: andrew.thorpe@craft4crafters.co.uk

Website: www.craft4crafters.co.uk

CRAFT, HOBBY AND STITCH INTERNATIONAL

Categories: Needlecraft and hobby products.

About: Europe's biggest and most popular trade show, giving crafters an opportunity to promote their products and improve sales. This show has several workshops and seminars for traders to enjoy.

Location: NEC Birmingham.

Month: February.

Organizer: International Craft and Hobby Fair Ltd (ICHF).

Address: Dominic House, Seaton Road, Highcliffe, Dorset BH23 5HW

Tel: 01425 272711

Email: info@ichf.co.uk

Website: www.ichf.co.uk

INTERNATIONAL JEWELLERY LONDON

Categories: Jewellery.

About: A fair purely for UK jewellery makers featuring several talks and speeches about new jewellery trends and retail strategies. You can also exhibit your products to an audience of approximately 9,000 buyers.

Location: Earls Court, London.

Month: September.

Organizer: Reed Exhibitions.

Address: Gateway House, 28 The Quadrant, Richmond, Surrey TW9 1DN

Tel: 020 8271 2134

Email: ijlteam@reedexpo.co.uk

Website: www.reedexpo.com

PINS AND NEEDLES

Categories: Cross stitch, embroidery, knitting, ribbon craft, quilting, patchwork, papercrafts, greeting cards and more.

About: Pins and Needles provides a variety of workshops, personal tutoring sessions, exhibitions and needlework supplies. This event has been running annually for several years and is increasing in its size and popularity every year.

Location: Newcastle Racecourse, Newcastle.

Month: February.

Organizer: Initial J Promotions Ltd.

Address: South Lough House, Stamfordham, Newcastle upon Tyne NE18 0QH

Tel: 01661 886814

Email: alison@initialj.co.uk

Website: www.initialj.co.uk

RENEGADE CRAFT FAIR

Categories: Jewellery, papercrafts, knitting, patchwork, quilting, ceramics, cross stitch, embroidery and more.

About: A large, international craft fair: Renegade tours around the US and makes a visit to London during the London Design Festival. Attracting thousands of visitors, RCF is particularly focused on enabling young and new crafters to showcase their talents as well as providing extensive workshops and classes.

Location: Old Truman Brewery, London.

Month: September.

Organizer: Renegade Craft Fair.

Address: 1932 S. Halstead Street Suite, 411 Chicago, Illinois 60608

Email: info@renegadecraft.com

Website: www.renegadecraft.com

ROSS PAPERCRAFT SHOW

Categories: Papercrafts, gift cards, decoupage, stamps and more.

About: A touring papercraft show that takes place over several dates throughout the year. Aiming to supply all papercraft needs at a low cost, as well as featuring up to 30 trade stalls at each venue.

Location: Leeds, Houghton, Sheffield, Hull, Middlesborough, Sunderland, Doncaster and Nottingham.

Month: Various dates throughout the year.

Organizer: Ross Papercraft Shows.

Tel: 07904 490904

Email: trosspaper@hotmail.co.uk

Website: www.rosspapercraftshows.co.uk

SCOTTISH QUILT CHAMPIONSHIPS

Categories: Quilting and patchwork.

About: A large show dedicated to patchwork and quilting, displaying hundreds of quilts from around the world. It features workshops and competitions.

Location: MacRobert Pavilions, Edinburgh.

Month: September.

Organizer: Grosvenor Shows Ltd.

Address: 282 High Road, Whaplode, Spalding, Lincolnshire PE12 6TG

Tel: 01406 372601

Email: grosvenorshows@btconnect.com

Website: www.grosvenorshows.co.uk

NATIONAL TRADE SHOWS

SEWING FOR PLEASURE

Categories: Stitching, beading and knitting.
About: The largest stitch craft show, with over 150 exhibitions, sewing machine workshops and free demonstrations, as well as supply stalls.
Location: NEC, Birmingham.
Month: March.
Organizer: International Craft and Hobby Fair Ltd.
Address: Dominic House, Seaton Road, Highcliffe, Dorset BH23 5HW
Tel: 01425 272711
Email: info@ichf.co.uk
Website: www.ichf.co.uk/sewingforpleasure

SPRING FAIR

Categories: Various arts and crafts.
About: Although this fair is not purely for homemade products, this could work to your advantage by allowing your creations to stand out. The fair is well known, it's the largest of its kind in Europe, and receives approximately 73,000 buyers.
Location: NEC, Birmingham.
Month: February.
Organizer: i2i Events.
Address: Greater London House, Hampstead Road, London NW1 7EJ
Tel: 020 7728 5000
Email: contact@i2ieventsgroup.com
Website: www.i2ieventsgroup.com

THE BEADWORK FAIRS

Categories: Beading, jewellery and equipment.
About: The Beadwork Fairs take place all over the country throughout the year, and include a vast amount of trade stalls, workshops and exhibitions.
Location: Various locations.
Month: Various dates throughout the year.
Organizer: The Craft Kit Company Ltd.
Address: 16 Kiln Lane, Betchworth, Surrey RH3 7LX
Tel: 01737 841080
Email: paul@thecraftkitcompany.co.uk
Website: www.thecraftkitcompany.com

THE FESTIVAL OF QUILTS

Categories: Textiles, patchwork and quilting.
About: A prestigious trade show specializing in an extremely large amount of textiles and equipment for all quilting and textile enthusiasts. With over 100 classes, workshops and lectures, the annual festival attracts over 30,000 people from around the world. A total of £30,000 in prize money is awarded to the finest quilts entered.
Location: NEC, Birmingham.
Month: August.
Organizer: Upper Street Events Ltd.
Address: 58 White Lion Street, Islington, London N1 9PP
Tel: 020 8692 2299
Email: agnes@twistedthread.com
Website: www.twistedthread.com

THE KNITTING AND STITCHING SHOW

Categories: Crochet, cross stitch, up-cycling, embroidery, patchwork, quilting, felting, jewellery, shibori dyeing, gift cards, embossing and more.
About: A prestigious trade show for all things textile: providing numerous workshops, lectures and demonstrations as well as featuring hundreds of trade stalls providing speciality supplies.

"I'd advise anyone starting out and wanting to attend a show to go along to it first and get a feel for it." Poppy Treffry

Location: London, Dublin and Harrogate.
Month: October and November.
Organizer: Upper Street Events Ltd.
Address: 58 White Lion Street, Islington, London N1 9PP
Tel: 020 8692 2299
Email: agnes@twistedthread.com
Website: www.twistedthread.com

NATIONAL CONSUMER SHOWS

ABINGDON CRAFT FAIR

Categories: Sculpture, glasswork, textiles and more.

About: The ultimate handmade shopping experience; there are several fairs throughout the year in various locations, featuring high quality exhibitors.

Location: Various locations.

Month: Various dates throughout the year.

Organizer: Abingdon Craft & Design Fairs Ltd.

Address: Unit FF2 Parkfield Business Centre, Park Street, Stafford, Staffordshire ST17 4AL

Tel: 01785 245312

Email: sales@acfcraftfairs.com

Website: www.acfcraftfairs.com

CAKE INTERNATIONAL

Categories: Sugarcraft, baking and cake decorating.

About: A large, international show featuring a wide variety of workshops, demonstrations and entertainment. Attracting visitors from all over the world, this is a fantastic event to attend to refine skills or learn new techniques.

Location: NEC, Birmingham; Event City, Manchester; ExCel, London.

Month: November, March and April.

Organizer: International Craft and Hobby Fair Ltd (ICHF).

Address: Dominic House, Seaton Road, Highcliffe, Dorset BH23 5HW

Tel: 01425 272711

Email: info@ichf.co.uk

Website: www.ichf.co.uk

CONTEMPORARY CRAFT SHOPPING EXPERIENCE

Categories: Various arts and crafts.

About: The perfect fair to find all of your special Christmas gifts. There are a wide range of unique products on offer, including jewellery, ceramics, furniture and much more.

Location: Warwickshire Exhibition Centre, Warwickshire.

Month: December.

Organizer: Meridienne Exhibitions.

Address: Fosse Way, Leamington Spa, Warwickshire CV31 1XN

Tel: 01926 614101

Email: info@meridienneexhibitions.co.uk

Website: www.meridienneexhibitions.co.uk

COUNTRY LIVING MAGAZINE CHRISTMAS FAIR

Categories: Ceramics, fine art, woodcraft, toys, prints, jewellery and more.

About: This large annual Christmas fair attracts in excess of 28,000 visitors each year. With over 200 exhibition stalls, there is something for everyone.

Location: Business Design Centre, London; SECC, Glasgow; Harrogate International Centre, Harrogate.

Month: November and December.

Organizer: Upper Street Events Ltd.

Address: 58 White Lion Street, Islington, London N1 9PP

Tel: 020 7288 6318

Email: HarrietL@upperstreetevents.co.uk

Website: www.countrylivingfair.com

COUNTRY LIVING MAGAZINE SPRING FAIR

Categories: Various arts and crafts, homes and interiors, fashion, nature and more.

About: This large annual Spring fair attracts in excess of 19,000 visitors each year. With over 400 exhibitions, workshops and shops, there is something for everyone.

Location: Business Design Centre, London.

Month: March.

Organizer: Upper Street Events Ltd.

Address: 58 White Lion Street, Islington, London N1 9PP

Tel: 020 7288 6318

Email: DanS@upperstreetevents.co.uk

Website: www.countrylivingfair.com

CRAFT 4 CRAFTERS

Categories: Knitting, sewing, papercrafts, painting, scrapbooking and more.

About: Displays a range of craft, has workshops and 'Make and Take' zones for all crafters to learn new skills.

Month: January.

Address: Clyst St Mary, Exeter EX5 1DH

Tel: 08453 040222

Email: andrew.thorpe@craft4crafters.co.uk

Website: www.craft4crafters.co.uk

CRAFT IN FOCUS

Categories: Various arts and crafts.

About: The latest designs from both established and relatively unknown British crafters. This is a well-respected

fair of the highest standard, accepting only high quality, homemade products.
Location: Various locations.
Month: Various dates throughout the year.
Organizer: Craft in Focus.
Address: PO BOX 942, Maidstone, Kent ME15 0YB
Tel: 01622 747325
Email: info@craftinfocus.com
Website: www.craftinfocus.com

CRAFTS FOR CHRISTMAS

Categories: Various arts and crafts.
About: An array of unique and inspiring gifts that you wouldn't usually find on the high street, plus meet the talented craftspeople behind the designs. Enjoy craft demonstrations from the *Prima* team as well as a variety of entertainment.
Location: SECC, Glasgow and NEC, Birmingham.
Month: October and November.
Organizer: International Craft and Hobby Fair Ltd.
Address: Dominic House, Seaton Road, Highcliffe, Dorset BH23 5HW
Tel: 01452 72711
Email: info@ichf.co.uk
Website: www.ichf.co.uk/indoorcraftsalive

CREATIVE STITCHES AND HOBBYCRAFTS

Categories: Knitting, embroidery, sewing, gift cards, papercrafts, beadwork and more.
About: This event consists of free fashion shows, workshops and demonstrations on a variety of crafts. See all the latest craft designs and stock up on supplies.
Location: Event City, Manchester;

Westpoint Centre, Exeter.
Month: May, September, October and November.
Organizer: International Craft and Hobby Fair Ltd.
Address: Dominic House, Seaton Road, Highcliffe, Dorset BH23 5HW
Tel: 01425 272711
Email: info@ichf.co.uk
Website: www.ichf.co.uk/csh

EARTH AND FIRE INTERNATIONAL CERAMICS FAIR

Categories: Ceramics.
About: A free event, attracting around 7,000 people from all around the world. The ultimate fair for any budding potters or ceramists; there are stalls, talks and free demonstrations, as well as trade stalls.
Location: Rufford Abbey, Nottinghamshire.
Month: June.
Organizer: Rufford Craft Centre.
Address: Ollerton, Newark, Nottinghamshire NG22 9DF
Tel: 01623 822944
Email: enquiries@nottscc.gov.uk
Website: www.nottinghamshire.gov.uk

FASHION, EMBROIDERY AND STITCH

Categories: Sewing, textiles and more.
About: This show features fashion shows, workshops and expert speakers, as well as exhibiting work from the UK's top textile talents. Also on offer is a vast range of fabric and embellishment supplies. Visitors holding a 'Sewing for Pleasure' ticket are able to attend free of charge.

Location: NEC, Birmingham.
Month: March.
Organizer: International Craft and Hobby Fair Ltd.
Address: Dominic House, Seaton Road, Highcliffe, Dorset BH23 5HW
Tel: 01425 272711
Email: info@ichf.co.uk
Website: www.ichf.co.uk/fashion/

LONDON DESIGN FESTIVAL

Categories: Various arts and crafts.
About: A truly massive fair spread over ten days with around 300 events, attracting an estimated 350,000 visitors. This event consists of trade and consumer stalls as well as workshops and trade seminars. This Festival takes place across London; further details can be found on the website.
Location: Various locations.
Month: September.
Organizer: London Design Festival Ltd.
Address: 60 Firth Street, London W1D 3JJ
Tel: 020 7734 6444
Email: hello@londondesignfestival.com
Website: www.londondesignfestival.com

MAKE IT

Categories: Knitting, stitching, felting, ceramics, beadwork, candles, preserves and more.
About: Representing new and traditional handmade crafts, this fair has several stalls as well as 'Make it and Take it' sessions and workshops.
Location: FIVE, Farnborough.
Month: February.
Email: enquiries@make-it.org.uk
Website: www.make-it.org.uk

NATIONAL CONSUMER SHOWS

PRIMA HOMEMADE SHOW

Categories: Gift cards, interior design, sewing, cake decorating and more.

About: A new Creative Stitches and Hobby Craft show taking place over four days for experienced and beginner crafters, featuring exciting displays, workshops and a variety of demonstrations.

Location: Bluewater Events Venue, Kent.

Month: September.

Organizer: International Craft and Hobby Fair Ltd.

Address: Dominic House, Seaton Road, Highcliffe, Dorset BH23 5HW

Tel: 01425 272711

Email: info@ichf.co.uk

Website: www.ichf.co.uk/csh/bluewater

SINCERELY YOURS

Categories: Papercraft

About: Providing 15 craft shows per year and touring from Scotland to Somerset; this show is a must for anyone interested in papercraft, offering a chance to purchase the latest papercraft supplies.

Location: Various locations.

Month: Various dates throughout the year.

Organizer: Sincerely Yours.

Address: Unit 11, Rochester Airport Ind Est, Laker Road, Rochester, Kent

Tel: 01684 561061

Website: www.sincerely-yours.co.uk

STAFFORDSHIRE COUNTY SHOW

Categories: Various arts and crafts.

About: A popular event, attracting up to 70,000 visitors every year and featuring numerous workshops, entertainment and agricultural produce. This is a large scale event featuring 400 trade stalls.

Location: Staffordshire County Showground, Staffordshire.

Month: May.

Organizer: Creative Crafts Association.

Address: Primrose Cottage, Howards Lane, Eccleston, Lancashire WA10 5QD

Tel: 01744 750606

Email: sandraCCA@aol.com

Website: www.creativecrafts-online.co.uk

THE CREATIVE CRAFTS SHOWS

Categories: Papercraft, beadwork, stitching, knitting, crochet and more.

About: This fair features many activities, such as workshops, demonstrations, idea exchanges and 'Make and Takes'. This is also a perfect chance to stock up on craft supplies

Location: Various locations.

Month: Various months throughout the year.

Organizer: Trident Exhibitions.

Address: West Devon Business Park, Tavistock, Devon PL19 9DP

Tel: 01822 614671

Email: info@trident-exhibitions.co.uk

Website: www.sccshows.co.uk

THE GREAT NORTHERN CONTEMPORARY CRAFT FAIR

Categories: Ceramics, glasswork, jewellery, textiles, woodcrafts, papercrafts, silver work, metalwork, printing and more.

About: Featuring over 150 exhibitors and attracting over 6,000 visitors per year, the Great Northern Contemporary Craft Fair has become an iconic event for all enthusiasts of craft. Visitors can enjoy workshops, demonstrations and competitions.

Location: Spinningfields, Manchester.

Month: October.

Organizer: Great Northern Events.

Address: 23 Belfield Road, Didsbury, Manchester M20 6BJ

Tel: 01612 839667

Email: enquiries@greatnorthernevents.co.uk

Website: www.greatnorthernevents.co.uk

REGIONAL SHOWS

EAST AND SOUTH EAST

CHILTERNS CRAFT SHOW

Categories: Jewellery, ceramics, textiles and more.

About: A fun family day out; attracting 8,000 visitors and providing workshops for adults and children on papercrafts, weaving, jewellery making and more. A great opportunity for crafters to exhibit and sell their work.

Location: Stonor Park, Henley-on-Thames.

Month: August.

Organizer: International Craft and Hobby Fair Ltd.

Address: Dominic House, Seaton Road, Highcliffe, Dorset BH23 5HW

Tel: 01452 72711

Email: info@ichf.co.uk

Website: www.ichf.co.uk

EAST ANGLIAN GAME & COUNTRY FAIR

Categories: Various arts and crafts.

About: Both children and adults can participate in the events at the Cornwall Design Fair, such as workshops and live demonstrations.

Location: Norfolk Showground, Norwich.

Month: April.

Organizer: Craft People 2000.

Address: 38 Eden Grove, Sheffield, South Yorkshire S26 4TP

Tel: 01142 879671

Email: info@craftpeople2000.co.uk

Website: www.craftpeople2000.co.uk

FESTIVAL OF CRAFTS

Categories: Textiles, ceramics, glasswork, woodcraft, embroidery, silverwork, jewellery and more.

About: This fair is long running and well established, featuring over 80 crafters and designers.

Location: Farnham Maltings, Surrey.

Month: October and February.

Organizer: Farnham Maltings.

Address: Bridge Square, Farnham, Surrey GU9 7Q4

Tel: 01252 745444

Email: info@farnhammaltings.com

Website: www.farnhammaltings.com

FIBRE-EAST

Categories: Spinning, knitting, weaving and more.

About: A celebration of UK sourced and produced wools and natural fibres. Fibre-East focuses on aiding individuals and small business, with numerous attractions, advice, demonstrations, workshops, over 80 exhibitors and trades.

Location: Scald End Farm, Bedford.

Month: July.

Organizer: Fibre-East.

Address: Scald End Farm, Mill Lane, Thurleigh, Bedford MK44 2DP

Tel: 07751 813681

Email: info@fibre-east.co.uk

Website: www.fibre-east.co.uk

HANDMADE WINCHESTER DESIGNER & MAKER CHRISTMAS FAIR

Categories: Textiles, soaps, silverwork, prints, glasswork, gift cards, jewellery and more.

About: A well-established event attracting over 6,000 customers each year; this annual Christmas fair has proven to be a favourite amongst local enthusiasts. The fair features over 70 stalls, all featuring genuine handmade crafts and artwork.

Location: Winchester Guildhall, Winchester.

Month: December.

Organizer: Handmade Winchester.

Address: 12b Laverstoke Lane, Laverstoke, Whitchurch, Hampshire RG28 7NY

Tel: 01392 219050

Email: applications@ handmadewinchester.co.uk

Website: www.handmadewinchester.co.uk

HYDE END CRAFT SHOW

Categories: Homemade clothes and jewellery, metalwork and woodcraft.

About: A well-organized and long running event, actively supporting local produce and crafts. The organizers make every effort to limit duplication of crafts and products to ensure maximum success.

Location: Hyde End, Norfolk.

Month: April and October.

Organizer: Eastern Events.

Address: Diggens Farm House, Buxton Road, Aylsham, Norfolk NR11 6UB

Tel: 01263 734711

Email: info@easternevents.com

Website: www.easternevents.com

KNEBWORTH HOUSE SHOWS

Categories: Ceramics, jewellery, woodcraft and stonemasonry.
About: A variety of stalls for both traditional and modern crafts, also features live craft demonstrations.
Location: Knebworth House, Hertfordshire.
Month: Various shows throughout the year.
Organizer: Romor Exhibitions.
Address: PO Box 448, MK40 2ZP
Tel: 01234 345725
Email: desk@romorexhibitions
Website: www.romorexhibitions.co.uk

MADE BRIGHTON

Categories: Knitting, glasswork, textiles and more.
About: A hugely successful and well-respected craft fair with approximately 6,000 visitors and 120 stalls.
Location: Corn Exchange, Brighton.
Month: November.
Organizer: Sarah Young and Jon Tutton.
Address: PO BOX 4729, Worthing, Sussex BN11 9LD
Tel: 01903 608757
Email: info@made11.co.uk
Website: www.brighton-made.co.uk

MADE IT MARKET

Categories: Jewellery, glasswork, ceramics and textiles.
About: A market with 70 selected crafters selling primarily handmade products, however digital crafts are also accepted.
Location: Various locations.
Month: Dates vary.
Organizer: Made-it Market.
Address: 8 Bois Field Terrace, Halstead, Essex CO9 2DF
Tel: 07793 889409
Email: hello@madeitmarket.co.uk
Website: www.madeitmarket.co.uk

MADE LONDON

Categories: Textiles, jewellery, clothes and more.
About: A relatively new fair created due to the success of Made Brighton, this fair has over 115 unique, original designers/crafters.
Location: One Marylebone, London.
Month: October.
Organizer: Sarah Young and Jon Tutton.
Address: PO BOX 4729, Worthing, Sussex BN11 9LD
Tel: 01903 608757
Email: info@madelondon.org
Website: www.madelondon.org

NATIONAL TRUST STOWE CRAFT AND DESIGN FESTIVAL

Categories: A wide variety of craft, including textiles and jewellery making.
About: Stalls and demonstrations for modern and traditional crafts.
Location: National Trust Stowe, Buckinghamshire.
Month: August.
Organizer: Romor Exhibitions.
Address: PO Box 448, MK40 2ZP
Tel: 01234 345725
Email: desk@romorexhibitions
Website: www.romorexhibitions.co.uk

SPIRALS CRAFT FAIR

Categories: Jewellery, woodcraft, textiles, glasswork, ceramics and more.
About: Fairs across Berkshire purely for selling local, homemade, quality products.
Location: Various locations.
Month: Various dates throughout the year.
Organizer: Spirals Craft Fair.
Address: 72 Eastcourt Road, Burbage, Marlborough, Wiltshire SN8 3AJ
Tel: 07979 498876
Email: hazel@spiralsmarket.co.uk
Website: www.spiralsmarket.co.uk

THE MALTINGS COMMUNITY HALL CRAFT FAIRS

Categories: Jewellery, textiles and more.
About: A regular craft fair, run by a non-profit organization, with the simple aim of promoting quality craftsmanship. Fairs take place at various times, usually at least two weekends every month.
Location: The Maltings Community Hall, Norfolk.
Month: Weekly.
Organizer: Wells Craft Group.
Address: The Maltings Community Hall, Staithe Street, Wells-next-the-Sea, Norfolk NR23 1AF
Tel: 01553 811403
Email: janwilson101@btinternet.com
Website: wellscraftsgroup.webs.com

WEALD OF KENT CRAFT SHOW

Categories: Jewellery, ceramics, woodcraft, glasswork, textiles and more.
About: A large craft show with over 250 exhibition stalls, demonstrations and entertainment for all the family.
Location: Penhurst Place, Tonbridge.
Month: May and September.
Organizer: International Craft and Hobby Fair Ltd.

Address: Dominic House, Seaton Road, Highcliffe, Dorset BH23 5HW
Tel: 01452 72711
Email: info@ichf.co.uk
Website: www.ichf.co.uk/outdoorcraftsalive/?show=tonbridge

WEST ANGLIA EASTER COUNTRY SHOW

Categories: Various arts and crafts.
About: A well-organized and long running event, actively supporting local produce and crafts. The organizers make every effort to limit duplication of crafts and products to ensure maximum success.
Location: Wood Green Animal Shelter, Cambridgeshire.
Month: April.
Organizer: Oakleigh Fairs.
Address: Thrift Farm House, Horkesley Hill, Nayland, Colchester CO6 4JP
Tel: 01206 263088
Email: web-contact@oakleighfairs.co.uk
Website: www.oakleighfairs.co.uk

THE LONDON BEAD FAIR

Categories: Beading, jewellery and equipment.
About: The London Bead Fair is a notable event that takes place twice annually; featuring over 40 trade stalls, exhibitions, demonstration and workshops.
Location: Kempton Park Racecourse, Sunbury.
Month: February and September.
Organizer: West of England Events.
Tel: 01747 840213
Email: stephenmobsby@westofenglandevents.co.uk
Website: www.westofenglandevents.co.uk

MIDLANDS

LUSTRE CONTEMPORARY CRAFT MARKET

Categories: Jewellery, ceramics, textiles, woodcraft and glasswork.
About: A fun family day out attracting approximately 8,000 visitors and providing workshops for adults and children on papercrafts, weaving, jewellery making and more. This is a great opportunity for crafters to exhibit and sell their work.
Location: Djanogly Art Gallery.
Month: November.
Organizer: Lakeside Arts Centre.
Address: University Park, Nottingham NG7 2RD
Tel: 01158 467777
Email: Djanogly-art-gallery@nottingham.ac.uk
Website: www.lakesidearts.org.uk

MERGE CONTEMPORARY CRAFT FAIR

Categories: Various arts and crafts.
About: Both children and adults can participate in the events at the Cornwall Design Fair, such as workshops and live demonstrations.
Location: Various locations around Oundle, Northampton.
Month: Fortnightly.
Organizer: Zoe Garner.
Address: National Glass Centre, Liberty Way, Sunderland SR6 0GL
Tel: 07860 783635
Email: mergecraft@hotmail.co.uk
Website: www.mergecontemporarycraftfairs.com

NEWARK AND NOTTINGHAMSHIRE COUNTY SHOW

Categories: Various arts and crafts including spinning.
About: This event marks the first Country show of the season, attracting over 50,000 visitors in 2012. There is a large craft and gift marquee within this show, celebrating rural life, farming and high quality food produce and livestock.
Location: Newark Showground, Nottinghamshire.
Month: May.
Organizer: Craft People 2000.
Address: 38 Eden Grove, Sheffield, South Yorkshire S26 4TP
Tel: 01142 879671
Email: info@craftpeople2000.co.uk
Website: www.craftpeople2000.co.uk

NOTTINGHAM BEAD & CRAFT SHOW

Categories: Jewellery, beadwork and glasswork.
About: This annual show includes work shops and demonstrations, trade stalls selling beading and craft supplies as well as numerous gift stalls.
Location: Nottingham Gateway Hotel, Nottingham.
Month: November.
Organizer: The Bead Shop Ltd.
Address: 7 Market Street, Nottingham NG1 6HY
Tel: 01159 588899
Email: info@mailorder-beads.co.uk
Website: www.mailorder-beads.co.uk

PAPER CRAFT FAIR

Categories: Papercrafts, gift cards, stamping, scrapbooking, découpage and more.

About: The Paper Craft Fair in Birmingham began successfully in 2010 and has continued to gain a positive reputation amongst crafters in and around the Midlands.

Location: National Motorcycle Museum, Birmingham.

Month: October and November.

Organizer: Excalibur Fairs and Events.

Address: The Techno Centre, Coventry University Technology Park, Puma Way, Coventry CV1 2TT

Tel: 07976 350520

Email: simon@excaliburfairs.co.uk

Website: www.papercraftfairs.co.uk

PRESTIGE CRAFT AND COLLECTORS FAIR

Categories: Ceramics, glasswork, candles, soaps, handbags, gift cards, jewellery and more.

About: These fairs contain unique, locally-handmade pieces and vintage items for sale.

Location: Newchurch Parish Hall, Culcheth.

Month: Several dates throughout the year.

Organizer: Prestige Craft and Collectors Fair.

Address: Newchurch Parish Hall, Common Lane, Culcheth WA3 4EH

Tel: 07411 154836

Email: sue_caller@hotmail.co.uk

Website: www.prestigecraftcollectorsfairs.vpweb.co.uk/default.html

QUALITY CRAFT FAIR

Categories: Various arts and crafts.

About: A regularly occurring village craft fair for handmade crafts, with approximately 12 stalls and some live demonstrations.

Location: Tissington Village Hall, Derbyshire.

Month: Several dates throughout the year.

Organizer: Quality Craft Fair.

Address: The Green, Tissington, Ashbourne, Derbyshire DE6 1RA

Email: denisebroadhurst@yahoo.co.uk

SOCK

Categories: Jewellery, ceramics, glasswork and sculptures.

About: A free weekend of crafts, with around 30 carefully selected crafters displaying their work.

Location: Loughborough Town Hall, Leicestershire.

Month: March.

Organizer: Loughborough Town Hall.

Address: Market Place, Loughborough, Leicestershire LE11 3EB

Tel: 01509 23191

Email: box.office@charnwood.gov.uk

Website: www.loughboroughtownhall.co.uk/events/2013/03/23/sock

THE GREAT BRITISH CRAFT FESTIVAL

Categories: Knitting, sewing, jewellery, beadwork and more.

About: A three-day fair with free demonstrations, workshops, and make and takes on découpage, stamping and more. There are also exhibitions from between 70–100 crafters, and appearances from well known crafters such as Dawn Bibby.

Location: Various locations.

Month: Several dates throughout the year.

Organizer: Hunkydory Crafts Ltd.

Address: Unit 2 15–19 Sedgwick Street, Preston, Lancashire PR1 1TP

Tel: 01772 5272561

Email: adam@hunkdorycrafts.co.uk

Website: www.hunkydorycrafts.co.uk

THE UK MOTORHOME AND CARAVAN SPRING FAIR

Categories: Various arts and crafts.

About: A large, annual weekend event that features over 150 trade stalls and a large arts and crafts marquee. This spring fair attracts over 10,000 visitors every year and is a celebration of rural and outdoor living, local produce and craftsmanship.

Location: Newark Showground, Nottinghamshire.

Month: March.

Organizer: Craft People 2000.

Address: 38 Eden Grove, Sheffield, South Yorkshire S26 4TP

Tel: 01142 879671

Email: info@craftpeople2000.co.uk

Website: www.craftpeople2000.co.uk

TOWCESTER CRAFT AND DESIGN SHOW

Categories: Ceramics, leather work, jewellery, photography, wood craft, soaps, glasswork, textiles and more.

About: This craft show features 45 handpicked exhibitors to display and sell their quality handmade gifts.

Location: Towcester Racecourse Conference Centre, Northamptonshire.

Month: March.

Organizer: Romor Exhibitions.
Address: PO BOX 448 MK40 2ZP
Tel: 01234 345 725
Email: desk@romorexhibitions.co.uk
Website: www.romorexhibitions.co.uk

STAFFORDSHIRE BEAD FAIR

Categories: Beading, jewellery and equipment.
About: Featuring exhibitions from all over the UK, the Staffordshire Bead Fair has been an annual event for several years and continues to be a popular attraction for visitors.
Location: Moat House Hotel.
Month: September.
Organizer: Staffordshire Bead Fair.
Address: 111a High Street, Wolstanton, Newcastle-under-Lyme, Staffordshire ST5 0EP
Tel: 01782 850108
Email: info@staffsbeadfair.co.uk
Website: www.staffsbeadfair.co.uk

NORTH EAST

FOOD AND CRAFT FAIR

Categories: Cakes, baking, cupcakes, silk painting, photography and more.
Location: Plants R Ross, Peterlee.
Month: Monthly.
Organizer: Plants R Ross.
Address: South Hetton Road, Easington, Peterlee, Durham SR8 3BZ
Tel: 01915 270855
Email: plantsrross@gmail.com
Website: www.plantsrrossnursery.co.uk

GEM 'N' BEAD AUTUMN SHOW

Categories: Jewellery, beadwork, glasswork and more.
Location: York Racecourse, Yorkshire.
Month: October.
Organizer: Craftworx.
Address: 12 Oriel Close, Walkington, Beverley, East Yorkshire HU17 8YD
Tel: 07961 883115
Email: tracey@craftworx.co.uk
Website: www.craftworx.co.uk

GRAINGER MARKET

Categories: Knitting, jewellery, embroidery, handbags, stonework, soaps and more.
About: This arts and crafts market takes place on the second Saturday of each month and is located in the popular indoor Grainger Market: a busy, central location attracting up to 140,000 visitors every week.
Location: Grainger Market, Newcastle upon Tyne.
Month: Monthly.

Organizer: Doreen Blakemore.
Address: Grainger Market, Grainger Street, Newcastle-upon-Tyne NE1 5QQ
Tel: 01912 115533
Email: markets@newcastle.gov.uk
Website: www.newcastle.gov.uk/business/markets/grainger-market

HELPING HANDS MAKER'S MARKET

Categories: Various arts and crafts.
About: A fortnightly craft fair that aims to assist local crafters by providing cheap stalls to exhibit their goods.
Location: Oxclose Church, Tyne and Wear.
Month: Fortnightly.
Organizer: Daniel Dunlavey.
Address: Oxclose Church, Brancepeth Road, Oxclose, Washington NE38 0LA
Tel: 07964 885667
Email: danieldunlavey@impossiblegears.co.uk
Website: www.facebook.com/HelpingHandsMarket

MAKE AND MEND MARKET

Categories: Jewellery, gift cards, textiles, cupcakes, baking, up-cycling and more.
About: One of Newcastle's biggest, independent markets, focusing on vintage, recycling and economical produce. Alternating between the Grainger Market and the Star and Shadow Cinema, Ouseburn each month.
Location: The Grainger Market and the Star and Shadow Cinema, Newcastle.
Month: Monthly.
Organizer: Brittany Coxon.

Email: makeandmendmarket@gmail.com

Website: www.makeandmendmarket.co.uk

MAKERS' FAIR FESTIVAL SPECIAL

Categories: Ceramics, glasswork, photography, painting, print, jewellery, illustrations, textiles, woodcraft and more.

About: The Saltaire annual Festival, set in the historic, World Heritage village of Saltaire, features in excess of 60 artists, crafters and designers.

Location: Victoria Hall, West Yorkshire.

Month: September.

Organizer: Saltaire Arts Trail.

Address: Saltaire Visitor Information Centre, Salts Mill, Victoria Road, Saltaire BD18 3LA

Email: hello@saltaireartstrail.co.uk

Website: www.saltaireartstrail.co.uk

MORPETH HAND CRAFT FAIR

Categories: Various arts and crafts.

About: A regular fair held in Morpeth Town Hall, specifically for handmade items only.

Location: Morpeth Town Hall, Northumberland.

Month: Various dates throughout the year.

Organizer: Quintet Promotions.

Tel: 01915 229533

Email: info@a-pac.net

Website: www.quintet-promotions.co.uk

THE LIVING NORTH ESSENCE OF CHRISTMAS FAIR

Categories: Jewellery, glasswork, photography, knitting, quilting, up-cycling, candles and more.

About: Showcasing 250 carefully selected exhibitors at what is reportedly the largest event of its kind in the North East.

Location: Newcastle Racecourse, Newcastle.

Month: November.

Organizer: Living North.

Address: Studio 2 St Nicholas Chare, Newcastle NE1 1RJ

Tel: 01912 618944

Email: ali@livingnorth.com

Website: www.livingnorthfair.com

YORK GUILD HALL CRAFT, COLLECTORS AND GIFT FAIR

Categories: Various arts and crafts.

About: Well-established and running for 20 years, this fair has up to 40 stalls containing unique crafts.

Location: York Guild Hall, North Yorkshire.

Month: August.

Organizer: Heritage Promotions.

Website: There is no contact information for Heritage Promotions, however you can contact them through their Facebook page; www.facebook.com/HeritagePromotionsUK

NORTH WEST

BOLTON CRAFT FAIR

Categories: Jewellery, soaps, confectionary, greeting cards, glasswork and more.

About: A fun family day out attracting approximately 8,000 visitors and providing workshops for adults and children on papercrafts, weaving, jewellery making and more. This is a great opportunity for crafters to exhibit and sell their work.

Location: The Last Drop Village, Bolton.

Month: Monthly.

Organizer: Bolton Crafts Association (BCA).

Address: The Hospital Road, Bromley Cross, Bolton, Lancashire BL7 9PZ

Tel: 07753 685000

Email: boltoncrafts@gmail.com

Website: www.boltoncrafts.co.uk

CHESHIRE FOOD FESTIVAL

Categories: Various arts and crafts.

About: Both children and adults can participate in the events at the Cornwall Design Fair, such as workshops and live demonstrations.

Location: Walton Hall, Cheshire.

Month: September.

Organizer: Manchester Craft Mafia.

Email: hello@manchestercraftmafia.co.uk

Website: www.manchestercraftmafia.co.uk

CRAFTY MARKET

Categories: Various arts and crafts.

About: This weekly craft market, nestled in amongst busy retail stores, is a great place to exhibit fine craft.

Strictly handmade and up-cycled items only.

Location: Neston Town Hall, Cheshire.
Month: Weekly.
Organizer: Fairangel Events.
Tel: 07895 059612
Email: info@fairangelevents.co.uk
Website: www.fairangelevents.co.uk

DACRE HALL LANERCOST CRAFT FAIR

Categories: Quilting, ceramics, glasswork, baking and more.
About: This event has been running for almost 40 years and takes place over a 10 day period in the historic, 13th century, Lanercost Priory.
Location: Dacre Hall, Carlisle.
Month: July and November.
Organizer: Elizabeth Harding.
Address: Dacre Hall, Lanercost Priory, Brampton, Cumbria CA8 2HG
Tel: 01697 72538
Email: elizabeth.harding@btinternet.com
Website: www.discovercarlisle.co.uk

HOPE STREET FEAST

Categories: Up-cycling, textiles, prints, jewellery, ceramics, soaps, knitting, illustrations and more.
About: Hope Street Feast is a large, family event providing a whole host of entertainment: music, theatre and dance, street food and drinks, fine produce and of course arts and crafts. This vibrant festival attracts more than 30,000 visitors every year.
Location: Blackburne House, Liverpool.
Month: September.
Organizer: Really Now.
Address: 67 Greenland Street, Liverpool, Merseyside L1 0BY
Tel: 07549 537606

Email: becky@reallynow.co.uk
Website: www.facebook.com/pages/Really-Now/468550329839054

LET'S GET CRAFTY

Categories: Glasswork, cupcakes, cross stitch, knitting, sewing, embroidery, soaps and more.
About: A quirky craft and food fair organized by young entrepreneur, Charlie Bolton. Exhibits Charlie's own products, as well as local crafters and designers, food and drinks.
Location: Whalley Village Hall, Lancashire.
Month: Monthly.
Organizer: Let's Get Crafty.
Address: Whalley Village Hall, Whalley, Lancashire BB7 9RG
Tel: 07837 641504
Email: charles.bolton@me.com
Website: www.facebook.com/whalleygetcrafty

LIVERPOOL ONE ARTS & CRAFT FAIRS

Categories: Jewellery, painting, textiles and more.
About: A relatively new event that has gained popularity since its success in 2011. 25 stalls feature various local, quality craft items and fresh produce.
Location: Thomas Street Way, Liverpool.
Month: May-September.
Organizer: Open Culture.
Address: World Museum Liverpool, William Brown Street, Liverpool L3 8EN
Tel: 01514 784928
Email: info@culture.org.uk
Website: www.culture.org.uk

RAWTENSTALL ANNUAL FAIR

Categories: Various arts and crafts including knitting.
About: Inspired by the traditional folk song, 'Rawtenstall Annual Fair', this fair has been organized to bring the local community together and promote local, quality crafts.
Location: The Valley Centre, Rawtenstall.
Month: May.
Organizer: Rossendale Revival.
Address: 1 Billington Avenue, Rawtenstall, Rossendale BB4 8UW
Tel: 07792 114638
Email: june.kw@ntlworld.com
Website: www.facebook.com/?ref=tn_tnmn#!/pages/Rossendale-Revival/136010459849605

THE CHESHIRE AUTUMN BEAD FAIR

Categories: Jewellery, beadwork, glasswork and more.
About: Celebrating all things bead related. From crystal beads, metal beads, plastic, silver, glass and ceramic; this show provides the opportunity to learn new skills and showcase existing pieces.
Location: Culcheth High School Community Campus, Warrington.
Month: November.
Organizer: Silver Orchid Beads & Silver Design.
Address: 111A High Street, Wolstanton, Newcastle-under-Lyme, Staffordshire ST5 0EP
Tel: 01782 850108
Email: Contact submission form available on website.
Website: www.beadyfairs.co.uk

THE CREATIVE CRAFTS SHOW

Categories: Crochet, cross stitch, découpage, sewing, embroidery, knitting, patchwork, quilting, ribboncraft, papercrafts, tapestry and more.

About: A long running event, ideal for beginners or experienced enthusiasts. Demonstrations and workshops are available to assist in developing new techniques and brushing up on skills.

Location: Manchester Central, Manchester.

Month: Varies annually.

Organizer: Trident Exhibitions Ltd.

Address: Atlas House, West Devon Business Park, Tavistock, Devon PL9 9DP

Tel: 01822 614671

Email: mc@trident-exhibitions.co.uk

Website: www.sscshows.co.uk

THE GIANT CHESTER FOOD, DRINK & LIFESTYLE FESTIVAL

Categories: Handbags, leather work, cupcakes, embroidery, ceramics, soaps, textiles, woodcraft and more.

About: A large annual festival that attracts in excess of 27,000 visitors over the duration of the weekend. Celebrating fine culinary skills and produce, with 120 exhibitions stalls.

Location: Chester Racecourse, Chester.

Month: March and April.

Organizer: Chester Food, Drink and Lifestyle.

Address: Chester Railway Station, 1st Floor West Wing Offices, Station Road, Chester CH1 3NT

Tel: 01244 405615

Email: helen@scwirrel.com

Website: www.chesterfoodanddrink. co.uk

THE GREAT NORTHERN CONTEMPORARY CRAFT FAIR

Categories: Ceramics, glasswork, jewellery, textiles, woodcrafts, papercrafts, silver work, metalwork, printing and more.

About: Featuring over 150 exhibitors and attracting over 6000 visitors per year, the Great Northern Contemporary Craft Fair has become an iconic event for all enthusiasts of craft. Visitors can enjoy workshops, demonstrations and competitions.

Location: Spinningfields, Manchester.

Month: October.

Organizer: Great Northern Events.

Address: 23 Belfield Road, Didsbury, Manchester M20 6BJ

Tel: 01612 839667

Email: enquiries@greatnorthernevents. co.uk

Website: www.greatnorthernevents. co.uk

THE RAZZLE DAZZLE TRAVELLING VINTAGE FAIR

Categories: Jewellery, glasswork, embroidery, silk painting, ceramics and more.

About: A monthly handmade and vintage fair boasting 40 stalls every month, featuring a variety of antiques and high quality handmade products.

Location: Cedar Farm, Ormskirk.

Month: Monthly.

Organizer: Jill Brindle.

Address: Cedar Farm, Back Lane, Mawdesley, Ormskirk L40 3SY

Tel: 07711 318466

NORTHERN IRELAND

ART OF CRAFT FAIR

Categories: Ceramics, glasswork, jewellery, textiles, basketry, woodcraft, woodturning and more.

Location: The Market Place Theatre & Arts Centre and Saint Patrick's Trian.

Month: June.

Organizer: Craft & Design Collective.

Address: Space Craft, 9b The Fountain Centre, College Street, Belfast BT1 6ET

Tel: 02890 329342

Email: info@craftanddesigncollective. com

Website: craftanddesigncollective. com

BLACK MARKET

Categories: Various arts and crafts.

Location: The Black Box, Belfast.

Month: Fortnightly.

Organizer: Ryan O'Reilly and Helen McDonnell.

Address: The Black Box, 18–22 Hill Street (Cathedral Quarter), Belfast BT1 2LA

Tel: 02890 244400

Email: office@blackboxbelfast.com

Website: www.blackboxbelfast.com

CRAFT FEST

Categories: Glasswork, metalwork, textiles, woodcraft, jewellery, ceramics and more.

About: An annual celebration of quality crafts with exhibitions, demonstrations and workshops. Located in Castle Ward in various

places: The House, The Tower and The Temple, visitors are treated to live music and entertainment as well as homemade foods and beverages.
Location: Castle Ward, Downpatrick.
Month: August.
Organizer: Craft & Design Collective.
Address: Space Craft, 9b The Fountain Centre, College Street, Belfast BT1 6ET
Tel: 02890 329342
Email: info@craftanddesigncollective.com
Website: craftanddesigncollective.com

GARVAGH CRAFT FAIR
Categories: Ceramics, glasswork, gift cards, woodcraft, artisan food, preserves and more.
About: An annual Christmas craft fair that boasts over 25 exhibition stalls of locally handcrafted pieces and homemade produce.
Location: Garvagh Community Building, Garvagh.
Month: November.
Organizer: Garvagh and District Development Association.
Address: Garvagh Community Building, 85 Main Street, Garvagh, Londonderry BT51 5AB
Tel: 02829 557325
Email: administrator@gadda.co.uk
Website: www.gadda.co.uk

PRIDE IN NEWRY
Categories: Various arts and crafts.
About: A parade and festival taking place over a week, celebrating Gay and Ethnic diversity. The week is packed full of entertainment including live music, film exhibitions, parades

and karaoke as well as numerous craft and food stalls. This event is fast becoming one of the most influential events of the year in Newry.
Location: Marcus Square, Newry.
Month: September.
Organizer: Newry Rainbow Community (NRC).
Address: 82a Hill Street, Newry, County Down BT34 1BE
Tel: 02830 250528
Email: getinvolved@prideinnewry.com
Website: www.prideinnewry.com

SUNDAY FAYRE AT VICTORIA SQUARE
Categories: Ceramics, preserves, gift cards, soaps, cupcakes, prints, painting, textiles, candles, glasswork and more.
About: Arguably one of Northern Ireland's largest shopping Centres, the Sunday Fayre has the pleasure of being surrounded by over 50 retail stores, cafes and restaurants. The Sunday Fayre, initially restricted to the summer, now takes place every Sunday due to increased success in this prime location.
Location: Victoria Square, Belfast.
Month: Weekly.
Organizer: Victoria Square.
Address: 1 Victoria Square, Belfast, County Antrim BT4 4QG
Tel: 02890 322277
Email: marketing@victoriasquare.com
Website: www.victoriasquare.com

THE LITTLE GREEN MARKET
Categories: Various arts and crafts.
About: The market takes place on the first Saturday of every month at The Little Green Allotments: featuring

live music and entertainment, a picnic area, BBQ, tea rooms, craft and food stalls and boasting breathtaking scenery.
Location: The Little Green Allotments, Lisburn.
Month: Weekly.
Organizer: The Little Green Allotments.
Address: 3 White Mountain Road, Lisburn, County Down BT28 3QY
Tel: 07867568976
Email: Contact submission form available on website.
Website: thelittlegreenallotments.com

THE STITCH AND CREATIVE CRAFT SHOW
Categories: Crochet, cross stitch, decoupage, sewing, embroidery, knitting, patchwork, quilting, ribboncraft, papercrafts, tapestry and more.
About: A well-known, long-running event that is ideal for beginners or experienced enthusiasts. Demonstrations and workshops are available to assist in developing new techniques and brushing up on skills.
Location: King's Hall, Belfast.
Month: Various dates throughout the year.
Organizer: Trident Exhibitions Ltd.
Address: Atlas House, West Devon Business Park, Tavistock, Devon PL9 9DP
Tel: 01822 614671
Email: mc@trident-exhibitions.co.uk
Website: www.sscshows.co.uk

WINTER CRAFT FAIR

Categories: Jewellery, ceramics, knitting, crochet, handbags and more.

About: The annual Winter Craft Fair has been providing visitors with a wide array of unique Christmas gift ideas for a few years now. Featuring work from well-known designers and crafters as well as welcoming newcomers each year.

Location: The Burnavon Arts and Cultural Centre, Cookstown.

Month: November.

Organizer: Arts and Cultural Development Cookstown District Council.

Address: The Burnavon Arts and Cultural Centre, Burn Road, Cookstown BT80 8DN

Tel: 028867 69949

Email: mary.crooks@cookstown.gov.uk

Website: www.burnavon.com

SCOTLAND

ABERDEEN COUNTRY FAIR

Categories: Paintings, metalwork, baking, woodcraft and more.

About: Continually growing and welcoming new traders, Aberdeen Country Fair attracts approximately 30,000 visitors to each event. The fair features numerous arts and craft stalls as well as locally produced foods, wines, cheeses and flowers.

Location: Belmont Street, Aberdeen.

Month: Monthly (including weekly events in December).

Organizer: Apardion Management Ltd.

Address: 18 Little Belmont Street, Aberdeen, Aberdeenshire AB10 1JG

Tel: 01224 649000

Email: info@aberdeencountryfair.co.uk

Website: www.aberdeencountryfair.co.uk

AFTERNOON TWEE

Categories: Various arts and crafts.

About: A young, vintage and craft show launched by entrepreneur, Amy Grew. A regular fair that takes place on the last Sunday of every month.

Location: Tusk, Glasgow.

Month: Monthly.

Organizer: Indy Traders.

Address: 18 Moss Side Road, Shawlands, Glasgow G41 3TN

Email: afternoontwee@hotmail.co.uk

Website: indytraders.com

BEST OF THE WEST FESTIVAL

Categories: Ceramics, paintings and photography.

About: This popular annual festival showcases a wide variety of arts, crafts, music, food and drink. A celebratory, two day event for all the family, featuring stalls from over 30 local artists and crafters.

Location: Inveraray Castle, Argyll.

Month: September.

Organizer: Argyll and The Isles Tourism (AIT).

Address: Inveraray Castle, Cherry Park, Inveraray, Argyll, PA32 8XE

Tel: 01499 302203

Email: info@bowfest.co.uk

Website: www.bowfest.co.uk/index.htm

BIGGAR LITTLE FESTIVAL

Categories: Paintings, jewellery, photography, stone carving, henna, textiles and more.

About: An extremely popular festival that has been running annually for many years now; Biggar Little Festival (BLF) spans over 10 days and passionately celebrates local traditions, culture, arts and crafts. Creating opportunities for novice exhibitors and crafters as well as being a staple event for the well established.

Location: Biggar, Lanarkshire.

Month: October.

Organizer: Biggar Little Festival Committee.

Address: Biggar, Lanarkshire,

Tel: 01899 220980

Email: info@biggar-little-festival.com

Website: www.biggar-little-festival.com

BYRES ROAD MAKERS MARKET

Categories: Ceramics, photography, silverwork, knitting, woodcraft, glasswork and more.

About: Taking place on the last Saturday of each month (February–November), a free, boutique market featuring 25 of Scotland's most talented artists, crafters and designers.

Location: Millhead Library, Glasgow.

Month: Monthly (excluding December and January).

Organizer: The Makers Markets.

Address: Millhead Library, 348 Byres Road, Glasgow G12 8AP

Email: getintouch@ byresroadmakersmarket.co.uk

Website: www. byresroadmakersmarket.co.uk

CEILIDH CULTURE STREET FAIR

Categories: Jewellery, knitting and more.

About: Organized specifically to promote Scottish handmade crafts and locally sourced and produced foods, attracting in excess of 20,000 visitors.

Location: Princes Street/Castle Street, Edinburgh.

Month: March and April.

Organizer: Hand Up Media.

Address: 32 Annanadale Street Lane, Edinburgh EH7 4LS

Tel: 01315 589644

Email: tania@handupmedia.co.uk

Website: www.handupmedia.co.uk

EXCLUSIVELY HIGHLANDS

Categories: Various arts and crafts.

About: A fine arts and crafts fair, exclusive to the Highlands of Scotland. This fair travels around to various locations in the Highlands (further details can be found on their website), however Eden Court has proven to be their largest event with over 60 exhibition stalls.

Location: Bishop's Palace and the Balcony, Eden Court, Inverness.

Month: November and December.

Organizer: Exclusively Highlands.

Tel: 01381 621962

Email: exclusivelyhighlands@hotmail.co.uk

Website: www.exclusivelyhighlands.co.uk

GRAND FIBRE FEST

Categories: Spinning, weaving, felting, knitting, cross stitch.

About: A celebration of all things textile: Grand Fibre Fest is now in its third year, allowing makers and designers to come together and showcase their pieces as well as allowing the community to take part and learn new skills.

Location: Dornoch Social Club, Dornoch.

Month: March.

Organizer: Dornoch and District Community Association.

Address: Dornoch Social Club, School Hill, Dornoch IV25 3PF

Tel: 01862 811898

Email: Contact submisison form available on website.

Website: www.dadca.org.uk

MARCH HARE MARKET

Categories: Jewellery, vintage clothing, hair accessories and more.

About: A monthly craft and vintage market featuring local fine crafters and vintage traders.

Location: Crimon Place, Aberdeen.

Month: Monthly.

Organizer: Kate Higgs, March Hare Market.

Address: Boys Brigade HQ, Crimon Place, Aberdeen, AB10 1RX

Tel: 07725 591866

Email: marchharemarket@gmail.com

Website: www.facebook.com/MarchHareMarket

MORNINGSIDE MAKERS MARKET

Categories: Ceramics, photography, silverwork, knitting, woodcraft, glasswork and more.

About: A free, monthly boutique market featuring 30 of Scotland's most talented artists, crafters and designers. Taking place on the first Saturday of each month, excluding January.

Location: Columcille Centre, Edinburgh.

Month: Monthly (excluding January).

Organizer: The Makers Markets.

Address: Columcille Centre, 2 Newbattle Terrace, Edinburgh EH10 4RT

Email: info@ morningsidemakersmarket.co.uk

Website: www. morningsidemakersmarket.co.uk

SPRING FLING

Categories: Ceramics, gilding, glasswork, jewellery, mosaic, prints, sculpture, woodcraft and more.

About: Established in 2003, this well known event is held annually in Dumfries and Galloway – Scotland's arts and crafts capital. The event showcases in excess of 76 artists and designers and is growing ever popular with every year. Studios are situated in various locations throughout the region and can make for a great family day out, attracting a large footfall.

Location: Various locations throughout the region of Dumfries and Galloway.

Month: June.

Organizer: The Spring Fling Management Committee.
Address: Gracefield Arts Centre, 28 Edinburgh Road, Dumfries DG1 1JQ
Tel: 01387 213218
Email: info@spring-fling.co.uk
Website: www.spring-fling.co.uk

THE ETHICAL CHRISTMAS FAIR

Categories: Jewellery, ceramics, soaps, candles, glasswork and more.
About: An Ethical Christmas Fair attracting in excess of 30,000 visitors in 2011, featuring exhibitions from crafters and designers from across the UK as well as pieces from overseas, such as Kenya, Zambia and Nepal.
Location: Princes Street/Castle Street, Edinburgh.
Month: December.
Organizer: Hand Up Media.
Address: 32 Annanadale Street Lane, Edinburgh EH7 4LS
Tel: 01315 589644
Email: tania@handupmedia.co.uk
Website: www.handupmedia.co.uk

THE REAL SCOTTISH CHRISTMAS FAIR

Categories: Jewellery, ceramics, soaps, candles, glasswork and more.
About: A popular Christmas Fair: 2011 attracted in excess of 30,000 visitors looking for that special gift.
Location: Princes Street/Castle Street, Edinburgh.
Month: December.
Organizer: Hand Up Media.
Address: 32 Annanadale Street Lane, Edinburgh EH7 4LS
Tel: 01315 589644
Email: tania@handupmedia.co.uk
Website: www.handupmedia.co.uk

SOUTH WEST

CONTEMPORARY CRAFT FESTIVAL

Categories: Fashion, woodcraft, textiles and more.
About: A fun family day out attracting approximately 8,000 visitors and providing workshops for adults and children on papercrafts, weaving, jewellery making and more. This is a great opportunity for crafters to exhibit and sell their work.
Location: Mill Marsh Park, Bovey Tracey, Devon.
Month: June.
Organizer: The Contemporary Craft Festival.
Address: Mill Marsh Park, St Johns Lane, Bovey Tracey, Devon TQ13 9AL
Tel: 01626 830612
Email: craftfair@craftsatboveytracey.co.uk
Website: www.craftsatboveytracey.co.uk

CORNWALL DESIGN FAIR

Categories: Fashion, textiles, jewellery, glasswork and more.
About: Both children and adults can participate in the events at the Cornwall Design Fair, such as workshops and live demonstrations.
Location: Trereife House.
Month: August.
Organizer: Cornwall Design Fair.
Address: Trereife House, Penzance, Cornwall TR20 8TJ
Tel: 01736 362750
Email: info@cornwalldesignfair.co.uk
Website: www.cornwalldesignfair.co.uk

CRAFTS @ THE CHEESE AND GRAIN

Categories: Various arts and crafts.
About: Around 45 stalls featuring completely homemade crafts.
Location: The Cheese and Grain, Frome, Somerset.
Month: The 4th Saturday of every month.
Organizer: D & K Art and Craft Fairs.
Address: 39 Corsham Road, Lacock, Chippenham, Wiltshire SN15 2NA
Tel: 01249 730985
Email: debora@dnk-artsandcraftfairs.co.uk
Website: www.dnk-artandcraftfairs.co.uk

CRUX CRAFT FAIR

Categories: Wood craft, weaving, textiles, mixed media, jewellery and ceramics.
About: Devon's long-running craft show for quality, homemade products by local designers.
Location: Rattery Village Hall, Devon.
Month: November.
Organizer: Crux Craft Fair.
Email: info@cruxcraftfair.co.uk
Website: www.cruxcraftfair.co.uk

EXETER CRAFT FESTIVAL

Categories: Soaps and skin care, jewellery, ceramics and textiles.
About: A free outdoor event in Exeter City Centre that has been annually taking place for over 30 years. Featuring approximately 100 stalls for local crafters to display and sell their products.
Location: Cathedral Green, Exeter.
Month: July.
Organizer: Exeter Craft Festival.

Address: 9 Westcombe, Alphington, Exeter EX2 8GH
Tel: 01392 219050
Email: admin@exetercraftfestival.co.uk
Website: www.exetercraftfestival.co.uk

FAIRS 4 YOU

Categories: Various arts and crafts.
About: A fun family day out with children's activities and over 25 stalls of unique, handcrafted local gifts for you to choose from. Usually held most weekends in various locations around the South West.
Location: Various locations.
Month: Various dates throughout the year.
Organizer: Fairs 4 You.
Tel: 01179 312941
Email: fairs4you@yahoo.co.uk
Website: www.fairs4you.co.uk

KEVIN MURPHY CRAFT SHOWS

Categories: A range of crafts are sold including knitwear and jewellery.
About: Craft Fairs at locations throughout the South West specializing in unique high quality and one-of-a kind items. Items sold are affordable and nothing is mass-produced.
Location: Various locations.
Month: April, October, November and December.
Organizer: Kevin Murphy Craft Shows.
Address: St John's Chapel Farm, Newton Tracey, Barnstable, Devon EX31 3PB
Tel: 01271 343160
Email: kevinmurphycraftfairs@hotmail.com
Website: www.kevinmurphycraftfairs.co.uk

MADE IN BRISTOL GIFT FAIR

Categories: Illustrations, jewellery, textiles, woodcraft and more.
About: A free two day festive craft fair, giving experienced and novice local crafters a chance to sell their handmade products.
Month: December.
Organizer: Made in Bristol.
Email: bryony@popupbristol.com
Website: www.madeinbristol.blogspot.com

NEELD HALL

Categories: Various arts and crafts.
About: Approximately 30 stalls of various unique handmade gifts, in Neeld Hall, Chippenham.
Location: Neeld Hall, Chippenham.
Month: The 4th Sunday of every month from March–December.
Organizer: D & K Art and Craft Fairs.
Address: 39 Corsham Road, Lacock, Chippenham, Wiltshire SN15 2NA
Tel: 01249 730985
Email: debora@dnk-artsandcraftfairs.co.uk
Website: www.dnk-artandcraftfairs.co.uk

THE BRISTOL HOME, FOOD AND CRAFT SHOW

Categories: Various arts and crafts.
About: Craft exhibitions, talks and demonstrations.
Location: UWE Exhibition and Conference Centre.
Month: October.
Organizer: Nationwide Exhibitions.
Address: PO BOX 20, Bristol BS16 5QU
Tel: 01179 070099

Email: martinc@nwe.co.uk
Website: www.thehomeshowbristol.co.uk

UNIVERSITY OF PLYMOUTH CRAFT FAYRE

Categories: Jewellery, soaps, bags, clothes and more.
About: A collection of locally produced, high quality craft, the Craft Fayres are organized by the students and are free for anyone to attend. There are several throughout the year and each have a different theme, i.e. Valentines Day and Christmas.
Location: Roland Levinsky Building, Plymouth.
Month: Various dates throughout the year.
Organizer: Plymouth University.
Address: Rowland Levinsky Building, University of Plymouth, Drakes Circus, Plymouth PL4 8AA
Tel: 01752 588388
Email: info@upsu.com
Website: www.plymouth.ac.uk

WANBOROUGH SHOW

Categories: Papercrafts, ceramics, jewellery, knitwear and more.
About: A long-running, small but friendly, one day crafting event, where you have the opportunity to set up a stall and sell homemade crafts.
Month: August.
Organizer: Wanborough Show.
Address: The Lynch Field, Wanborough, Swindon, Wiltshire SN4 0DA
Email: info@wanboroughshow.org
Website: www.wanboroughshow.org

WALES

AMELIA TRUST FARM HARVEST FESTIVAL

Categories: Various arts and crafts.
About: A fun family day out, attracting approximately 8,000 visitors and providing workshops for adults and children on papercrafts, weaving, jewellery making and more. This is a great opportunity for crafters to exhibit and sell their work.
Location: Amelia Trust Farm, Barry.
Month: September.
Organizer: Amelia Trust Farm.
Address: Amelia Trust Farm, Five Mile Lane, Llancarfan, Barry CF62 3AS
Tel: 01446 782030
Email: general@ameliatrust.org.uk
Website: www.ameliatrust.org.uk

BRECON CRAFT FAIR

Categories: Woodcraft, woodturning, jewellery, patchwork, soaps and beauty products, knitting, crochet, weaving and more.
About: Both children and adults can participate in the events at the Cornwall Design Fair, such as workshops and live demonstrations.
Location: The Market Hall, Powys.
Month: Monthly.
Organizer: Michael Mulqueen.
Address: Market Street, The Market Hall, Brecon, Powys LD3 9AH
Tel: 01495 753782
Email: michael.mulqueen@homecall.co.uk
Website: www.breconcraftfair.co.uk

CELTIC SPRING FAYRE

Categories: Artisan food and beverage, jewellery, leather work, photography, woodturning, gift cards, toys, handbags and more.
About: Conwy Quay Spring Fayre was born out of the success of the many other fayres organized by Celtic Fayres and Event ~Reality that have seen up to 30,000 visitors attend each year. A traditional Welsh affair specializing in quality craft, gift and food exhibitions, as well as craft demonstrations, situated on the banks of Conwy Quay.
Location: Conwy Quay, Conwy.
Month: May.
Organizer: Celtic Fayres & Event ~Reality.
Address: The Old Garage, Conwy Road, Tal y Bont, Conwy LL32 8SE
Tel: 01492 660209
Email: esorlegin@aol.com
Website: www.celticfayres.co.uk

CELTIC SUMMER FAYRE

Categories: Artisan food and beverage, jewellery, leather work, photography, woodturning, gift cards, toys, handbags and more.
About: Conwy Quay Summer Fayre was born out of the success of the many other fayres organized by Celtic Fayres and Event ~Reality that have seen up to 30,000 visitors attend each year. A traditional Welsh affair specializing in quality craft, gift and food exhibitions, as well as craft demonstrations, situated on the banks of Conwy Quay.
Location: Conwy Quay, Conwy.
Month: September.
Organizer: Celtic Fayres & Event ~Reality.

Address: The Old Garage, Conwy Road, Tal y Bont, Conwy LL32 8SE
Tel: 01492 660209
Email: esorlegin@aol.com
Website: www.celticfayres.co.uk

CONTEMPORARY ARTS, GIFTS AND CRAFTS FAIR

Categories: Various arts and crafts.
About: Organized by Gilded Lili Fairs, this is a regular fair held in the St Elli Shopping Centre every Thursday, Friday and Saturday, as well as some longer events and the majority of December. The shopping centre attracts 145,000 visitors every week, making this an optimum venue for exhibiting local skills and talents.
Location: St Elli Shopping Centre, Llanelli.
Month: Three times weekly.
Organizer: Gilded Lili Fairs.
Address: Nant y Celyn, Cynheidre, Llanelli, Carmarthenshire SA15 5YD
Tel: 07854 762595
Email: gildedlilifairs@hotmail.co.uk
Website: www.gildedlilifairs.co.uk

COWBRIDGE FOOD & DRINK FESTIVAL

Categories: Cake decorating, cupcakes, sugarcraft, chocolates, confectionary, artisan food brewing, baking and more.
About: Attracting over 15,000 visitors each year to the 80 stalls, this renowned festival is an ideal venue for all food and beverage enthusiasts looking to exhibit their tasty treats.
Location: Sheepleys, Cowbridge.
Month: October.
Organizer: Cowbridge Food & Drink.
Address: Sheepleys, Llandow,

Cowbridge CF71 7DF
Tel: 07875 290428
Email: info@cowbridgefoodanddrink.org
Website: cowbridgefoodanddrink.org

CRAFT IN THE BAY SUMMER SHOW

Categories: Various arts and crafts.
About: An annual summer show held at Cardiff's Craft in the Bay. UK artists and crafters are selected to exhibit their pieces over a three month period.
Location: Craft in the Bay, Cardiff.
Month: July, August and September.
Organizer: The Makers Guild in Wales.
Address: Craft in the Bay, The Flourish, Lloyd George Avenue, Cardiff CF10 4QH
Tel: 02920 484611
Email: admin@makersguildinwales.org.uk
Website: www.makersguildinwales.org.uk

LLANDUDNO CHRISTMAS FAYRE

Categories: Jewellery, handbags, gift cards, photography, silverwork, artwork, soaps, glasswork, candles, tapestry, woodcrafts, embroidery and more.
About: An annual Christmas event showcasing the works of over 100 local artisan crafters. Previous years has seen the fayre attract over 20,000 visitors.
Location: Madoc Street, Llandudno.
Month: November.
Organizer: Llandudno Development Partnership.
Address: The Victoria Centre, Management Suite, 48 Mostyn Street, Llandudno LL30 2RH

Tel: 07725 237667
Email: enquiries@llandudnochristmasfayre.co.uk
Website: www.llandudnochristmasfayre.co.uk

MONMOUTHSHIRE SHOW

Categories: Various arts and crafts.
About: This prestigious show celebrated its 150th anniversary in 2007. Acclaimed as the largest one day show, Monmouth celebrates local agricultural livestock, produce, craft and rural life.
Location: Monmouthshire Showground, Monmouthshire.
Month: August.
Organizer: Monmouthshire Show Society Ltd.
Address: Monmouthshire Showground, Redbrook Road, Monmouth, Monmouthshire NP25 3LX
Tel: 01981 580710
Email: anna@monmouthshow.co.uk
Website: www.monmouthshow.co.uk

NEWPORT ART, CRAFT AND GIFT FAIR

Categories: Painting, prints, gift cards, jewellery, decoupage, textiles, ceramics, photography and more.
About: Providing something for everyone, this art, craft and gift fair exhibits some of the finest pieces of artwork and handmade crafts in South Wales. The fair can usually be found each month, with additional dates in December; in The Gallery, above Newport Provisional Market.
Location: The Gallery, Newport.
Month: Monthly.
Organizer: Ty Celf Fine Art.
Address: The Gallery, Newport Provision Market, Upper Dock Street,

Newport NP20 1DD
Tel: 07922 277887
Email: info@Ty-Celf.com
Website: www.ty-celf.com

ORIEL 2 – UPCOMING DESIGNERS

Categories: Jewellery, ceramics and sculpture.
About: Held at Cardiff's Craft in the Bay, this exhibition showcases the latest designs from graduates of Hereford College of Art as well as already established designers and makers.
Location: Craft in the Bay, Cardiff.
Month: September and November.
Organizer: The Makers Guild in Wales.
Address: Craft in the Bay, The Flourish, Lloyd George Avenue, Cardiff CF10 4QH
Tel: 02920 484611
Email: admin@makersguildinwales.org.uk
Website: www.makersguildinwales.org.uk

ROATH CRAFT MARKET

Categories: Textiles, cross stitch, crochet, patchwork, quilting, knitting, buttons, soap, ceramics, gift cards and more.
About: Every Saturday morning, all year round, this market consists of a huge variety of stalls featuring the handiwork of local craftspeople.
Location: Mackintosh Community Centre, Cardiff.
Month: Weekly.
Organizer: Linda Ditchburn.
Address: Makintosh Community Centre, 38 Keppoch Street, Roath, Cardiff CF24 3JW
Tel: 07806 772792

Email: Craft@RoathMarket.co.uk
Website: www.roathmarket.co.uk

ROYAL WELSH WINTER FAIR

Categories: Woodturning, knitting, handmade shoes, welsh blankets, ceramics, hand spun fibres and more.
About: Held in the CLA pavilion in Powys, this annual Winter Fair is made up of 300 stalls and attracts more than 26,000 customers every year. From handmade, bespoke gifts to agricultural livestock and locally produced food, this fair is a popular attraction.
Location: CLA Pavilion, Powys.
Month: November.
Organizer: Wales Craft Council.
Address: Royal Welsh Showground, Llandelwedd, Builth Wells, Powys LD2 3SY
Tel: 01982 554401
Email: tradestands@rwas.co.uk
Website: www.rwas.co.uk

ST MARY STREET MARKET

Categories: Jewellery, knitting, textiles, vintage clothing, antiques and more.
About: Recently pedestrianized, St Mary Street has proved the perfect location for a vibrant street market. Situated outside of the already existing Cardiff Market, the St Mary Street Market has gone from strength to strength since launching in the summer of 2012. An average of 30 stalls and increasing, the market attracts a buzzing throng of visitors every Saturday.
Location: St Mary Street, Cardiff.
Month: Weekly.
Organizer: Riverside Community Market Association (RCMA).

Address: St Mary Street, Cardiff CF10
Tel: 02920 190036
Email: gareth@riversidemarket.org.uk
Website: www.riversidemarket.org.uk

TRULY HANDMADE SUMMER FAYRE

Categories: Dolls, cupcakes, candles, jewellery, glasswork, sculpture, pin art, cross stitch, soap, ceramics and more.
About: A large variety of craft stalls as well as entertainment, refreshments and prize draws. Truly Handmade promises to be a great family day out, with proceeds from the raffle going to Tenovus Cancer Trust.
Location: Paget Rooms, Penarth.
Month: Monthly.
Organizer: Bea Roberts.
Address: Paget Rooms, Victoria Road, Penarth CF64 3EG
Tel: 02920 213287
Email: tidal.creations@gmail.com
Website: www.tidaldreamcreations.co.uk

USK SHOW

Categories: Tapestry, embroidery, cross stitch, crochet, quilting, knitting, woodcraft, metalwork, knitting and more.
About: A large agricultural show attracting over 20,000 visitors every year. Featuring entertainment, arena events, horticulture and homecraft displays and homemade refreshments at the 125 acre Usk Showground. The Usk Show's roots stem back to 1848 when it began as the Usk Farmer's Club.
Location: Usk Showground, Monmouthshire.

Month: September.
Organizer: Usk Farmer's Club Ltd.
Address: Llanerthil Mill, Llandenny, Usk, Monmouthshire NP15 1DJ
Tel: 01291 672773
Email: usk.show@virgin.net
Website: www.uskshow.co.uk

WONDERWOOL WALES

Categories: Felting, knitting, weaving, spinning, crochet, textiles and more.
About: A large festival showcasing the production and use of Welsh wools and natural fibres. Numerous stalls, workshops and demonstrations such as hooking & progging, felting, weaving and spinning are featured at this event.
Location: The Royal Welsh Showground,.
Month: April.
Organizer: Wonderwool Wales Ltd.
Address: Ty Mawr Uchaf, Llanerfyl, Welshpool, Powys SY21 0JE
Tel: 01938 820495
Email: bookings@wonderwoolwales.co.uk
Website: www.wonderwoolwales.co.uk

BRICKS AND MORTAR SHOPS

INTERVIEW

GILLIAN HARRIS

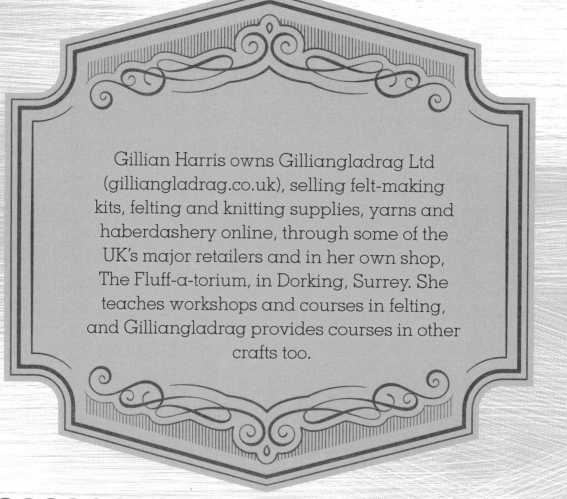

Gillian Harris owns Gilliangladrag Ltd
(gilliangladrag.co.uk), selling felt-making
kits, felting and knitting supplies, yarns and
haberdashery online, through some of the
UK's major retailers and in her own shop,
The Fluff-a-torium, in Dorking, Surrey. She
teaches workshops and courses in felting,
and Gilliangladrag provides courses in other
crafts too.

I used to be a graphic designer but I gave it up when I had my second daughter. We were quite an arty family – my grandfather was a tailor – and I knew I wanted to go back to textiles. I tried lots of things and fell into felt-making: found out about it, started to do it, become totally obsessed with it, and Gilliangladrag grew organically from there. I never set out to be a felt-maker, but I am quite entrepreneurial and have a good business sense, so it all came along at the right time in my life, when I was looking for a way to reinvent myself, if you like.

Selling Wholesale

We sell online, in our shop and into other shops – again that happened organically, but is now definitely part of a plan. When you're running a business, you need to look at all the different aspects of it.

We've never had to deal with the problem of approaching big businesses, such as John Lewis, and asking them to stock our products, because they approached us. We were exhibiting at

> All you can do is send in your product and hope that they like it.

a trade show, they saw what we were doing and liked it. It may be cheaper to approach large retailers directly, because then you aren't spending money on a stand at a show and gambling as to whether or not someone will be interested. But it is terribly difficult. To be frank, it's sometimes hard to get hold of the right person in a big company even when they've placed an order, so approaching them cold would be even harder. All you can do is send in your product and hope that they like it. If they do they do and if they don't they don't: you can't perform any magic to persuade them. But you have to believe in what you're doing. Yes, you have to market it, you have to do PR and advertising and all the rest, but if you have a great product, it will be successful.

Negotiating on price and payment terms and so on with big companies can be difficult. I was quite hard-

> When you're running a business, you need to look at all the different aspects of it.

nosed about it, probably naively so, when we first started, but over the years I've come to learn that they pretty much call the shots. You have to look at it from different angles, though. If you're supplying a big store, it's almost like a PR and marketing exercise. They're giving you a massive advertising space that you could never have bought. Although obviously the primary objective is to make money, your being there really improves brand awareness.

We manufacture all our kits ourselves, so in my mind – though my staff probably wouldn't agree with me – supplying big orders is the easy bit! It's all the rest of it, getting the orders in the first place, that's tricky. When it comes to making things and getting them out the door, my attitude is, 'If you need that many, you make that many. If you need more people to make them, you find more people.' We export large numbers of kits now, and that can be hard – because of course you're still dealing with everything else and you can't shut the shop or ignore the website just because you're trying to fulfil a big order. But most of the time it is doable.

As for nurturing clients, we keep them up-to date with newsletters and we tend to launch new products roughly once a year. We also advertise in the trade and the retail press, in different sorts of publications, which feed off one another and create further business.

> When it comes to making things and getting them out the door, my attitude is, 'If you need that many, you make that many. If you need more people to make them, you find more people.'

OUR RANGE

We're currently the UK distributor for some Australian knitting products and for an American range of handspun yarns, but everything else we sell – everything in our own range – comes from what I like and what I think is going to work.

If someone suggested I make a red handbag with blue spots, I wouldn't listen, because that's not the way I operate. The only time that changes is when I'm ordering, say, knitting wools for the shop – then I can't just do what I like, I have to have a range that will please everyone.

Of course if a big customer came to me and said, 'Will you make us a red handbag with blue spots?' and wanted enough of them, that would be different. But I'd have to design it so that I was happy with the red and blue and happy with the shape – it would still have to have my look about it. My branding is hugely important, and I won't have it compromised in any way.

RIGHT PLACE, RIGHT TIME

Some of our smaller kits have been hugely successful, in particular a needle-felting kit called Chirpy Chappy that we launched in the spring. Needle felting is popular at the moment, there's a lot of interest in birds, the product looks right – it's sweet and quirky – and it's a good price. All those things came together at the right time and made it our fastest selling kit ever.

EVENTS IN THE SHOP

The events we hold are really important to us: people have flown in from France and the Netherlands to come to one of my felting courses. The fact that I've written a couple of books helps: if people have read your book, they're more likely to want to come on one of your courses. Again, it all feeds off itself. Each different facet of the business is like a little cog in the bigger machine.

People are very keen on workshops and courses at the moment – that's something that has grown partly from the recession, from the 'Make Do and Mend' mentality. Most of what Gilliangladrag sells is for you to make your own things and I think a lot of people are moving away from the whole mass-produced thing, towards something they feel is more sustainable and 'worthwhile'. It's (rightly) seen as more worthwhile to buy something that's been handmade in Britain than a mass-produced piece from halfway round the world. And there's the question of longevity – if you've bought something for a pound, you're happy to throw it away next week and buy another. If you've bought something handmade, or if someone else has made it for you, you're hopefully going to cherish it for much longer.

RUNNING THE BUSINESS

I've got 13 people working for me part-time, making up kits, sending out website orders, working in the shop, and it's a huge juggling act all the time. I feel lucky that I'm able to work in this environment, doing what I want to do and being surrounded by things that I like, but it is incredibly hard work and I'm never truly away from it.

It's really, really difficult to make proper money out of craft unless you have a good business head. I can't stress that enough – so many people try to turn their hobby into a business without thinking about the costs involved in making things and what they need to charge a make a proper profit. I say this all the time to people who come on my courses: add up your cost of sales and your overheads, even if you're working at home, so that you can work out what your prices should be and how much you need to earn in order to make a living. If you've given up a £20,000-a-year job to do this, how many brooches, bracelets, bags and key rings do you have to sell to make £20,000 a year? Quite a few. And that's £20,000 profit, so you probably need to be turning over in excess of £40,000. It's all very well making two or three things and charging £5 for them at the local craft fair, and it's terribly flattering when somebody buys something you've made – but what if they ask you to make 40 more? How long is that going to take? Are you still going to charge £5?

> If you've given up a £20,000-a-year job to do this, how many brooches, bracelets, bags, key rings do you have to sell to make £20,000 a year? Quite a few.

My husband always says, 'Turnover is vanity, but profit is sanity' and he's right. When you remove yourself from the fluffy loveliness and the colours and the gorgeousness of it all, you have to look at the balance sheet and it has to work out.

That would be my top tip to anyone wanting to turn a hobby into a business: you have to think about the financial aspect of it. Although people will pay for handmade, they will only pay so much. You are up against a lot of chains selling things made cheaply in the Far East and it can be tough out there. Try not to let those thoughts ruin your plans – but always keep it in mind!

BRICKS AND MORTAR SHOPS

EAST AND SOUTH EAST

37 OLD LONDON ROAD

About: Featured on the popular television programme, 'Mary Queen of Shops', 37 Old London Road is a unique homeware boutique that provides an eclectic selection of up-cycled furnishings and home accessories. This contemporary shop adapts and reworks old, vintage and worn out items, creating chic and original pieces for the home.
Address: 37 Old London Road, Kingston-upon-Thames, Surrey KT2 6ND
Tel: 02085 414774
Email: Contact submission form available on website.
Website: www.37oldlondonroad. co.uk

A LITTLE BIRD TOLD ME GALLERY

About: Established in 2009 and authorized to deal with famous works by Quentin Blake, Dick Bruna and Clinton Branbury, A Little Bird Told Me Gallery specializes in classic illustrations, prints, paintings and photographs.
Address: 25 The High Street, Wendover, Buckinghamshire HP22 6DU
Tel: 07854 787733
Email: littlebirdtold@me.com
Website: www. alittlebirdtoldmegallery.com

APPENDAGE

About: Appendage is a gallery that showcases the works of designers and makers from Brighton and the UK. Exhibitions featured here tend to be contemporary, brightly coloured and ranging in skills and media, such as ceramics, mosaics, glasswork, jewellery, felt work, embroidery, knitwear, prints and much more.
Address: 36 Kensington Gardens, Brighton, East Sussex BN1 4AL
Tel: 01273 605901
Email: info@openhouseonline.co.uk
Website: www.openhouseonline. co.uk

ARCADIA

About: Established in 1993, Arcadia is a contemporary craft and design gallery showcasing unique and original works by high quality, British designers. Exhibitions consist of jewellery, woodcraft, ceramics, textiles and more.
Address: 12 Benet Street, Cambridge CB2 3PT
Tel: 01223 314411
Email: andrey.pronin@gmail.com
Website: www.arcadiagallery.co.uk

ARTY GIRAFFE

About: Arty Giraffe is a welcoming craft shop offering pottery painting, casting and workshops, as well as selling a range of locally handmade and nationally produced gifts.
Address: 850 Oxford Road, Reading, Berkshire RG30 1EL
Tel: 01189 418683
Email: enquiries@artygiraffe.com
Website: www.artygiraffe.com

BETWEEN DREAMS

About: Established in 2005, Between Dreams sells and exhibits art and craft by a variety of local artists, representing up-and-coming as well as established artists. Crafts featured include glasswork, jewellery, textiles, woodcraft, ceramics and more.
Contact: Cathy & Lisa
Address: Hillier Garden Centre, Woodhouse Lane, Botley, Southampton SO30 2EZ
Tel: 01489 786878
Email: shop@betweendreams.co.uk
Website: www.betweendreams.co.uk

BIG BEAD BOUTIQUE

About: Inspired by the beautiful variety of beads available in Venice, Joanne opened Big Bead Boutique which supplies high quality beads and equipment to create individual pieces. The boutique also hosts a variety of events and workshops and offers a bespoke service that can include restoring sentimental pieces.
Contact: Joanne Tomlin
Address: 12 Dyke Road, Brighton, East Sussex BN1 3FE
Tel: 01273 383983
Email: joanne_tomlin@hotmail.com
Website: www.bigbeadboutique. com

BIG BLUE SKY

About: Achieving prestigious recognition from Vogue as one of the best shops outside London, Big Blue Sky is a proud craft boutique that features only the best local, handmade items. A vibrant selection of paintings, photography, prints, ceramics and sculptures can be discovered at this quaint boutique.

Address: Warham Road, Wells-Next-The-Sea, Norfolk NR23 1QA
Tel: 01328 712023
Email: shop@bigbluesky.uk.com
Website: www.bigbluesky.uk.com

BLACKBIRD

About: Blackbird represents handmade, contemporary craft and design, and promotes local artists who use materials that are ethical and responsibly sourced. Featuring handbags, jewellery, artwork, ceramics, craft kits, textiles and gift cards; Blackbird also provides a host of workshops within its studio.

Contact: Maxine Sutton
Address: 2 Market Place, Margate, Kent CT9 1ER
Tel: 01843 229533
Email: info@blackbird-england.com
Website: www.blackbird-england.com

BUTTONS & BOWS

About: Established by young entrepreneur and illustrator, Hannah Clear, Buttons & Bows features handmade crafts made by herself and other local artists. Hannah creates unique textiles pieces from her illustrations, recycling old clothing where possible.

Contact: Hannah Clear

Address: Almshouse Arcade, 19 The Hornet, Chichester, West Sussex PO19 7JL
Tel: 07824 806717
Email: Contact submission form available on website.
Website: www.buttonsandbows-shop.com

BY JOVE!

About: By Jove! is a unique tearoom that features 25 loose-leaf teas and a huge variety of home-baked goods. A large array of unique gifts and local produce can also be found at this beautiful establishment.

Address: The Old School, 30a High Street, Burwell, Cambridge CB25 0HD
Tel: 01638 602086
Email: Contact submission form available on website.
Website: www.byjovetearooms.co.uk

CALLADOODLES

About: Dedicated to promoting emerging artists and designers, Calladoodles is an ethically conscious, craft retail store that provides a range of one-off products and bespoke gifts. A wide range of skills and media are featured at Calladoodles, such as glasswork, ceramics, beadwork, textiles, candles, soaps, jewellery, gift cards and much more.

Address: 18 The High Street, Carshalton, Surrey, SM5 3AG
Tel: 02086 699054
Email: clare@calladoodles.com
Website: www.calladoodles.uk.com

CAMBRIDGE CONTEMPORARY CRAFTS

About: Born out of its sister gallery – Cambridge Contemporary Arts – this bright and welcoming craft shop showcases a unique variety of work by emerging crafters as well as established. Cambridge Contemporary Crafts features fine, handmade ceramics, glasswork, jewellery, textiles, prints, woodcraft and more.

Address: 5 Benet Street, Cambridge CB2 3QN
Tel: 01223 361200
Email: nfo@cambridgecrafts.co.uk
Website: www.cambridgecrafts.co.uk

CHURCH STREET GALLERY

About: Church Street Gallery specializes in unique, contemporary arts and crafts in a range of media, such as painting, prints, photography, glassworks, ceramics, sculpture, jewellery, gift cards and more.

Address: 17 Church Street, Saffron Walden, Essex CB10 1JW
Tel: 01799 522947
Email: info@church-street-gallery.co.uk
Website: www.church-street-gallery.co.uk

COCOAPOD

About: Cocoapod is a unique and innovative chocolate shop that features brightly coloured, imaginative delicacies created by sisters, Linda and Phillipa.

Contact: Linda and Phillipa
Address: 197 Petts Wood Road, Petts Wood, Kent BR5 1LA
Tel: 01689 834108
Email: info@cocoapod.co.uk
Website: www.cocoapod.co.uk

COMMA

About: This couple-owned store provides a mix of eclectic and unique

handmade items, sourced from crafters and designers across the UK and locally.

Contact: Sally & Dave Emery
Address: 247 Iffley Road, Oxford OX4 1SJ
Tel: 01865 202400
Email: hello@oxfordcomma.co.uk
Website: www.oxfordcomma.co.uk

CUCKOO CUCKOO CONTEMPORARY CRAFTS GALLERY

About: This stylish and original arts and crafts gallery is dedicated to supporting the local economy by providing local and British designers with a venue to showcase their unique products. Cuckoo Cuckoo features a variety of ceramics, glasswork, jewellery, papercraft, prints, textiles and much more.

Address: 2 Westhill Arcade, 43a George Street, Hastings TN34 3EA
Tel: 01424 428999
Email: thecuckoodesk@gmail.com
Website: www.cuckoocuckoo.co.uk

DANDELION WOOD

About: Dandelion Wood is a beautiful craft boutique that features carefully selected, handmade pieces ranging from ceramics, embroidery, handbags, jewellery, soft furnishings, soaps, vintage items and much more. Products are sourced locally as well as reaching farther a-field to France, Italy and Denmark.

Address: The Shop, The Street, Selborne, Hampshire GU34 3JP
Tel: 01420 511412
Email: Contact submission form available on website.
Website: www.dandelionwood.co.uk

EDEN ROSE

About: A well-established homeware and fashion store, Eden Rose features works by well known designers, such as Lisbeth Dahl, Tutti, House Doctor, Mina UK and more.

Address: 14 Lower Road, Chorleywood, Hertfordshire WD3 5LH
Tel: 01923 282124
Website: www.edenroseboutique.com

FIRE AND IRON GALLERY

About: Situated in a 14th century farmhouse outbuilding, Fire and Iron exhibits a fascinating collection of work by international artists in the medium of metal. Visitors will find delicate pieces of jewellery, sculptures, furniture and more, crafted from iron, steel, gold, silver, platinum, titanium, copper, bronze, tin, aluminium, pewter and zinc.

Contact: Lucy Quinnell
Address: Rowhurst Forge, Oxshott Road, Leatherhead, Surrey KT22 0EN
Tel: 01372 386453
Email: Lucy@fireandiron.co.uk
Website: www.fireandiron.co.uk

GALLERY 2

About: The Suffolk Craft Society formed in 1970 to celebrate and promote local craftsmanship. Now supporting over 140 members, the Society founded Ipswhich's Gallery 2, which showcases a carefully selected variety of high quality, unique pieces.

Contact: Sarah Young
Address: The Town Hall Galleries, Cornhill, Ipswhich IP1 1DH
Tel: 01473 432865
Email: development@ suffolkcraftsociety.com
Website: www.suffolkcraftsociety.com

GUILDFORD HOUSE GALLERY SHOP

About: Guildford House gallery and craft shop features a varied programme of exhibitions, workshops and craft shows. The newly established craft shop contains a varied selection of local arts and crafts, including gift cards, glasswork, jewellery, ceramics and more.

Address: 155 High Street, Guildford, Surrey GU1 3AJ
Tel: 01483 444751
Email: heritageservices@guildford. gov.uk
Website: www.guildford.gov.uk

HADDENHAM GALLERIES CRAFT CENTRE

About: This vibrant gallery features an array of changing exhibitions each year. Exhibitions include a variety of skills and crafts, such as up-cycling, ceramics, textiles and more.

Address: 20 High Street, Haddenham, Ely, Cambridge CB6 3XA
Tel: 01353 749188
Email: haddenhamgalleries@tiscali. co.uk
Website: www.haddenhamgallery. co.uk

HANDMADE

About: Handmade is a community of local artists, designers, crafters and collectors all based in Brighton, who share, exhibit and enjoy each others handcrafted and unique works.

Address: 106 St James Street, Brighton BN2 1TP
Email: handmade.co@hotmail.com
Website: www.facebook.com/ groups/handmadeco

JAM ETON

About: Established in 1994, JaM exhibits the high quality craftsmanship of over 100 makers. Exhibitions change regularly and feature works in ceramic, glass and jewellery.
Contact: Mike and Jacqueline Turner
Address: 81 High Street, Eton, Windsor SL4 6AF
Tel: 01753 622333
Email: info@jam-eton.co.uk
Website: www.jam-eton.co.uk

KENT AND LONDON

About: Kent and London is a quality, bespoke furniture business. Pieces can be entirely customized for the customers exact specifications.
Address: The Boat Shed, Horsebridge Road, Whitstable, Kent CT5 1BU
Tel: 01227 275500
Email: info@kentandlondon.co.uk
Website: www.kentandlondon.co.uk

MADE IN HASTINGS

About: Made In Hastings carefully selects handmade products from local makers in and around Hastings. Always happy to welcome new crafters, Made in Hastings exhibits a variety of work, such as textiles, woodcraft, knitwear, ceramics, paintings, hand bound books and more.
Address: 82 High Street, Old Town, Hastings TN34 3EL
Tel: 01424 719110
Email: info@madeinhastings.co.uk
Website: www.madeinhastings.co.uk

MARGATE GALLERY

About: Margate Gallery is dedicated to seeking out and promoting the best emerging artists and designers locally, nationally and internationally. Items exhibited include jewellery, ceramics, photography, textiles, paintings, glasswork, woodcraft and more.
Address: No. 2 Lombard Street, Margate Old Town, Kent CT9 1EJ
Tel: 01843 292779
Email: janet@margategallery.co.uk
Website: www.margategallery.co.uk

NEW ASHGATE GALLERY

About: The New Ashgate Gallery is a not-for-profit organization that supports emerging artists and campaigns. The gallery also provides an extensive range of workshops, professional seminars and school visits. Items such as ceramics, sculpture, glassworks, jewellery, textiles, woodcraft, metalwork, paintings and prints can all be found on display at this gallery.
Address: Wagon Yard, Farnham, Surrey GU9 7PS
Tel: 01252 713208
Email: gallery@newashgate.org.uk
Website: www.newashgate.org.uk

NICE THINGS

About: Showcasing work by local artists and crafters from the East Kent area, as well as work from makers around the UK and abroad, Nice Things features paintings, photography, prints, jewellery, gift cards, ceramics, felt work and more.
Contact: Suzy Humphries and Bella Goyarts
Address: The Custom House, Harbour Parade, Ramsgate CT11 8LP
Tel: 07939 542990
Email: info@nice-things.co.uk
Website: www.nice-things.co.uk

NUMBER 83

About: Number 83 is a craft and gift shop stocking locally sourced products and vintage gifts, from locally fired glass, handbags and jewellery to photography and original paintings.
Address: 83 Pool Road, Westbourne, Dorset BH4 9BB
Tel: 01202 764494
Email: info@number83.net
Website: www.number83.net

POLKADOT

About: This lovely craft shop is full of vintage and handmade products, all sourced locally. Polkadot offers a wide variety of gifts and craft pieces, such as woodcraft items, silver work, jewellery, ceramics and much more.
Contact: Lisa Wright
Address: 14 Market Square, Winslow, Buckinghamshire MK18 3AF
Tel: 07932 330197
Email: info@polkadotwinslow.co.uk
Website: www.polkadotwinslow.co.uk

PRETTY SCRUFFY

About: Pretty Scruffy provides local artisans and crafters a venue to exhibit and sell their handmade wares, such as ceramics, jewellery, silver work, textiles and more.
Address: Shop 3, No.1 Cooper Street, Chichester, West Sussex PO19 1EB
Tel: 01243 779715
Email: mail@prettyscruffy.com
Website: www.prettyscruffy.com

QUAY ARTS CRAFT SHOP

About: Quay Arts features work from over 60 artists and designers from the Isle of Wight. Work displayed and

on sale includes ceramics, glasswork, woodcraft, textiles, metalwork, jewellery, gift cards and much more.

Contact: Sam Mitchell
Address: 15 Sea Street, Newport Harbour, Isle of Wight PO30 5BD
Tel: 01983 824162
Email: s.mitchell@quayarts.org
Website: www.quayarts.org/shop

QUINTESSENTIAL DESIGN

About: Jill and Massimo opened Quintessential Design after years of working in Europe and creating their innovative standing jigsaw puzzles. As well as their original creation, Jill and Massimo also create a wide variety of handmade homeware and accessories

Contact: Jill & Massimo
Address: 65 The Old High Street, Folkestone, Kent CT20 1RN
Tel: 01303 488141
Email: sales@quintessentialdesign. co.uk
Website: www.quintessentialdesign. co.uk

ROCKET AND FAIRYDUST

About: Rocket and Fairydust is a craft shop that provides a bespoke hand-painting service for any furniture, as well as a small collection of handmade crafts and gifts.

Address: 38 Nutfield Road, Merstham, Redhill, Surrey RH1 3EP
Tel: 07881 906861
Email: info@rocketandfairydust.co.uk
Website: www.rocketandfairydust. co.uk

SEALE CRAFT SHOP

About: This craft and gift shop, run by mother and daughter, features a vibrant and eclectic collection of handcrafted items and handmade foods. Seale Craft Shop stocks homemade cakes, conserves, chutney, honey and mustards; jewellery, glasswork, woodcraft, knitwear, gift cards and much more.

Contact: Shirley Harrington
Address: Manor Farm Craft Centre, Wood Lane, Seale, Farnham GU10 1HR
Tel: 01252 783488
Email: sealecraftshop@ntlworld.com
Website: www.sealecraftshop.co.uk

SURREY GUILD CRAFT GALLERY

About: Organized by the Surrey Guild of Craftsmen, the gallery is a permanent exhibition space for professional contemporary and traditional designers and artists.

Address: 1 Moushill Lane, Milford, Surrey GU8 5BH
Tel: 01483 424769
Email: acholloway@hotmail.co.uk
Website: www.surreyguild.com

THE GILLIANGLADRAG FLUFF-a-TORIUM

About: The Fluff-a-torium is dedicated to all things felt; stocking felting kits and equipment and hosting a range of classes and felt workshops. Gillian Harris has found success in her passion for felt and her kits are now sold in John Lewis, Liberty, Hobbycraft and many independent retailers.

Contact: Gillian Harris
Address: 20 West Street, Dorking, Surrey RH4 1BL
Tel: 01306 898144
Email: gill@gilliangladrag.co.uk
Website: www.gilliangladrag.co.uk

THE HANDMADE GIFT CO.

About: The Handmade Gift Co. are passionate about promoting British crafters and designers. Artisans and crafters can expect to receive a great deal of support with promotions, marketing and selling their work. The Handmade Gift Co. features a variety of products, such as soaps, jewellery, textiles, handbags, prints and more.

Contact: Liz King
Address: Stuart Porter Antiques & Craft Centre, 15 Broad Street, Stamford, Lincolnshire PE9 1PJ
Tel: 01780 766214
Email: info@thehandmadegiftco.com
Website: www.thehandmadegiftco. com

THE WHITE GALLERY

About: The White Gallery centres around providing local artists and crafters of Surrey with the opportunity to exhibit their work, and the residents of surrey with the opportunity to buy original and affordable art. Collections at The White Gallery consist of ceramics, original paintings, prints, photography, glasswork, jewellery, sculptures and much more.

Contact: Michael Palmer and Rachel Benneworth
Address: 17 St. Martins Walk, Dorking, Surrey RH4 1UX
Tel: 01306 881066
Email: admin@ thewhitegallerydorking.co.uk
Website: www. thewhitegallerydorking.co.uk

MIDLANDS

ALL FIRED ARTS

About: All Fired Arts is an open pottery studio in which visitors can choose from a range of pottery blanks and paint their own designs. The studio also supports local artists by displaying drawings, paintings, prints and more.

Contact: Annie

Address: 12 Poplar Road, Kings Heath, Birmingham B14 7AD

Tel: 01214 440940

Email: allfiredarts@gmail.com

Website: www.allfiredarts.co.uk

ALTERED CHIC

About: Inspired by French interiors and country living, Altered Chic provides stylish, affordable homeware and accessories, handmade by local artists.

Contact: Lisa and John

Address: 7 Falcon Yard, Chesterfield, Derbyshire S40 1PF

Tel: 01246 767428

Email: info@alteredchic.co.uk

Website: www.alteredchic.com

BILSTON CRAFT GALLERY

About: Bilston Craft Gallery celebrates the talent of crafting in its historic exhibit, showcasing 300 years worth of craft. Visitors can then compare historic crafts with that of new, contemporary crafts by local artists and makers. Exhibitions feature ceramics, glasswork, jewellery, textiles, metalwork, woodcraft and more.

Address: Mount Pleasant, Wolverhampton WV14 7LU

Tel: 01902 552507

Email: bilstoncraftgallery@ wolverhampton.gov.uk

Website: www.wolverhamptonart. org.uk/bilston

BOW BOUTIQUE

About: Featuring vintage pieces and contemporary handmade gifts and homeware; Bow Boutique is an eclectic mix of local craftsmanship and design. The shop features collections of ceramics, candles, handbags, soaps, jewellery, artwork and more.

Address: 8 Causeway Lane, Matlock, Derbyshire DE4 3AR

Tel: 01629 580239

Email: hello@bow-boutique.co.uk

Website: www.bow-boutique.co.uk

CREATED

About: This family gallery opened in 2008 and showcases the handmade creations of crafters and artists from all over the UK. The gallery stocks a range of pieces, such as ceramics, felt items, paintings, photography and prints.

Contact: Deirdre Gage

Address: 420 Chatsworth Road, Chesterfield, Derbyshire S40 3BQ

Tel: 01246 232205

Email: info@createdgallery.co.uk

Website: www.createdgallery.co.uk

Debbie BRYAN STUDIO & SHOP

About: Debbie Bryan is an award winning crafter specializing in traditional, British craftsmanship, using raw materials to create scarves, brooches, gloves and lace knits.

Contact: Debbie Bryan

Address: 18 St. Mary's Gate, The Lace Market, Nottingham NG1 1PF

Tel: 01159 507776

Email: info@debbiebryan.co.uk

Website: www.debbiebryan.co.uk

DOWN TO EARTH GALLERY

About: Down to Earth Gallery was originally established to showcase the metalwork of Phil Rogers, however since its opening in 2008, the gallery has become a vibrant mix of art from some of the best British crafters. Down to Earth features glasswork, jewellery, ceramics, prints, paintings and more.

Contact: Phil Rogers

Address: 4 The Craft Centre, St. Mary's Street, Whitchurch, Shropshire SY13 1QY

Tel: 01948 667712

Email: down.2.earth@btconnect.com

Website: www.downtoearthgallery. co.uk

ESKIMO BLUE

About: Eskimo blue is a pottery gallery and workshop. Ceramist Charlotte Barker creates wonderful handmade ornaments and functional ceramic pieces, as well as hosting pottery parties for special occasions and various workshops.

Contact: Charlotte Barker

Address: The Old Coach House, 192c Clarendon Park Road, Clarendon Park, Leicester LE2 3AF

Tel: 01162 125469

Email: charlotte@eskimoblue.co.uk

Website: www.eskimoblue.co.uk

FOCUS GALLERY

About: Established in 1971, Focus Gallery has been celebrating British handmade art for over 40 years. The gallery features ceramics, metalwork, silver work, jewellery, glasswork, woodcraft, textiles and more.

Contact: Lorraine Murphy

Address: 108 Derby Road, Nottingham, Nottinghamshire NG1 5FB

Tel: 01159 537575
Email: focusgallerynottingham@hotmail.com
Website: www.focusgallerynottingham.com

Gallery 52

About: A small, independent art gallery showcasing a wide variety of artwork, ceramics, jewellery, gift cards, handcrafted gifts and trinkets.
Contact: Rae Alton
Address: Main Road, Brailsford, Ashbourne, Derbyshire DE6 3DA
Tel: 01335 360368
Email: rae@gallery52.co.uk
Website: www.gallery52.co.uk

IAPETUS

About: A large craft and gift shop stocking work and art by over 150 crafters and makers. Handmade art and gifts include jewellery, gift cards, ceramics and various other artworks.
Contact: Anna Brook and Chris Marks
Address: 34 Belle Vue Terrace, Great Malvern, Worcestershire WR14 4PZ
Tel: 01684 566929
Email: hello@iapetus.co.uk
Website: www.iapetus.co.uk

ITCH Gallery

About: Jenny Creasey runs this innovative and contemporary gallery in the heart of Rutland, the smallest county in the UK. Itch Gallery showcases a host of talented British crafters and makers working in the field of painting, ceramics, jewellery, papercraft, prints, textiles, glasswork and woodcraft.
Contact: Jenny Creasey
Address: 4 Knights Yard, Gaol Street, Oakham, Rutland LE15 6AQ

Tel: 01572 756760
Email: info@itchgallery.co.uk
Website: www.itchgallery.co.uk

Leabrooks Gallery

About: Providing over 1000 square feet of exhibition space, Leabrooks gallery displays a wide range of original art in oil, watercolour and mixed media, as well as handcrafted jewellery, ceramics and gift cards.
Address: 36 Leabrooks Road, Somercotes, Alfreton, Derbyshire DE55 4HB
Tel: 01773 602961
Email: sales@leabrooksgallery.co.uk
Website: www.leabrooksgallery.co.uk

MADE Gallery

About: Made Gallery passionately promotes the tradition of personally designing and hand making art and craft pieces. The gallery is continually changing and welcoming new talent; featuring works of art, jewellery, ceramics, leather work, gift cards, glasswork, textiles and much more.
Contact: Julia Groundsell
Address: 14a Orange Street, Uppingham, Rutland LE15 9SQ
Tel: 01572 822002
Email: julia@madegallery.co.uk
Website: www.madegallery.co.uk

MAKING THE BEST

About: A small, high quality craft shop that focuses around hand-crafting and up-cycling. The shop stocks prints, woodcraft, soft furnishings, chalk paints, jewellery and a variety of other wonders. Patricia also offers a range of classes and workshops.
Contact: Patricia Mellet

Address: 11 Bridge Street, Leighton, Buzzard, Bedfordshire LU7 1AH
Tel: 01525 372409
Email: patricia@makingthebest.co.uk
Website: www.makingthebest.co.uk

MANGOJUICE GALLERY & WORKSHOP

About: Mangojuice began as a family run gallery, mainly exhibiting Mangojuice jewellery and accessories. Today the gallery hosts a vibrant collection of artwork, prints, ceramics, glass and metalwork by the whole family and various local artists.
Address: 9A New Street, Worcester WR1 2DN
Tel: 07834 283471
Email: workncolour@aol.com
Website: www.mangojuicegallery.com

MICHAELMAS HOUSE

About: An exhibition space and supplier of handmade, country furniture, homeware and accessories, all sourced from quality British crafters and designers.
Contact: Tim and Lorraine
Address: 4 Main Street, Market Bosworth, Warwickshire CV13 0JW
Tel: 01455 291303
Email: info@michaelmashouse.co.uk
Website: www.michaelmashouse.co.uk

NO TWO THINGS

Contact: Di Chesterman and Beth Revell
Address: 208a The Broadway, Didcot, Oxon OX11 8RN
Tel: 01235 511550
Email: info@notwothings.co.uk
Website: www.notwothings.co.uk

STUDIO 61 GALLERY BOUTIQUE

About: Karina's boutique gallery features the works of over 100 British artists and designers, as well as her own ceramics, textiles, woodcraft, glasswork and bath products. The theme of the gallery generally reflects Karina's love for Cornwall and the coast.

Contact: Karina Goodman

Address: Leashaw, Holloway, Derbyshire DE4 5AT

Tel: 01629 534532

Email: karinagoodman@btinternet.com

Website: www.karinagoodman.com

THE ARTER

About: A welcoming craft and gift boutique that celebrates local art and design; The Arter features a variety of unique and special pieces such as glasswork, ceramics, up-cycled items, knitted jewellery, millinery, textiles and more.

Contact: Paula & Rachael

Address: Hall's Croft, Old Town, Stratford-upon-Avon CV37 6BG

Tel: 01789 267353

Email: the_arter@hotmail.com

Website: www.facebook.com/thearterNT

THE BEETROOT TREE

About: Located in a restored, 17th century Jacobean barn, The Beetroot Tree presents a contrasting and vibrant collection of contemporary works of art, delicate textiles, unique furnishings and fine crafts.

Contact: Alysn Midgelow-Marsden

Address: South Street, Draycott, Derbyshire DE72 3PP

Tel: 01332 873929

Email: info@thebeetroottree.com

Website: www.thebeetroottree.com

THE HARLEY GALLERY

About: A tranquil gallery and workspace that prides itself on providing a beautiful exhibition location for contemporary, traditional and historic pieces of art and local handicrafts. Each piece of artwork is carefully selected and includes jewellery, ceramics, paintings, woodcraft, silver work and much more.

Contact: Susan Sherrit

Address: Welbeck, Worksop, Nottinghamshire S80 3LW

Tel: 01909 501700

Email: info@harleygallery.co.uk

Website: www.harleygallery.co.uk

THE HOUSE GALLERY

About: The House Gallery is indeed a house and even has a resident dog. The exhibits and artwork are displayed over two floors within this homely gallery and consist of pieces of jewellery, glasswork, ceramics, artwork, textiles and more.

Address: 7 Rose Court, Olney, Buckinghamshire MK46 4BY

Tel: 01234 711840

Email: arija@thehousegallery.co.uk

Website: www.thehousegallery.co.uk

THE NATIONAL CENTRE FOR CRAFT & DESIGN

About: This vast exhibition centre is the largest in the UK, boasting four spacious galleries. The National Centre for Craft and Design showcases work by artists and designers from across the world, featuring a huge variety of media and craftsmanship.

Address: Navigation Wharf, Carre Street, Sleaford, Lincolnshire NG34 7TW

Tel: 01529 308710

Email: info@nationalcraftanddesign.org.uk

Website: www.nationalcraftanddesign.org.uk

THE SEED GALLERY AND STUDIO

About: The Seed Gallery specializes in supporting emerging talent and applied arts graduates. Works featured include ceramics, glasswork, jewellery, textiles, prints, gift cards and more.

Address: The Croft, Market Place, Crich, Matlock DE4 5BQ

Tel: 01773 852322

Email: info@seedgallery.co.uk

Website: www.seedgallery.co.uk

THE STRAWBERRY TREE

About: This quaint and homely boutique features a wide variety of unique gift ideas and locally handmade works of art. The Strawberry Tree provides a mixture of artwork, gift cards, candles, jewellery, woodcraft and much more.

Contact: Kerry

Address: 17 Market Street, Loughborough, Leicestershire LE11 3EP

Tel: 01509 768064

Email: Contact submission form available on website.

Website: www.thestrawberrytreegifts.co.uk

THEGALLERY

About: theGALLERY focuses on the importance of handcrafted, local work using local, unique materials. The collections include jewellery, ceramics,

glass and metalwork, woodcraft, textiles, paintings, prints and more.
Contact: Jacs Collins
Address: 3 Market Square, Bishop's Castle, Shropshire SY9 5BN
Tel: 01588 630128
Email: jacs@thegallerybc.co.uk
Website: www.thegallerybc.co.uk

THREE LITTLE PIGS

About: Three Little Pigs is a unique boutique offering an eclectic range of gifts and crafts sourced from local and regional makers. Stocking jewellery, homeware, garden accessories, furnishings and more, Three Little Pigs also offers workshops and classes for beginners or the more experienced.
Contact: 68 High Street
Address: Pershore, Worcestershire WR10 1DU
Tel: 01386 555210
Email: enquiries@threelittlepigs.eu
Website: www.threelittlepigs.eu

TIGERLILY MAKES

About: Tigerlily Makes is a wool and felt-making boutique stocking a wide range of wool and felt-making kits and supplies. Lisa also hosts a range of parties and events for hen parties, families, schools and children.
Contact: Lisa Marie Olsen
Address: 1st Floor Monty's Vintage Shop, Curborough Craft & Antique Centre, Watery Lane, Lichfield WS13 8ES
Tel: 08455 439046
Email: info@tigerlilymakes.co.uk
Website: www.tigerlilymakes.co.uk

TUTBURY CRAFTS

About: This tiny little shop features a large selection of crafts and supplies as well as hosting a variety of workshops and demonstrations. Tutbury Crafts specializes in knitting, crochet, jewellery, papercraft, needlecraft and various other artworks.
Contact: Frances Murray
Address: 3 Tutbury Mill Mews, Lower High Street, Tutbury, Staffordshire DE13 9LU
Tel: 01283 520115
Email: tutburycrafts@gmail.com
Website: www.tutburycrafts.co.uk

UNIT TWELVE

About: Unit Twelve is a bright contemporary gallery and workshop that hosts a variety of events run by local artists. The gallery features exhibitions of papercraft, hand woven accessories, illustrations, wire sculptures, ceramics, prints and more.
Contact: Jennifer Collier
Address: Tixall Heath Farm, Tixall, Stafford ST18 0XX
Tel: 07811 460494
Email: jcolliertextiles@yahoo.co.uk
Website: www.unittwelve.co.uk

"If you're supplying a big store, it's almost like a PR and marketing exercise."
Gillian Harris

NORTH EAST

ANGEL

About: Retro and vintage-inspired gift and homeware; the Angel brand is world renowned for its French Linen. The Angel boutique stocks a variety of antique French furniture, mirrors, jewellery and various other vintage items and accessories.
Contact: Kirstin Hodgson
Address: 2 Tyler's Walk, Easingwold, North Yorkshire YO61 3QP
Tel: 01347 822044
Email: enquiries@angel-lifestyle.com
Website: www.angel-lifestyle.com

BIRD'S YARD

About: Established in 2010, within its first year Bird's Yard was Awarded the 'Best Newcomer' award at the Retail Therapy Awards 2010. Spread over three floors, this charming boutique harbours an abundance of nooks and crannies for crafters and designers to showcase their works from.
Address: 83 Kirkgate, Leeds LS2 7DJ
Tel: 07976 017057
Email: michelle@birdsyard.co.uk
Website: www.birdsyard.co.uk

COCCUVEDA GIFTS & CRAFTS

About: Coccuveda functions as a workshop and craft boutique in the market town of Rothbury. Various collections of crafts include handmade headpieces and fascinators, glasswork, textiles, woodcraft, jewellery and more.
Contact: Loraine Lawson
Address: 155 Bridge Street, Rothbury, Northumberland NE65 7QW

Tel: 01669 621847
Email: coccuveda@live.co.uk
Website: www.coccuveda-crafts.co.uk

CREATIVE COHESION

About: Creative Cohesion is a centre that organizes workshops, tutorials and activities for artists and families as well as providing workspace for artists to hire and exhibit from. Works exhibited at Creative Cohesian range from glasswork and ceramics to artwork and photography.
Address: 20–21 Nile Street, Sunnyside, Sunderland SR1 1EY
Tel: 01915 655331
Email: creativecohesion@btconnect.com
Website: www.facebook.com/CreativeCohesion

GALLERY 49

About: Spread over two floors of a listed Georgian building, Gallery 49 accommodates a wide variety of contemporary local and national art.
Address: 1 Market Place, Bridlington, East Yorkshire YO16 4QJ
Tel: 01262 679472
Email: galleryforty-nine@live.co.uk
Website: www.galleryforty-nine.com

HAD2BUY

About: Had2Buy is a boutique and art gallery featuring exquisite handmade crafts from local designers. The boutique features jewellery, gift cards, handbags, up-cycled items, patchwork and more.
Address: 15 Bondgate, Darlington, County Durham DL3 7JE
Tel: 01325 286080
Email: had2buy@hotmail.co.uk
Website: www.had2buy.co.uk

HANNI MAY'S GIFT EMPORIUM

About: Hanni May's is a unique craft and gift shop that offers local and regional crafters a permanent location to showcase their wares. The shop features collections of candles, jewellery, vintage items, textiles, bespoke gifts and more.
Contact: Danielle Monden
Address: 6 Clarks Yard, Darlington, County Durham DL3 7QH
Tel: 01325 380741
Email: info@hannimays.co.uk
Website: www.hannimays.co.uk

HEART GALLERY

About: Heart Gallery provides an eclectic and exciting mix of British jewellery design and contemporary craft, such as ceramics, glasswork, painting, papercraft, photography, textiles, woodcraft and more.
Address: The Arts Centre, 4a Market Street, Hebden Bridge HX7 6AA
Tel: 04122 845845
Email: enquiries@heartgallery.co.uk
Website: www.heartgallery.co.uk

KIRSTY HOPKINS

About: The Kirsty Hopkins studio features all of Kirsty's own original textile designs and gifts. Located in the crafty area of Kings Street, Kirsty's studio is surrounded by creativity and inspiration.
Contact: Kirsty Hopkins
Address: Studio 10 King Street Workshops, Pateley Bridge, North Yorkshire HG3 5LE
Email: kirsty@kirstyhopkins.co.uk
Website: www.kirstyhopkins.co.uk

LIVE, LOVE AND CREATE

About: Live, Love and Create is a thriving workshop, café and craft shop. The workshop provides a range of activities such as decoupage, pottery painting and parties. The café serves a selection of homemade cakes and pastries, whilst the gift shop features a quality selection of ceramics, jewellery, homeware, gift cards and craft kits.
Address: 23 Wrawby Street, Brigg, North Lincolnshire DN20 8JJ
Tel: 01652 600992
Email: info@livelovecreate.co.uk
Website: www.livelovecreate.co.uk

MASHAM GALLERY

About: A popular gallery and gift shop; the Masham Gallery features the work of over 50 artists and crafters. Works displayed consist of ceramics, jewellery, glasswork, textiles and more.
Contact: Josie Beszant
Address: 24 Market Place, Masham, North Yorkshire HG4 4EB
Tel: 01765 689554
Email: enquiry@mashamgallery.co.uk
Website: www.mashamgallery.co.uk

No.1 THE STONE BARN

About: An open studio featuring the work of silhouette papercut artist, John Speight. Visitors to the shop can observe John at work or browse the beautiful gifts that consist of his handmade gift cards and Spirit of Colour Jewellery by Lorna Speight. Also in stock are soaps, Murana glass jewellery and a variety of other craft items.
Contact: John Speight
Address: Kirkhale Courtyard, Kirkhale, Newcastle-upon-Tyne NE19 2PE

Tel: 01830 540428
Email: info@onethestonebarn.co.uk
Website: www.onethestonebarn.co.uk

NO.18 MAISON BOUTIQUE

About: An individual boutique situated in the heart of Newcastle-upon-Tyne, No.18 Maison Boutique features the works of UK crafters and designers as well as offering bespoke services for those special occasions. The shop stocks a variety of items, from knitwear and textiles to ceramics and prints.
Address: 18a Blanford Square, Newcastle, Tyne and Wear NE1 4HZ
Tel: 01912 328181
Email: hello@no18maisonboutique.co.uk
Website: www.no18maisonboutique.co.uk

PINS AND RIBBONS

About: Pins and Ribbons specializes in homeware, soft furnishings, textiles, candles and other accessories. What began as a hobby for Kerrie Murray has exploded into an enterprise; now supplying to hundreds of retail outlets, from niche boutiques to department stores. All items are handmade.
Contact: Kerrie Murray
Address: 15 Station Road, Eaglescliffe TS16 0BU
Tel: 01642 786777
Email: enquiries@pinsandribbons.co.uk
Website: www.pinsandribbons.co.uk

RADIANCE LIGHTING

About: A truly unique craft boutique consisting of creative lighting and lampshades in a variety of media, such as ceramics, glass and paper. Radiance welcomes crafters from across the UK and beyond.

Contact: Hannah
Address: 26 Market Street, Hebden Bridge, West Yorkshire HX7 6AA
Tel: 01422 845764
Email: hannah@radiancelighting.co.uk
Website: www.radiancelighting.co.uk

ROOBARB GIFTS

About: A bright, quirky little gift and craft shop that stocks a range of handmade homeware, handbags, sock toys, candles, textiles and much more.
Contact: Sarah Foster
Address: 1 Peel Street, Marsden, Huddersfield HD7 6B
Tel: 01484 846226
Email: roobarbgifts@hotmail.co.uk
Website: www.facebook.com/RoobarbGifts

ROSEWILL COTTAGE

About: Rosewill Cottage is a small, friendly, bead boutique. This community of beaders host jewellery making parties, workshops and various other events, as well as stocking local handmade craft items. The shop stocks a dazzling array of beads of various materials, bead kits, craft wire, jewellery and much more.
Contact: Dawn McLean
Address: 148 Tynemouth Road, North Shields NE30 1EG
Tel: 01912 583310
Email: rosewillcottage@gmail.com
Website: www.rosewill-cottage.co.uk

THE BRIDGE GALLERY

About: The Bridge Gallery is home to unique, original pieces of artwork, as well as some limited edition prints. Handmade jewellery, gift cards, sculptures and other handcrafted gifts can also be found at the Bridge Gallery.
Address: The Bridge, Bedale, North Yorkshire DL8 1AN
Tel: 01677 427824
Email: bedalegallery@gmail.com
Website: www.thebridgegallery.co.uk

THE BUTTERFLY ROOMS

About: The Butterfly Rooms proudly stocks the work and products of independent British artists and companies. Specializing in original designs and gifts, ranging from candles and toiletries to jewellery and textiles. The Butterfly Rooms also provides classes in which visitors can paint pottery and stitch their own bespoke creations.
Address: 74 Bingley Road, Saltaire BD18 4SB
Tel: 01274 581806
Email: angela@thebutterflyrooms.co.uk
Website: www.thebutterflyrooms.co.uk

THE GIFT GALLERY

About: Established in 2010, The Gift Gallery presents the handiwork of over 150 crafters from the UK and Ireland. The gallery showcases a variety of collections, including ceramics and jewellery.
Address: 19 Shambles, York YO1 7LZ
Tel: 01904 541851
Email: info@giftgalleryyork.co.uk
Website: www.thegiftgalleryyork.co.uk

THE GIFT TAG

About: This family-run boutique stocks a wide range of eclectic, handmade gifts. The Gift Tag offers a bespoke service on a variety of items and features local handcrafted products, such as patchwork gifts, candles, soaps, jewellery and more.

Address: 44 Halifax Road, Cullingworth, Bradford, West Yorkshire BD13 5DE

Tel: 01535 275151

Email: jenibaildon@aol.com

Website: www.thegifttag.vpweb.co.uk

UNIQUE ARTS

About: Unique Arts was established in 2005 with the intention of selling local crafts and handmade gifts, however the business has somewhat evolved into a community project, providing a variety of workshops, private classes and parties.

Address: South Square Centre, Thornton, Bradford BD13 3LD

Tel: 07981 691556

Email: info@uniquearts.co.uk

Website: www.uniquearts.co.uk

WESTSIDE CONTEMPORARY GALLERY

About: A contemporary art gallery featuring the famous animal portraits of Sue Moffit along with other local artists' collections in the media of ceramics, glasswork, prints and much more.

Contact: Sue Moffit

Address: Westside Farm, Newton, Northumberland NE43 7TW

Tel: 01661 843778

Email: sue@westsidecontemporary.com

Website: www.westsidecontemporary.com

NORTH WEST

ARTERIA

About: Located in Gallery 23, Arteria stocks a unique range of modern homeware, gifts and crafts.

Address: 23 Brock Street, Lancaster, Lancashire LA1 1UR

Tel: 01524 61111

Email: info@arteriashop.co.uk

Website: www.arteriashop.co.uk

ASCOT STUDIOS

About: Established in 2005, Ascot Studios represents local, national and international artists. Regarded as one of the leading independent art galleries in Britain, Ascot Studios features an inspirational collection of original paintings.

Contact: Phil Harwood

Address: Bee Mill, Preston Road, Ribchester, Preston PR3 3XJ

Tel: 01254 878100

Email: info@ascotstudios.com

Website: www.ascotstudios.com

CEDAR FARM GALLERIES

About: Cedar Farm is a community of unique shops and galleries selling contemporary and traditional crafts, homeware, prints, jewellery and much more.

Address: Back Lane, Mawdesley, Ormskirk, Lancashire L40 3SY

Tel: 01704 822038

Email: cedarfarm@live.co.uk

Website: www.cedarfarm.net

CETRA GALLERY & STUDIO

About: Cetra Gallery is a contemporary photography studio and agency specializing in wedding, fashion, family and commercial photography with a unique and relaxed style. The art gallery was created to allow local and national artists to showcase and sell their own work and services.

Address: 50 Pensby Road, Heswall, Wirral CH60 7RE

Tel: 01513 427777

Email: richard@cetra.co.uk

Website: www.cetra.co.uk

CRAFT SHOP ROYAL EXCHANGE THEATRE

About: Established in 1981, the Craft Shop in the Royal Exchange Theatre has been celebrating British craft for over 30 years. The shop stocks gift cards, jewellery, ceramics, woodcrafts, glassworks, textiles and more.

Address: St Ann's Square, Manchester M2 7DH

Tel: 01616 156767

Email: craft.shop@royalexchange.co.uk

Website: www.royalexchange.org.uk

FARFIELD MILL ARTS & HERITAGE CENTRE

About: This arts and heritage centre is lavishly spread over four floors in a restored Victorian house. Farfield Mill holds regular art and craft events, such as demonstrations, fairs and exhibitions.

Address: Farfield Mill, Garsdale Road, Sedbergh, Cumbria LA10 5LW

Tel: 01539 621958

Email: exhibitions@farfieldmill.org

Website: www.farfieldmill.org

GOSFORTH POTTERY SHOP

About: Gosforth Pottery provides a wide range of activities for the family to partake in: visitors can create their own pots, or paint a pre-made pot. Gosforth Pottery also exhibits an extensive variety of their own pottery and ceramics, as well as those of local crafters.

Contact: Barbara and Dick Wright

Address: Gosforth, Cumbria CA20 1AH

Tel: 01946 725296

Email: mail@gosforth-pottery.co.uk

Website: www.gosforth-pottery.co.uk

HEARTS DESIGNS

About: Hearts Designs stocks a wide variety of handmade gifts sourced from local artists and craftswomen in the South Lakeland area. Supporting disadvantaged young women in Nepal and Peru through their range of fairtrade crafts, such as handmade rugs, tapestries, handbags, jewellery and more.

Address: 14 Thornfield Road, Grange-Over-Sand, Cumbria LA11 7DR

Tel: 01539 535267

Email: info@hearts-designs.co.uk

Website: www.hearts-designs.co.uk

LANDBABY AT THE BLUECOAT

About: For Claire, Landbaby began as a way to make money during the summer and soon evolved into a thriving business. Claire launched her shop with a meagre £50, and is inspirational to other newly emerging crafters. Landbaby welcomes new designers with the only rule being that work must be handmade and unique.

Contact: Claire

Address: The Bluecoat, School Lane, Liverpool L1 3BX

Tel: 07504 479440

Email: landbabyshop@gmail.com

Website: www.landbaby.co.uk

POPPI RED GIFT AND COFFEE SHOP

About: Located in the exquisite Lake District, Poppi Red is a cheery, welcoming gift shop, stocking a wide range of homeware and gifts, as well as up-cycled items.

Address: Main Street, Hawkshead, Cumbria LA22 0NT

Tel: 01539 436434

Email: Contact submission form available on website.

Website: www.poppi-red.co.uk

RENNIES GALLERY

About: Rennies Gallery is steeped in family history; originally established in 1965 by Jean and Ronald Rennie to promote Jean's oil paintings. Rennies is now a widely recognized gallery showcasing quality prints, illustrations, paintings and photography by world famous artists, such as Quentin Blake, Todd White and Hamish Blakely

Address: 61 Bold Street, Liverpool L1 4EZ

Tel: 01517 080599

Email: sales@renniesgallery.co.uk

Website: www.renniesgallery.co.uk

SOEL

About: SOEL is a high-end, ethical, luxury designer store featuring classic ladies fashion, accessories and gifts. SOEL only stocks organic and ethical products. Handcrafted stock includes jewellery, handbags, textiles and up-cycled items.

Address: Backridge Farm, Twitter Lane, Waddington BB7 3LG

Tel: 01200 423363

Email: lynn@soelboutique.co.uk

Website: www.soelboutique.co.uk

STAACKS

About: Staacks celebrates traditional and contemporary work by British based crafters. In stock are a range of craft pieces, such as ceramics, candles, soaps, glasswork, textiles, jewellery, artwork and much more.

Address: 144 Banks Road, West Kirby CH48 0QB

Tel: 01516 250229

Email: kara@staacks.co.uk

Website: www.staacks.co.uk

THE BLUECOAT

About: The Bluecoat is Liverpool's thriving, artistic hub. Its four galleries open their doors to artists and crafters of all varieties, including regular fixtures such as Landbaby.

Address: School Lane, Liverpool L1 3BX

Tel: 01517 025324

Email: info@thebluecoat.org.uk

Website: www.thebluecoat.org.uk

THE SHOP FLOOR PROJECT

About: The Shop Floor Project's vision is to stock beautiful, handcrafted pieces that can be passed down through family generations as an heirloom – quality is of the utmost importance. The shop features collections of jewellery, ceramics, gift cards, prints, handbags and more.

Contact: Samantha and Denise Allan

Address: Studio 214 Ulverston Business Centre, 25 New Market Street, Ulverston LA12 7LQ

Tel: 01229 584537

Email: samantha@theshopfloorproject.com

Website: www.theshopfloorproject.com

THE WOOL CLIP

About: The Wool Clip is for lovers of all things woollen. The shop stocks a vast array of woollen products as well as buttons, felt and crochet items; jewellery, craft equipment and more.

Address: Priest's Mill, Caldbeck, Cumbria CA7 8DR

Tel: 01697 478707

Email: info@woolclip.com

Website: www.woolclip.com

NORTHERN IRELAND

ABACUS BEADS

About: Established in 1991, Abacus Beads was the first bead shop in Northern Ireland. A wide variety of supplies and beads are available, such as glass beads, bone, felt, metal, acrylic, wooden and resin beads.

Address: 1 McAuley House, Castle Street, Belfast, County Down BT1 1HB

Tel: 02890 236087

Email: info@abacusbeads.co.uk

Website: www.abacusbeads.co.uk

AMANDA'S WOOL & CRAFT SHOP

About: Amanda's Wool and Craft Shop is a supplier of high quality wools, yarns, haberdashery, jewellery and accessories.

Contact: Amanda

Address: 137–139 Main Street, Fivemiletown, County Tyrone BT75 0PG

Tel: 02889 522154

Website: www.amandaswoolandcraftshop.co.uk

ANN MCNULTY POTTERY

About: Ann has been a full-time ceramicist since 1978 and specializes in stoneware and the unusual process of raku.

Contact: Ann McNulty

Address: 1 The Buttermarket Craft & Design Centre, Down Street, Enniskillen, County Fermanagh BT74 7DU

Tel: 02866 324721

Email: annmcnulty@talk21.com

Website: www.annmcnultypottery.com

ANNIE'S COUNTRY CRAFTS

About: Annie's Country Crafts consists of entirely handcrafted gifts, homeware and furnishings, all lovingly designed and made by Annie. Products include quilted soft furnishings, patchwork and a variety of textile accessories.

Contact: Annie

Address: Homefarm, 3 Drumawhey Road, Newtownards, County Down BT23 8RS

Tel: 02891 814788

Email: orders@anniescrafts.com

Website: www.anniescrafts.com

ART & HOME

About: Art & Home is a gallery and art supply store with over 50 years of experience in the art industry. Supplying branded art supplies and hosting regular exhibitions, Art & Home welcomes interest from local and international artists.

Address: 145–147 High Street, Holywood, Belfast County Down BT18 9LG

Tel: 02890 428168

Email: sales@artandhomeweb.com

Website: www.artandhomeweb.com

AURA – HANDMADE JEWELLERY & CRAFTS

About: Aura showcases handmade art and crafts by local designers and artists. Collections consist of jewellery, felt work, ceramics, soft furnishings, textiles, glasswork and more.

Address: Unit 1 59 High Street, Bangor, County Down BT20 5BE

Tel: 02891 229839

Email: info@auracrafts.com

Website: www.auracrafts.com

BLUE BEANS

About: Blue Beans sits in the foothills of the Mountains of Mourne and showcases a vibrant selection of Irish crafts. Exhibits consist of ceramics, iron and copper work, glasswork, jewellery, textiles, soaps, handbags, gift cards and more.

Contact: Claire Warn

Address: 67 Main Street, Castlewellan, County Down BT31 9DQ

Tel: 02843 770414

Email: clairewarn@utvinternet.com

Website: www.bluebeanscraft.co.uk

COPPERMOON

About: Established in 1992, Copppermoon have always supported local and national arts and crafts. The boutique features jewellery, ceramics, leather works, homeware, glassworks, textiles and much more.

Address: 3 Wellington Street, Belfast, County Antrim BT1 6HT

Tel: 02890 235325

Email: inbox@coppermoon.co.uk

Website: www.coppermoon.co.uk

DOGHOUSE GALLERY

About: Initially established by Pamela to showcase her world renowned jewellery, the business has continued to grow, allowing Pamela to invite other crafters to exhibit their own creations.

Contact: Pamela

Address: 97–99 Mill Street, Comber BT23 5EG

Tel: 02891 871261

Email: info@doghousegallery.co.uk

Website: www.doghousegallery.co.uk

EDEN POTTERY

About: Established over 21 years ago, Eden Pottery is run by husband and wife Phillip and Heather Walton. The shop stocks an extensive array of their own creations, whilst allowing visitors to paint their own pottery.

Contact: Phillip and Heather Walton

Address: 218 Abbey Road, Millisle, Newtownards, County Down BT22 2DH

Tel: 02891 862300

Email: sales@edenpotteryshop.co.uk

Website: www.edenpotteryshop.co.uk

G. E. KEE

About: G.E. Kee is a long established arts and craft shop that features an extensive collection of local paintings and prints.

Address: 17 Bridge Street, Coleraine, County Derry BT52 1DR

Tel: 02870 343525

Email: shop@kee-arts.demon.co.uk

Website: www.kee-arts.demon.co.uk

GLOONAN GALLERY

About: Gloonan Gallery showcases a large variety of artwork amd craft pieces over two floors. Original paintings, glasswork, woodcraft, handbags, textiles, puzzles, jewellery, ceramics and collections by well known designers can be found here.

Contact: James and Patricia

Address: 13 Church Street, Ahoghill, Ballymena, County Antrim BT42 2PA

Tel: 02825 878470

Email: hello@gloonangallery.com

Website: www.gloonangallery.com

GREENWOOD & CO HANDMADE JEWELLERY

About: Beautifully crafted, handmade jewellery made from high quality materials sourced from all over the world.

Contact: Gloria Greenwood

Address: 64 Main Street, Saintfield, County Down BT24 7AB

Tel: 02897 519587

Email: info@ greenwoodandcojewellery.com

Website: www. greenwoodandcojewellery.com

I DO CARTWHEELS

About: I Do Cartwheels is a unique, furniture design studio that collaborates with small, local companies and craftspeople to create their designs.

Address: Comber Courtyard, 5 High Street, Comber, County Down BT23 5HQ

Tel: 07837 529469

Email: donna@idocartwheels.com

Website: www.idocartwheels.com

KILLYLISS STUDIO

About: Killyliss Studio was established in 1991 and specializes in handcrafted items, inspired by the Irish and Celtic culture. Colm crafts a variety of ornaments and pendants using high quality materials, such as cold-cast metals, slate and cast limestone.

Contact: Colm McCann

Address: 40 Killyliss Road, Dungannon, County Tyrone BT70 1QQ

Tel: 02887 725689

Email: info@killylissstudio.com

Website: www.killylissstudio.com

LIMEHOUSE CRAFTS AND GIFTS

About: Limehouse is a family run business that specializes in sourcing original and affordable gifts, such as handmade jewellery, gift cards, candles, ceramics and much more.
Contact: David and Sarah Tully
Address: 13 Hill Street, Newry BT34 2BN
Tel: 02830 825767
Website: www.limehousecraftsandgifts.com

LITTLE GEMS ARTS & CRAFTS

About: A small but friendly arts and crafts shop that features local handmade crafts, such as jewellery, textiles, soft furnishings and more.
Contact: Lisa Currie
Address: 92A Woodburn Road, Carrickfergus, County Antrim BT38 9AB
Tel: 07779 570104
Email: lisamck31@googlemail.com
Website: www.littlegemsartscrafts.co.uk

MISHA'S COUNTRY WORKSHOP

About: Handcrafted, refurbished or up-cycled, Misha makes and sells homeware and furniture by upholstering, hand-painting and repairing second-hand, vintage furinture.
Contact: Misha
Address: 34 Lancasterian Street, Carrickfergus, County Antrim BT38 7AG
Tel: 07933 233155

Email: info@mishascountryworkshop.co.uk
Website: www.mishascountryworkshop.co.uk

PAINTED EARTH

About: A traditional craft and gift shop that showcases a variety of work from local artists and designers. Painted Earth stocks a range of items, such as ceramics, jewellery, prints, paintings, textiles and more.
Address: 98 Main Street, Newcastle, County Down BT33 0AE
Tel: 02843 722510
Email: shop@paintedearth-ni.co.uk
Website: www.paintedearth-ni.co.uk

SIOPA AN CARN

About: Siopa An Carn is a craft and gift shop that celebrates traditional Irish fare as well as contemporary crafts and gifts. Featuring a variety of handcrafted products, such as candles, jewellery, ceramics, paintings, prints, gift cards, glasswork, candles, soaps and more.
Address: 132 Tirkane Road, Derry BT46 5NH
Tel: 02879 549978
Email: info@siopaancarn.com
Website: www.siopaancarn.com

SPACE CRAFT

About: The Space CRAFT gallery shop is organized and run by the Craft & Design Collective (CDC). The CDC's priority is to support and promote independent and quality craftmanship, applied art and design.
Address: 9b The Fountain Centre, College Street, Belfast BT1 6ET
Tel: 02890 329342

Email: info@craftanddesigncollective.com
Website: www.craftanddesigncollective.com

SUGAR & SPICE CREATIONS

About: Sugar & Spice are passionate about baking and creating delicious treats for special occasions. Professional and high quality, Sugar & Spice offer a bespoke service, be it contemporary wedding cakes, traditional cakes or cupcakes.
Address: 26 Collinward Avenue, Newtownabbey, County Antrim BT36 6DZ
Tel: 07703 800521
Email: info@sugarandspicecreations.co.uk
Website: www.sugarandspicecreations.co.uk

SWAN POTTERY AND CRAFT STUDIO

About: Swan Pottery and Craft Studio provides a mixture of craft supplies and classes in ceramics, beading, découpage, soap making and more.
Address: 30 St. Patrick's Road, Downpatrick, County Down BT30 7JQ
Tel: 02891 819873
Email: ionabarry@swanpotteryandcraftstudio.co.uk
Website: www.swanpotteryandcraftstudio.co.uk

THE BUSHMILLS GALLERY

About: Located near to the Giant's Causeway, The Bushmills Gallery is in an ideal location, providing a wide variety of local arts and crafts.

Contact: Joan and James White

Address: 53 Main Street, Bushmills, County Antrim BT57 8QA

Tel: 02820 731911

Email: Contact submission form available on website.

Website: www.thebushmillsgallery.com

THE WICKER MAN

About: The Wicker Man is a large provider of arts and craft pieces and supplies. The shop features the work of local painters, photographers, sculptors, jewellers and provides monthly exhibitions to support newly emerging artists.

Address: River House, 46 Hight Street, Belfast, County Antrim BT1 2BE

Tel: 02890 243550

Email: Contact submission form available on website.

Website: www.thewickerman.co.uk

SCOTLAND

AZURE

About: A contemporary handmade gift shop in the style of a gallery, stocking items from UK crafters and artists. Azure stock a wide range of items, such as silver and gold jewellery, metalwork, woodcrafts, ceramics, textiles, gift cards and more.

Address: 7 Sandgate, Ayr, Ayrshire KA7 1BG

Tel: 01292 290267

Email: somethingdifferent@azuregivingandliving.co.uk

Website: azuregivingandliving.co.uk

BOHO

About: BOHO is a unique boutique that showcases a distinctive collection of quality, handcrafted jewellery. Designed and created by Scottish crafters, BOHO's jewellery collection is made from a variety of materials, such as Scottish sea glass, tin, enamel and silver.

Contact: Anne

Address: 6 Shore Road, Aberdour, Fife, Scotland KY3 0TR

Tel: 01383 861430

Email: Contact submission form available on website.

Website: www.iloveboho.co.uk

CLEMENTINE DESIGNS

About: Established in 2005, Clementine Designs is located close to Edinburgh's busy city centre and provides a wide range of home accessories and gifts. Stocking ceramics, textiles, knitted and quilted items, Clementine celebrates all things handcrafted.

Address: 141 Bruntsfield Place, Edinburgh EH10 4EB

Tel: 01314 772237

Email: info@clementinehomeandgifts.co.uk

Website: www.clementinehomeandgifts.co.uk

CONCRETE WARDROBE

About: Concrete Wardrobe primarily promotes the high quality work of local Scottish artists and crafters, however they also source handcrafted pieces nationally and internationally. This boutique stocks a huge variety of handmade items, such as ceramics, jewellery, textiles, gift cards, leather work, handbags; woven, printed and knitted items – the list is endless.

Contact: Fiona McIntosh and James Donald

Address: 50A Broughton Street, Edinburgh EH1 3SA

Tel: 01315 587130

Email: concretewardrobe@hotmail.co.uk

Website: www.concretewardrobe.blogspot.com

CUSHION AND CAKE

About: Cushion and Cake is a quirky little tearoom located in Glasgow's west-end, serving a range of homemade delicacies and quality teas. As well as serving up tasty treats, Cushion and Cake stock range of local crafts and handmade items, such as crochet and felt accessories, jewellery, prints, textiles and handmade cushions.

Address: 35 Old Dumbarton Road, Glasgow G3 8RD

Tel: 07982 308563

Email: tea@cushionandcake.com

Website: www.cushionandcake.com

DREAMTIME STUDIO

About: A boutique crystal and craft shop, as well as a gallery founded by Polish artist, Agnieszka Mizia. It exhibits Agnieszka's own oil paintings, ceramics, glassworks and gift cards, as well as a variety of other handmade gifts.

Contact: Agnieszka Mizia

Address: Tigh-Na-Mara, Inverlounan Road, Lochgoilhead, Argyll

Tel: 07982 308563

Email: amizia@dreamtimestudio.co.uk

Website: www.dreamtimestudio.co.uk

FLOURISH

About: Located in Aberdeen's west-end, this adorable gift shop stocks a variety of quirky handmade ceramic items, jewellery, toiletries, gift cards and many other home accessories.

Contact: Mairie Eddie

Address: 162 Union Grove, Aberdeen AB10 6SR

Tel: 01224 467372

Email: info@flourishhome.co.uk

Website: www.flourishhome.co.uk

FLUX

About: Flux is an individual and unique boutique, stocking a variety of jewellery, ornaments, gifts and art. Passionately dedicated to recycling and fairtrade, Steph and Bea have strict criteria when it comes to stocking crafts: 'they must be quirky, unique, never cute and most importantly, well made.'

Contact: Steph and Bea Taylor

Address: 55 Bernard Street, Leith, Edinburgh EH6 6SL

Tel: 01315 544075

Email: bea@get2flux.co.uk

Website: www.get2flux.co.uk

GIFTED

About: A boutique dedicated to local crafters and artists, Gifted stock a wide range of artwork, woodcrafts, prints, ceramics, glassworks, jewellery, textiles and more.

Address: 36 Busby Road, Clarkston, Glasgow G76 8LW

Tel: 01416 200346

Email: sales@gifted-shop.com

Website: www.gifted-shop.com

HAT IN THE CAT

About: A unique studio featuring beautifully designed, handmade hats, fascinators and hair accessories by textile artist Jeanette Sendler.

Contact: Jeanette Sendler

Address: 2 Main Street, Bridgend, Perth PH2 7HB

Tel: 01738 624213

Email: info@hatinthecat.co.uk

Website: www.hatinthecat.co.uk

LADY DRAWERS

About: Lady Drawers is a small boutique featuring exclusive female clothing, handbags, jewellery, gift cards and artwork sourced from local designers and crafters.

Address: 66 Nithsdale Road, Glasgow G41 2AN

Tel: 01414 234230

Email: info@LadyDrawers.co.uk

Website: www.facebook.com/pages/Lady-Drawers/10150090373455602

MARCHMONT GALLERY

About: Marchmont is an art gallery and craft shop displaying a wide range of pieces from both established and emerging designers and crafters. Items stocked include woodcrafts, jewellery, recycled accessories, gift cards, ceramics, knitted items and more.

Address: 56 Warrender Park Road, Edinburgh EH9 1EX

Tel: 01312 288228

Email: enquiries@marchmontgallery.com

Website: www.marchmontgallery.com

NEO DESIGN

About: A fine jewellery boutique stocking silver work by artist Tracey McSporran and other European designers.

Contact: Tracey McSporran

Address: 17 Whitehall Crescent, Dundee DD1 4BB

Tel: 01382 206658

Email: t_mcsporran@hotmail.co.uk

Website: www.traceymcsporran.co.uk

ORSAY

About: A bright and contemporary boutique featuring handmade work from Scottish and UK artists, Orsay exhibits fine jewellery, metalwork, woodcrafts, ceramics, prints, textiles, gift cards and more.

Address: 2 Stevenson Street, Oban, Argyll PA34 5NA

Tel: 01631 569988

Email: orsay@btconnect.com

Website: www.facebook.com/orsayoban

OWL & LION

About: Master Bookbinder, Isabelle Ting, created the Owl & Lion to promote the art of quality binding, hand-printing and letter press. Isabelle runs classes in her studio alongside the shop, where she creates the luxurious books and prints.

Contact: Isabelle Ting

Address: 66 Westport, Edinburgh EH1 2LD

Email: hello@owlandlion.com

Website: www.owlandlion.com

PETER POTTER GALLERY

About: Peter Potter is a gallery, café and craft shop celebrating the wonderful handcrafted work of local and national designers. The gallery features a mix of traditional and contemporary pieces such as, jewellery, ceramics, beadwork, textiles and much more.

Address: 10 The Sands, Haddington EH41 3EY

Tel: 01620 822080

Email: hello.ppgallery@yahoo.co.uk

Website: www.peterpottergallery.org

PLAISIR

About: This award-winning modern boutique stocks a wide range of unique fashion, gifts and homeware. Supporting a variety of artists and designers and selling wonderful handmade items, such as jewellery, prints, gift cards, papercraft, artwork and much more.

Contact: Clare and Anthony

Address: 33–35 High Street, Biggar ML12 6DA

Tel: 01899 220600

Email: hello@plaisirshop.co.uk

Website: www.plaisirshop.co.uk

PRECIOUS SPARKLE BEADS

About: A premier retailer of semi-precious gemstone beads and beadwork, providing a huge variety of beautiful beads, in a multitude of materials.

Contact: Dawn Cotton Fuge

Address: 8 Bridge Land, Perth PH1 5JJ

Tel: 01738 563264

Email: info@precioussparklebeads.co.uk

Website: www.precioussparklebeads.co.uk

REMADE

About: ReMade are promoters of handcrafted items that have been ethically produced, up-cycled, fairtrade or vintage. This environmentally conscious boutique stocks a variety of homeware, jewellery and up-cycled furnishings.

Address: 147 North High Street, Musselburgh EH21 6AN

Tel: 07540 089797

Email: frugalcool@hotmail.co.uk

Website: www.frugalcool.co.uk

STICK FACTORY (SF) GALLERY

About: The Stick Factory consists of a fine arts and crafts gallery that stocks a multitude of handmade items from local artists. However, the main purpose of the Stick Factory is to create bespoke items out of local hardwoods, such as elm, oak, ash and beech.

Contact: Mike Usher

Address: Stick Factory Creative Projects, 69b/69c Mayfield Road, Edinburgh EH9 3AA

Tel: 01316 295171

Email: caroline@stickfactory.co.uk

Website: www.stickfactory.co.uk

STARFISH STUDIO

About: Located in the picturesque fishing town of Johnshaven, Starfish Studio features only handmade, quality items. Artist Kate Mackenzie features some of her own work alongside other British crafters in the line of soaps, jewellery, glassworks, ceramics, up-cycling, textiles and more.

Contact: Kate Mackenzie

Address: 3 Anchor Lane, Johnshaven, Aberdeenshire DD10 0EN

Tel: 01561 360118

Website: www.starfishstudio.co.uk

TEMPT

About: Tempt features the handmade craft and wares of the talented local women of Scotland. This quaint boutique stocks a mixture of craft items: jewellery, textiles, prints, ceramics, up-cycled pieces, artwork and more.

Address: 20 Lady Wynd, Cupar, Fife KY15 4ED

Tel: 01334 652687

Email: sales@temptdirect.co.uk

Website: www.temptfife.blogspot.com

THE CRAFTERS

About: Established in 1998, a group of crafters created this retail location to sell their handmade crafts and support one another. The Crafters community has since grown in size and stocks a wide range of handmade gifts, such as prints, gift cards, paintings, jewellery, candles, knitted items, ceramics and much more.

Address: 5 Market Square, Melrose TD6 9PQ
Tel: 01896 823823
Email: sales@thecrafters.co.uk
Website: www.thecrafters.co.uk

THE RED DOOR GALLERY

About: Supporting local emerging artists as well as stocking a vast mixture of artwork, indie prints, homeware gifts and crafts, The Red Door Gallery really is a melting pot of skills. The gallery features over 100 artists showcasing prints, jewellery, gift cards, artwork, ceramics, glasswork, textiles and more.

Address: 42 Victoria Street, Edinburgh EH1 2JW
Tel: 01314 773255
Email: info@edinburghart.com
Website: www.edinburghart.com

THE SHOP OF INTEREST

About: Established in 2010 by artists, May and Martin, The Shop of Interest lives up to its name: a shop stocked with all things that May and Martin love, as well as functioning as an art gallery. The shop features jewellery, prints, papercraft items, textiles and much more.

Contact: May and Martin
Address: 1058 Argyle Street, Glasgow G3 8LY
Tel: 01412 217316
Email: hello@theshopofinterest.co.uk
Website: www.theshopofinterest.co.uk

TOUCHED BY SCOTLAND

About: Showcasing some of the best work from artists and designers throughout Scotland, Touched by Scotland exhibits paintings, ceramics, jewellery, textiles, woodcrafts and more.

Contact: Jan Hobbs and Robin Baird
Address: Ryehill, Oyne, Aberdeenshire AB52 6QS
Tel: 01464 851489
Email: info@touchedbyscotland.com
Website: www.touchedbyscotland.com

URBAN IGLOO

About: Urban Igloo is an interior design business and gallery showcasing up-cycled furniture and quality artwork.

Contact: Rosanne Erskine
Address: 240a Portobello High Street, Portobello, Edinburgh EH15 2AU
Tel: 07882 713641
Email: info@urbanigloo.co.uk
Website: www.urbanigloo.co.uk

SOUTH WEST

ARTWORKS

About: Located in the friendly little village of South Brent, Artworks showcases the original and unique works of over 100 artists. Works on display include ceramics, jewellery, beadwork, glassware, knitwear, sculptures and more.

Address: 9 Station Road, South Brent, Devon TQ10 9BE
Tel: 01364 649424
Email: shop@artworks.entadsl.com
Website: www.artworksouthbrent.co.uk

ATELIER CONTEMPORARY CRAFT GALLERY

About: Atelier is a unique and orignial craft gallery that exhibits an interesting collection of hand-picked items. The gallery consists of ceramics, textiles, glasswork, metalwork and much more.

Address: 12 Tuly Street, Barnstaple, Devon EX31 1DH
Tel: 01271 268244
Email: crafts@gallery-atelier.co.uk
Website: www.gallery-atelier.co.uk

BAXTERS GALLERY

About: Baxters is a spacious and welcoming art gallery that features a mixture of pieces, such as jewellery, ceramics, prints, artwork and more.

Contact: Sarah Duggan
Address: 12 Foss Street, Dartmouth TQ6 9DR
Tel: 01803 839000
Email: info@baxtersgallery.co.uk
Website: www.baxtersgallery.co.uk

BRICKS AND MORTAR SHOPS – SOUTH WEST

BUY THE SEA

About: Inspired by everything associated with the sea and the coast, Buy the Sea stocks a wide variety of nautical themed crafts and gifts.

Address: 34 East Street, Ilminster, Somerset TA19 0AN

Tel: 01460 258970

Email: info@buythesea.co.uk

Website: www.buythesea.co.uk

CHARLIE BOOTS

About: Charlie Boots is a fashion retail outlet that specializes in independent designer items, particularly those that use ethically sourced materials, such as organic, fair trade, vintage, hemp, bamboo and recycled fabrics.

Address: 35 Broad Street, Bath BA1 5LP

Tel: 07824 533672

Email: charlie@charlieboots.com

Website: www.charlieboots.com

CHIC ABODE

About: Located in the centre of beautiful St Ives, Chic Abode is home to the work of over 25 local designers and artists. Many items featured at Chic Abode are inspired by the coast and surrounding area; these consist of paintings, textiles, handbags, ceramics and Spanish Terracotta ware.

Contact: Lorraine Field

Address: Unit 1 The Drill Hall, Chapel Street, St Ives, Cornwall TR26 2LR

Tel: 07766 145068

Email: info@chicabode.co.uk

Website: www.chicabode.co.uk

CLIFTON ROCKS

About: Clifton Rocks is a contemporary jewellery boutique, featuring collections by local and national designers. Clare also offers an alterations and repair service, as well as bespoke commissions.

Contact: Clare Chandler

Address: 100 Queens Road, Clifton, Bristol BS8 1NF

Tel: 01179 731342

Email: info@cliftonrocks.co.uk

Website: www.cliftonrocks.co.uk

CRY OF THE GULLS

About: Cry of the Gulls is always on the look out for new and innovative crafters and artists to expand their collection of local Cornish work. This bright and homely gallery features paintings, ceramics, sculptures, glasswork, jewellery, textiles and more

Address: 2 Webb Street, Fowey, Cornwall PL23 1AP

Tel: 01726 833838

Email: info@cryofthegulls.co.uk

Website: www.cryofthegulls.co.uk

EVERY CLOUD

About: Every Cloud is an independent and ethical jewellery, accessories and gift boutique, stocking glasswork, jewellery, felt work, ceramics, textiles, prints and gift cards.

Contact: Charlotte

Address: 3 Napper's Court, Charles Street, Dorchester, Dorset DT1 1EE

Tel: 01305 269731

Email: email@everycloudboutique. co.uk

Website: www.everycloudboutique. co.uk

FISHERTON MILL

About: Winner of 'The South Wilts Business of the year 2011' and the largest independent gallery in the South West; Fisherton Mill is renowned for its collections. Exhibitions at the gallery consist of prints, stonework, ceramics, up-cycling, woodcraft, jewellery, textiles, felt work and much more.

Contact: Michael Main and Deborah Fox

Address: 108 Fisherton Street, Salisbury, Wiltshire SP2 7QY

Tel: 01722 415121

Email: thegallery@fishertonmill.co.uk

Website: www.fishertonmill.co.uk

GALLERY @ 500FT

About: A bright, spacious gallery located 500 feet above sea level, exhibiting work by artists and crafters from the surrounding area. The gallery is passionate about supporting newly emerging artists and displays ceramics, glasswork, jewellery and more.

Address: The Old Bank House, Church Hill, Lynton, Devon EX35 6HQ

Tel: 01598 752560

Email: info@gallery500feet.com

Website: www.gallery500feet.com

GALLERY LATITUDE 50

About: Gallery Latitude 50 is located in the beautiful Penwith countryside and owned by experienced designer, Corinne Carr. The gallery exhibits jewellery, paintings, sculpture, ceramics, textiles and much more.

Contact: Corinne Carr

Address: Cripplesease, St Ives, Cornwall TR20 8NF

Tel: 01736 741052

Email: info@gallerylatitude50.co.uk

Website: www.gallerylatitude50.co.uk

GIFTED2 – MADE BY HAND

About: Showcasing beautiful and unique gifts from over 14 countries, Gifted2 – Made By Hand promotes the traditional crafting techniques used by different cultures. The handmade items instore consist of woodcraft, furniture, handbags, jewellery, textiles, ceramics, glasswork and more.

Contact: Diana and Richard John

Address: 77 Fore Street, Brixham, Devon TQ5 8AG

Tel: 01803 858133

Email: Contact submission form available on website.

Website: www.gifted2.co.uk

HAWTHORN CONTEMPORARY ARTS AND CRAFT

About: Hawthorn is a unique and original craft gallery and haberdashery, featuring handmade art and crafts from over 35 local designers. Collections feature felt sculptures, ceramics, textiles, jewellery, paintings and much more, including an extensive range of fabrics and equipment.

Contact: Stephanie Carswell

Address: 13 Salisbury Street, Blandford Forum, Dorset DT11 7AU

Tel: 01258 268007

Email: info@hawthorncraft.co.uk

Website: www.hawthorncraft.co.uk

HOOPER & SHAW

About: A creative and exciting boutique that mixes traditional techniques with imaginative ideas. Hooper & Shaw offers a variety of prints, textiles, soft furnishings and more.

Contact: Nicole Heidaripour and Daniel Scott

Address: 60 Fore Street, Port Isaac, Cornwall PL29 3RE

Tel: 01208 880845

Email: Contact submission form available on website.

Website: www.hooperandshaw.com

LIME SQUARE

About: Lime Square is a bright and spacious gift shop and gallery featuring artwork from local artists and crafts from local designers. Collections consist of original paintings, ceramics, jewellery, gift cards, soaps, candles, woodcraft, glasswork and more.

Address: 15 Glanvilles Mill, Ivybridge, Devon PL21 9PS

Tel: 01752 698119

Email: info@lime-square.co.uk

Website: www.lime-square.co.uk

M.A.D.E MAKERS AND DESIGNERS EMPORIUM

About: Displaying collections from over 250 British artists and designers, M.A.D.E represents a wide variety of disciplines and skills and is always looking for emerging talents. Featuring textiles, homeware, ceramics, woodcraft, jewellery, gift cards, photography and more, M.A.D.E really is an emporium for all designers and makers alike.

Contact: Louise Bonham and Sheena Jennings Dash

Address: 9 Silver Street, Cirencester, Gloucestershire GL7 2BJ

Tel: 01285 658225

Email: info@made-gallery.com

Website: www.made-gallery.com

MADE IN STROUD

About: Established in 2000, and specializing in the works of crafters and makers in and around Stroud, Made In Stroud showcases a variety of homeware and gifts, such as jewellery, soft furnishings, prints, knitwear, glassworks, gift cards and much more.

Address: 16 Kendrick Street, Stroud GL5 1AA

Tel: 01453 840265

Email: online@madeinstroud.co.uk

Website: www.madeinstroud.co.uk

MALCOLM SUTCLIFFE GLASS GALLERY

About: The Malcolm Sutcliffe Glass Gallery predominantly exhibits Malcolm's own extraordinary and widely renowned glassworks. The gallery also features work by other British artists and crafters, such as paintings, prints, jewellery, gift cards and more.

Contact: Malcolm Sutcliffe

Address: 2 West Street, Penryn, Cornwall TR10 8EW

Tel: 01326 377020

Email: info@malcolm-sutcliffe.co.uk

Website: www.malcolm-sutcliffe.co.uk

MERLIN GLASS

About: Merlin Glass specializes in glass door-handles in a vast array of colours and designs. Liam's service is entirely unique and bespoke.

Contact: Liam Carey

Address: Barn Street, Station Road, Liskeard, Cornwall PL14 4BL

Tel: 01579 342399

Email: info@merlinglass.co.uk

Website: www.merlinglass.co.uk

NEWLYN ART GALLERY SHOP

About: The Newlyn Art Gallery has been in operation for almost 120 years. The Gallery Shop features a variety of art books and equipments as

well as craft items, such as jewellery, ceramics and textiles.

Contact: James Green
Address: New Road, Newlyn TR18 5PZ
Tel: 01736 363715
Email: mail@newlynartgallery.co.uk
Website: www.newlynartgallery.co.uk

ONE BROWN COW

About: One Brown Cow was established in 2007 with the desire to source items and collections that have been designed and manufactured in the UK. Of the items that have been carefully selected for import, One Brown Cow insists on organic, recycled, fair trade pieces. As well as stocking well known designers, such as Cath Kidston and Orla Kiely, One Brown Cow also supports the work of emerging designers.

Address: 40 High Street, Amesbury, Wiltshire SP4 7DL
Tel: 01980 626420
Email: sales@onebrowncow.co.uk
Website: www.onebrowncow.co.uk

POPPY TREFFRY

About: Poppy Treffry's designs are known internationally and can be found in stores across the USA and Japan as well as the UK. The quirky boutique, based in St Ives, stocks a range of Poppy's own designs, textiles and embroidered items.

Address: Drill Hall, Chapel Street, St Ives, Cornwall TR26 2LR
Tel: 01736 795494
Email: hello@poppytreffry.co.uk
Website: www.poppytreffry.co.uk

REDHOUSE GIFTS

About: Redhouse Gifts aims to provide visitors with a unique shopping experience and a range of original homeware and gifts that cannot be found on the high-street. All products within the store are sourced from in and around Britain and feature knitted items, handbags, ceramics, textiles, soft furnishings, woodcraft, candles, soaps, jewellery and much more.

Contact: Maggie
Address: 75 High Street, Totnes, Devon TQ9 5PB
Tel: 01803 840111
Email: maggie@redhousegifts.co.uk
Website: www.redhousegifts.co.uk

ROSABLUE HAND-MADE ORIGINALS

About: Penelope and Luca commission, buy, design and make the fabric that is used to create the products at Rosablue. All items are 100% cotton and range from aprons, bags and cushions to tea towels, dolls and bunting.

Contact: Penelope and Luca Menato
Address: 215 Bath Road, Cheltenham GL53 7NA
Tel: 01242 521234
Email: rosablue@rosablue.com
Website: www.rosablue.com

ROSTRA & ROOKSMOOR GALLERIES

About: A contemporary and friendly art gallery that features a diverse range of collections, such as jewellery, lighting, ceramics, sculptures, painting, prints, glasswork, woodcraft and much more.

Address: 5 George Street, Bath BA1 2EJ
Tel: 01225 448121
Email: info@rostragallery.co.uk
Website: www.rostragallery.co.uk

SHAKSPEARE GLASS

About: Shakspeare Glass showcases a wide variety of handmade and blown glass products, such as bowls, vases, kitchenware, paperweights, sculptures and much more.

Address: Riverside Place, Taunton, Somerset TA1 1JJ
Tel: 01823 333422
Email: sales@shakspeareglass.co.uk
Website: www.shakspeareglass.co.uk

SHY VIOLET

About: Shy Violet is an eclectic interior and homeware shop that stocks a huge array of handcrafted gifts, furniture and home accessories. Ranges include jewellery, candles, soft furnishings, toys, textiles, glasswork ceramics and more.

Address: 27 High Street, Stalbridge, Dorset DT10 2LH
Tel: 01963 362428
Email: shyvioletdesigns@aol.com
Website: www.shy-violet.co.uk

SOMA

About: Soma is a contemporary gallery and shop that promotes modern art and illustration as well as a variety of artworks and crafts, such as textiles, jewellery, ceramics, gift cards, prints and more.
Address: 4 Boyces Avenue, Clifton, Bristol BS8 4AA
Tel: 01179 739838
Email: gallery@somagallery.co.uk
Website: www.somagallery.co.uk/somashop

TAURUS CRAFTS

About: Taurus Crafts was established with the purpose of offering work experience, training and employment to individuals with special needs. The business is made up of 15 artisan businesses each specializing in a variety of disciplines and media such as leather work, photography, stone carving, knitting, jewellery and textiles, as well as locally sourced and produced foods.
Contact: Dirk and Isa Rohwedder
Address: The Old Park, Lydney, Gloucestershire GL15 6BU
Tel: 01594 844841
Email: enquire@tauruscrafts.co.uk
Website: www.tauruscrafts.co.uk

TENDERFOOT GIFTS, CRAFTS & WORKSHOPS

About: Tenderfoot is a small craft workshop featuring a large variety of local art and crafts, such as ceramics, soaps, candles, knitted items, glassworks and more. Tenderfoot also caters for parties and provides regular workshop events.
Contact: Helen England and Lori MacAlpine-Smith
Address: 100 Wick Road, Brislington, Bristol BS4 4HF
Tel: 01179 717138
Email: tenderfooting@gmail.com
Website: www.tenderfooting.co.uk

THE ROUND HOUSE & CAPSTAN GALLERY

About: The Round House and Capstan Gallery is home to some of Cornwall's finest artists and crafters. Works exhibited include ceramics, prints, glasswork, knitwear, photography, sculptures, woodcraft, paintings, jewellery and more.
Address: Sennen Cove, Lands End, Cornwall TR19 7DF
Tel: 01736 871859
Email: roundhouse.gallery@btconnect.com

THE SUMMER HOUSE

About: With over ten years of experience, June has had shops in several locations across Cornwall. Padstow is the new location of The Summer House and features a variety of collections, including candles, patchwork quilts and cushions, ceramics, vintage items and more.
Contact: June
Address: 28 Duke Street, Padstow, Cornwall PL28 8AB
Tel: 01841 533138
Email: thesummerhouse1@btinternet.com
Website: www.thesummerhouse.co.uk

WALFORD MILL CRAFTS

About: The Walford Mill Crafts shop showcases work by local designers and makers, featuring ceramics, woodcraft, textiles, jewellery, glasswork, metalwork and more.
Address: Stone Lane, Wimborne, Dorset BH21 1NL
Tel: 01202 840400
Email: info@walfordmillcrafts.co.uk
Website: www.walfordmillcrafts.co.uk

WORLD OF BEADS

About: A family run business that is dedicated to providing an enormous supply of beads and beading equipment. Beads consist of Murano glass, semi-precious stones, fresh water pearls, Swarovski crystals, silver, wood, shell and bone. World of Beads are also happy to create bespoke jewellery from beads chosen by the customer.
Address: 1 Stonemasons Court, Parchment Street, Winchester, Hampshire SO23 8AT
Tel: 01962 861255
Email: info@worldofbeads.co.uk
Website: www.worldofbeads.co.uk

WALES

BEACH HUT BOUTIQUE

About: This cosy gift boutique has a passion for all things coastal. The Beach Hut Boutique is always looking for new artists and crafters to add to their collection of unique gifts and homeware.

Address: 28 Main Street, Pembroke, Pembrokeshire SA71 4NP

Tel: 01646 682002

Email: info@thebeachhutboutique.co.uk

Website: www.thebeachhutboutique.co.uk

COOPER'S

About: This quirky homeware and gift shop supplies an eclectic array of furniture, kitchenware and a variety of other handmade pieces.

Address: 24 High Street, Caerleon, Newport, Gwent NP18 1AG

Tel: 01633 422138

Email: mail@coopersvintage.co.uk

Website: www.coopersvintage.co.uk

CORRIS CRAFT CENTRE

About: A centre of nine workshops in which visitors can observe crafters at work and purchase directly from the artists themselves. The Corris Craft Centre features a variety of crafts, such as glasswork, ceramics, jewellery, leather work, woodcraft and more.

Address: Corris, Machynlleth, Powys SY20 9RF

Tel: 01654 761584

Email: web@kingarthurslabyrinth.co.uk

Website: www.corriscraftcentre.com

CORWENT MANOR CRAFT CENTRE

About: A long-established craft centre and workshop that is renowned for its candles; Corwent Manor Craft Centre features a variety of handmade products from in and around North Wales.

Address: 8 London Road, Corwen, Denbighshire LL21 0DR

Tel: 01490 413196

Email: alansandra@corwenmanor.com

Website: www.corwenmanor.com

COURT CUPBOARD CRAFT GALLERY

About: Located in the foothills of the Black Mountains, Court Cupboard Craft Gallery celebrates traditional Welsh arts and crafts. Showcasing the work of members of the Black Mountains Circle, the gallery features a variety of ceramics, jewellery, Welsh lovespoons, textiles, soaps, felt work, spinning, beadwork, calligraphy and much more.

Address: New Court Farm, Llantilio Pertholey, Abergavenny, Monmouthshire NP7 8AU

Tel: 01873 852011

Email: admin@courtcupboard.com

Website: www.courtcupboard.com

CRAFT RENAISSANCE

About: A warm and friendly gallery, Craft Renaissance is dedicated to supporting the talents of local artists and crafters and providing them with an ideal venue to make, exhibit and sell their work from. Collections include woodcrafts, paintings, textiles, felt work, jewellery, handbags, ceramics, glasswork and more.

Contact: Helen Mitchell and John Bruce

Address: Kemys Commander, Usk, Monmouthshire NP15 1JU

Tel: 01873 880879

Email: info@craftrenaissance.co.uk

Website: www.craftrenaissance.co.uk

CRAFTS ALIVE

About: Crafts Alive is a locally run craft shop that supports local arts and crafts. A vibrant mix of traditional and temporary gifts and crafts are available, such as woodcraft, glasswork, knitwear, soaps, up-cycling, patchwork and more.

Address: 133b Rhosmaen Street, Llandeilo, Carmarthenshire SA19 6EN

Tel: 01558 822010

Email: Contact submission form available on website.

Website: www.crafts-alive.co.uk/join-us

CURIG CRAFTS AND WOOLLENS

About: An extensive collection of handmade gifts and products, the majority of which are made in Wales; Curig Crafts and Woollens showcases traditional and contemporary jewellery, Welsh lovespoons, ceramics, glasswork, woodcraft and more.

Address: Curig House, 2 Long Bridge Street, Llanidloes, Powys SY18 6EE

Tel: 01686 414916

Email: sales@curigwelshgifts.co.uk

Website: www.curigwelshgifts.co.uk

CUSTOM HOUSE SHOP AND GALLERY

About: Steeped in Welsh history, Custom House Shop and Gallery has been supporting local designers and makers for over 17 years. The gallery features jewellery, knitwear, prints, ceramics, soap and much more.

Contact: Karina Servini

Address: 44 Saint Mary Street, Cardigan, Ceredigion SA43 1HA

Tel: 01239 615541

Email: info@customhousecardigan.com

Website: www.customhousecardigan.com

ERWOOD STATION CRAFT CENTRE & GALLERY

About: Located in an old railway station, this unique craft shop showcases the work of over 80 artists and makers, with new exhibitions taking place every six weeks. Collections include glasswork, ceramics, photography, jewellery, ironwork, weaving, painting, leather work, woodcraft and much more.

Address: Llandeilo Graban, Builth Wells, Powys LD2 3SJ

Tel: 01982 560674

Email: mc@erwood-station.co.uk

Website: www.erwood-station.co.uk

GIFT OF GLASS

About: Gift of Glass exhibits an extensive range of glassworks by David and Lucy themselves, as well as various other local makers. As well as featuring a huge variety of beautiful glass products, David and Lucy are happy to create bespoke gifts for special occasions.

Contact: David and Lucy

Address: 1a Trafalgar Road, Tenby, Pembrokeshire SA70 7DW

Tel: 01834 845886

Email: info@giftofglass.co.uk

Website: www.giftofglass.co.uk

GLASSBLOBBERY LTD

About: The Glassblobbery is a family run glass workshop located in an old church hall in Glanrafon. David and Wendy create an exciting variety of glass ornaments and homewares.

Contact: David and Wendy Pryce-Jones

Address: Glanrafon Hall, Glanrafon, Corwen, Denbighshire LL21 0HA

Tel: 01490 460440

Email: info@glassblobbery.com

Website: www.glassblobbery.com

GLYN-COCH CRAFT CENTRE

About: Featuring the works of over 40 crafters and artists, Gly-Coch Craft Centre showcases a variety of talent. Knitted garments and wool sourced from the centre's own flock of rare Norfolk Horn sheep, is just one of the authentic Welsh products on offer.

Address: Pwll Trap, St. Clears, Carmarthenshire SA33 4AR

Tel: 01994 231867

Email: info@glyn-coch.com

Website: www.glyn-coch.com

IN THE PINK

About: In The Pink is a studio and gallery that promotes the work of local craftspeople in and around Powys. Exhibitions include photography, jewellery, gift cards, quilting, ceramics, felt work and a variety of artisan foods; conserves, honey, chutneys and more.

Address: Ty Barcud, The Square, Llanwrtyd Wells, Powys LD5 4RB

Tel: 01591 610122

Email: info@in-the-pink.net

Website: www.in-the-pink.net

JANET BELL GALLERY

About: The Janet Bell Gallery initially began as a small studio, selling original paintings, prints and gift cards. This soon expanded, relocated and accumulated over 25 local artists and crafters, now stocking a variety of artwork including ceramics, jewellery, textiles, prints, gift cards and more.

Contact: Janet Bell

Address: Ariandy, 15 Castle Street, Beaumaris, Anglesey, LL58 8AP

Tel: 01248 810043

Email: info@janetbellgallery.com

Website: www.janetbellgallery.com

ORIEL MAKERS GALLERY

About: Established in 1991, Oriel Makers is run by a community of crafters and designers; featuring collections of glassworks, textiles, leather work, woodcraft, jewellery, prints, ceramics, paintings and more.

Address: 37 Pen-y-Lan Road, Cardiff CF24 3PG

Tel: 02920 472595

Email: info@orielmakers.co.uk

Website: www.orielmakers.co.uk

ORIEL MYRDDIN GALLERY SHOP

About: Located in Carmarthen's Old Art School, Oriel Myrddin presents a variety of regularly changing exhibitions. The gallery features an equal balance between fine art, and craft and design. Local artists and designers are invited to submit expressions of interest to take part in exhibitions.

Contact: Meg Anthony
Address: Church Lane, Carmarthen SA31 1LH
Tel: 01267 222775
Email: MAnthony@carmarthenshire. gov.uk
Website: www.orielmyrddingallery. co.uk

PETHAU MELYS

About: Tom – contemporary kitchen-ware potter, and Myfanwy – textile jewellery and homewares designer, created the vintage feel of Pethau Melys together. Everything in the shop is made by hand, up-cycled or second hand.
Contact: Tom Gloster and Myfanwy Griffiths
Address: 10 Corn Hill, Porthmadog, Gwynedd LL49 9AT
Tel: 01766 512569
Email: Contact submission form available on website.
Website: www.pethaumelys.co.uk

PORTICUS

About: Porticus combines the work of some of Britain's finest designers and crafters with the emerging local talent of Llandrindod Wells. Exhibitions feature woodcraft, knitwear, jewellery, glasswork, ceramics and more.
Address: 1 Middleton Street, Llandrindod Wells, Powys LD1 5ET
Tel: 01597 823989
Email: info@porticus.co.uk
Website: www.porticus.co.uk

STABLES HOME & GARDEN

About: A relatively young venture, established by Hannah and Joe, Stable Home & Garden showcases the couple's own talents in the fields of woodcraft and joinery, up-cycling, renovating and various other skills. The shop contains a vibrant mixture of chic furniture and homeware.
Contact: Hannah and Joe
Address: Oakcroft House, Station Avenue, Chirk, Wrexham LL14 5LU
Tel: 01691 773545
Email: stableshomeandgarden@ hotmail.co.uk
Website: www. stableshomeandgarden.co.uk

THE JEWELLERY JUNKY

About: Established in 2009, The Jewellery Junky is a treasure trove of carefully handcrafted jewellery and beautiful, gourmet, cupcake soaps.
Address: Upper Frog Street, Tenby, Pembrokeshire SA70 7JD
Tel: 01834 843499
Email: info@thejewelleryjunkee.co.uk
Website: www.thejewelleryjunkee. co.uk

THE ORIEL CRIC GALLERY

About: The Oriel CRiC Gallery features six exhibitions every year, showcasing the work of local Welsh artists and crafters.
Address: Crickhowell Resource and Information Centre, Beaufort Street, Crickhowell NP8 1BN
Tel: 01873 811970
Email: Contact submission form available on website.
Website: www.crickhowellinfo.org. uk/group/OrielCRiCGallery

THE WOOL CROFT

About: The Wool Croft is a fresh and bright boutique stocking a vast array of quality yarns and wools sourced from all over the UK. The boutique features an array of locally handcrafted items and provides regular workshops for new and experienced crafters.
Address: 9 Cross Street, Abergavenny, Monmouthshire NP7 5EH
Tel: 01873 851551
Email: info@thewoolcroft.co.uk
Website: www.thewoolcroft.co.uk

THE WYE VALLEY CRAFTS ASSOCIATION

About: The Wye Valley Crafts Association is a community run organization. The craft shop, located in the stunning surroundings of Abbey Mill, features a huge variety of crafts, such as leather work, jewellery, patchwork, photography, glasswork, woodcraft, gift cards, ceramics and much more.
Contact: Helen Carter
Address: Abbey Mill, Tintern, Monmouthshire NP16 6SE
Tel: 01291 689346
Email: helencarter2006@yahoo. co.uk
Website: www.wyevalleycrafts.co.uk

VICTORIA FEARN GALLERY

About: Specializing in contemporary works of art ranging from the affordable to the exquisite; Victoria Fearn Gallery showcases a large selection of glasswork, ceramics, paintings, prints, jewellery and more.
Contact: Victoria Fearn
Address: 6b Heol y Deri, Rhiwbina, Cardiff CF14 6HF
Tel: 02920 520884
Email: victoriafearngallery@hotmail. com
Website: www.victoriafearngallery. co.uk

AMANDA WARING

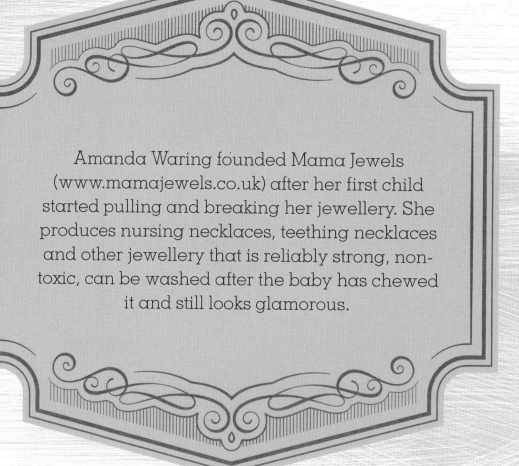

Amanda Waring founded Mama Jewels
(www.mamajewels.co.uk) after her first child
started pulling and breaking her jewellery. She
produces nursing necklaces, teething necklaces
and other jewellery that is reliably strong, non-
toxic, can be washed after the baby has chewed
it and still looks glamorous.

I had a proper job before my children were born, but I made jewellery as a side line. I went to craft fairs and held jewellery parties – it was a hobby business. Then my first son was born and he would tug and break whatever I was wearing – not just things I had made, but jewellery I'd bought. I searched high and low, mainly on the internet, for baby-proof jewellery, but I couldn't find anything. There were some necklaces that were more like toys, designed for the baby to interact with it, but nothing that you'd want to wear on a fashion level.

I talked to a lot of other mums and found that they were in the same position as I was – looking for beautiful things to wear that wouldn't harm their babies and that their babies wouldn't destroy. So I thought, 'There's a gap here. I can do something about it.' As it happens the recession hit while I was on maternity leave and I was made redundant. I had no money, I had nothing to lose and I decided to go for it.

> I talked to a lot of other mums and found that they were in the same position as I was. So I thought, 'There's a gap here. I can do something about it.'

Coincidentally, the local Sure Start Centre was offering a short course on 'Do you think you're the right kind of person to start your own business?' I went on that, found that it was run by Business Link, approached them and got a fantastic advisor who guided me through putting together a business plan. With his help I approached my local council and the bank for funding. The bank turned me down straight away. That was a slightly Catch-22 situation in that I didn't have any income, so they weren't going to lend me any money to help me generate an income. But both Business Link and the council agreed to give me some funding, as long as I matched it 50/50.

PREPARING A BUSINESS PLAN

This is quite tricky, because when you're starting a business you're looking at an unknown entity, especially if you have

> When you're starting a business you're looking at an unknown entity, especially if you have a new product ... It was incredibly helpful to me, because there were loads of things I hadn't a clue about.

a new product, as I did. Business Link and the council were looking for all sorts of information that I hadn't even considered. They wanted to know how much I thought I would sell, how much profit I would make, where I would advertise, where I would find my customers, where I would source my materials – everything, really, about putting the structure of the business together. It was incredibly helpful to me, because there were loads of things I hadn't a clue about. Particularly marketing and PR: I'd never done anything like that and just sitting down and thinking about how I was going to get customers to find out about my products was a very useful exercise.

By this time I was determined to start the company whether I got funding or not, but being given that money did make a difference to the quality of what I was doing. The main thing was the website: I was able to pay someone to design a really professional site, rather than having to spend my own time on it when I needed to be concentrating on the business.

PUTTING YOURSELF FORWARD

This is another area where Business Link helped me: at a very early stage my advisor asked if I had thought of entering myself for any awards. My first reaction was, 'Hold on a minute – I've just started! What can I win?' But actually it was helpful in a lot of ways. When you start a business it's good to have something like that to motivate you and to push you forward. If you're working on your own, you don't have anyone saying, 'Well done, you've done a good job.' You can pat yourself on the back, but it's not the same! Quite often you win because customers have recommended you, and that does make you feel good.

Also, if you win something, you get a badge to put on your website that says, 'These people think my product's good'. It's difficult to assess how much all this has helped, because I don't know any different – right from the beginning I was led in that PR direction to promote my business, so I've always had this sort of accolade. But although I don't think it automatically brings in lots of new custom straight away, it does mean that people visiting my website see that I've been endorsed by Mumsnet and Mumpreneur UK and other people they have heard of, and that all adds to my credibility.

REPEAT BUSINESS

My business is a strange one, because my jewellery is aimed exclusively at the mothers of young babies. Obviously mums who are at home with their babies don't tend to have a lot of money, so they might buy one thing in the course of a year and then come back and buy another for Christmas. But then they buy presents for their friends too. I do get a lot of repeat business.

The flip side is that once the babies are older, the mums go back to wearing regular jewellery. Which leaves me with the problem of having to look constantly

MAKING PLANS

I still design everything I sell, but I outsource the making of it to a number of local mums. They've been with me from the beginning, because I simply haven't been able to do everything myself, particularly now that I have three children. But they do everything to my specification and that helps me to maintain quality.

A year ago I had plans for expansion, but then I found out that baby number three was coming. Since then we've been consolidating: making sure customer service is good, fulfilling orders. But the plan for the future is definitely to expand – to get into more retailers and to build a bigger online presence.

for new business. That's the crux of what I do, day in, day out – many ways of trying to generate new business.

RUNNING THE BUSINESS

At the moment we have 160 designs, so we tend to keep a small level of stock of each item – we've got a workshop to house it all – and then we do a stock take each week and spend the next week making up the designs we're short of.

I also have to keep an eye on all the designs and make sure I'm happy with them. Often I look at a design and decide to rejig it slightly. Then I have to draw my customers' attention to it. I have a blog on the website and I recently rejigged a very popular design, so I wrote a blog about it, 'introducing' the new improved version. Or I may have to redevelop a design because I can no longer get the materials. Everything we use is washable, non-toxic and smooth, with no sharp edges, so my designs tend to be based round what the suppliers can come up with. If that changes and I can no longer source a particular material, it can be very frustrating!

Some of my designs are perhaps too expensive for some, but that's because they are produced in the UK and packaged really well. The higher priced items take a little longer to make, so they have to be priced accordingly: you're not in business to lose money. I have a range of items, some cheaper, some more expensive and some mid-range, and that seems to work.

MISTAKES I WOULDN'T MAKE AGAIN

At the beginning I was approached by various magazines, asking me to advertise in them. It's flattering when someone from a well-known magazine phones you and says, 'We've seen this fantastic this and fantastic that that you're doing.' I did sometimes fall for it and paid out quite a bit of money for an ad that I have no idea whether it was successful or not.

I wouldn't recommend anyone to advertise when they first start, because I don't think it's very effective, but if you do, put a code in the advert that will tell you who's seen it and who's responding to it, so you can assess if it was worth it. But my real advice would be, rather than spending money on advertising, look at employing someone to provide you with PR services. That way you get someone else's recommendation, rather than paying to recommend yourself.

But my real advice would be, rather than spending money on advertising, look at employing someone to provide you with PR services. That way you get someone else's recommendation, rather than paying to recommend yourself.

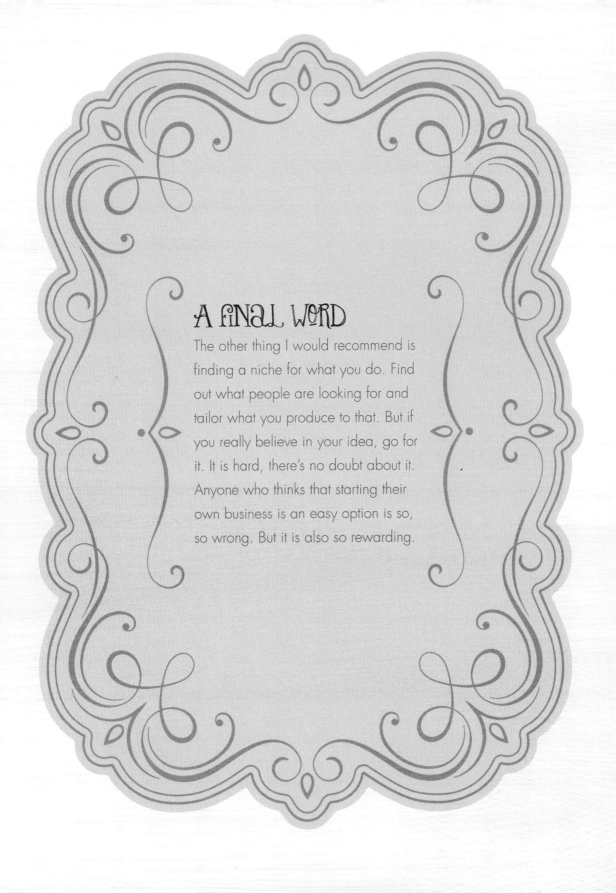

A FINAL WORD

The other thing I would recommend is finding a niche for what you do. Find out what people are looking for and tailor what you produce to that. But if you really believe in your idea, go for it. It is hard, there's no doubt about it. Anyone who thinks that starting their own business is an easy option is so, so wrong. But it is also so rewarding.

NATIONAL FUNDING SOURCES

ANGEL INVESTMENT

About: Angels are affluent entrepreneurs looking to invest in start-up or small businesses. There are many different Angel investment sites and networks available online; some require a membership fee, whereas others are free to join. Working with a Business Angel gives you the advantage of their expertise and support. Angel Investment Network is one social network that consists of investors advertising their particular preferences of investment opportunity and what expertise they have to offer. Entrepreneurs also may advertise their brief business plans.

Organization: Angel Investment Network Ltd.

Fund Value: N/A.

Eligibility Criteria: Every single investment is personal and private and therefore tailored to each party's needs and requests.

Application Process: Entrepreneurs can register to the website to begin advertising and networking with registered investors.

Address: 238 St Margaret's Road, Twickenham, Middlesex TW1 1NL

Tel: 07277 334053

Email: Contact submission form available on website.

Website: www. angelinvestmentnetwork.co.uk

ARTS COUNCIL ENGLAND

About: This organization provides funding and support for a wide range of arts activities. The Arts Council funds activities that engage the people of England, and funds artists and organizations to allow them the financial viability to continue their work. Various grants and programmes are active at any one time.

Organization: Arts Council England.

Fund Value: £1,000–£100,000.

Eligibility Criteria: Grants are awarded to individuals or organizations whose majority of activities take place in England.

Application Process: The application process involves writing a proposal and filling in an application form.

Address: PO Box 4353, Manchester M61 0DQ

Tel: 08453 006200

Email: enquiries@artscouncil.org.uk

Website: www.artscouncil.org.uk

BOOST THE BUSINESS IN YOU COMPETITION

About: Developed by the Government's Department for Business, Innovation and Skills (BIS) and Guardian News and Media Ltd, this annual competition is designed for small and medium-sized business in their first year of trading, or those that require funding in order to develop, including business support and advertising campaigns.

Organization: BIS and Guardian News and Media Ltd.

Fund Value: £15,000 worth of advertising.

Eligibility Criteria: UK businesses that are in their start-up phase, first year of trading or require additional funding to help expand and develop.

Application Process: Applications can be submitted via the website.

Address: Kings Place, 90 York Way, London N1 9GU

Tel: 020 3353 2000

Email: userhelp@guardian.co.uk

Website: www.guardian.co.uk/business-in-you

CROWD FUNDING

About: Crowd Funding is similar to Angel Investment in that it is an online network of investors and entrepreneurs. Entrepreneurs create a pitch online and offer some form of reward or steak in their business in exchange for funding.

Organization: Crowdcube Ltd.

Fund Value: Up to £250,000.

Eligibility Criteria: Anyone can register to the website and begin pitching ideas to the investors.

Application Process: Entrepreneurs can register to the website to begin advertising and networking with registered investors.

Address: The Innovation Centre, University of Exeter, Exeter EX4 4RN

Tel: 01392 241319

Email: support@crowdcube.com

Website: www.crowdcube.com

ENTERPRISE ANSWERS

About: Enterprise Answers provide loans as well as advice and support for new business ideas and small and

medium enterprises (SMEs). Loans are repayable over ten years.

Organization: Enterprise Answers.
Fund Value: £3,000–£100,000.
Eligibility Criteria: N/A.
Application Process: Applicants may enquire about applications for a loan via the provided telephone number, email address or enquiry submission form.
Address: The Office, Mardale Road, Penrith, Cumbria CA11 9EH
Tel: 01768 867118
Email: enquiries@enterpriseanswers.co.uk
Website: www.enterpriseanswers.co.uk

FINDING FINANCE

About: This website is a group of organizations, powered by the Community Development Finance Institution (CDFI), that source financial funding for individuals and businesses that may have had difficulty securing financial help from traditional sources. They specifically target ethnic minorities, women and businesses located in economically fragile areas.
Organization: Community Development Finance Institution (CDFI).
Fund Value: £50–£1,000,000.
Eligibility Criteria: The CDFI have a variety of different lending schemes dependent upon whether the applicant is an individual, business, charity, or applying from a specific area.
Address: Room 101 Hatton Square Business Centre, 16/16a Baldwins Gardens, London EC1N 7RJ
Tel: 020 7430 0222
Email: info@cdfa.org.uk
Website: www.findingfinance.org.uk

FREDERICKS FOUNDATION

About: Financial support for start-up and established businesses located in specific regions nationwide. Available to applicants who have been refused funding from traditional sources.
Organization: Fredericks Foundation.
Fund Value: Up to £10,000 for start-ups, up to £20,000 for established businesses.
Eligibility Criteria: Businesses that have been refused funding from traditional sources.
Application Process: Applications can be submitted via the website.
Address: Fredericks House, 39 Guildford Road, Lightwater, Surrey GU18 5SA
Tel: 01276 472722
Email: mail@fredericksfoundation.net
Website: www.fredericksfoundation.org

FUND 101

About: An innovative way of applying for a small start-up grant, Fund 101 allows entrepreneurs to apply for a small grant. To be successful the applicant must achieve the same amount of votes as the amount of money requested, for example, if an applicant applies for £70, then 70 votes are needed to secure the funding. Voters can be friends, family or interested third parties.
Organization: Enterprise Nation.
Fund Value: £50–£500.
Eligibility Criteria: Anyone with a new business idea, or development idea can apply.
Application Process: Applicants are required to fill out a form explaining their business proposal.

Address: Redbrick House, 9 Town Walls, Shrewsbury SY1 1TW
Tel: 01743 272555
Email: Contact submission form available on website.
Website: www.enterprisenation.com

JERWOOD MAKERS OPEN

About: This award allows emerging contemporary applied artists, working across craft practices, the opportunity to exhibit their pieces as part of the Jerwood Visual Arts programme in London and on tour. Five artists will be awarded £7,500 to create their exhibition pieces. A fantastic opportunity to showcase work at a prestigious event.
Organization: Jerwood Charitable Foundation.
Fund Value: £7,500.
Eligibility Criteria: UK residents. Applicants that have graduated or set up their practice within the last ten years.
Application Process: Applicants are required to apply online, providing a current CV and up to six images of current work. Applicants are also required to pay an entry fee of £20.
Address: 117 Union Street, Bankside, London SE1 0LN
Tel: 01372 462190
Email: jmo@parkerharris.co.uk
Website: www.jerwoodvisualarts.org

LEADER GRANTS

About: An initiative designed to improve the local economy and tourism sector within the stipulated rural areas. Most projects will require match funding.
Organization: Rural Development Programme for England (RDPE).

Fund Value: Up to £50,000.
Eligibility Criteria: Farmers, forresters and small rural businesses located within the stipulated rural areas. Proposals must be able to evidence a contribution to either one of the following categories: creating opportunities to enjoy the local areas, supporting community development and business transformation, promoting local food or climate change adaptation and mitigation.
Application Process: Applications can be made via the website.
Address: Temple Quay House, 2 The Square, Bristol BS1 6EB
Tel: 01173 723634
Email: rdpenetwork@defra.gsi.gov.uk
Website: www.rdpenetwork.defra.gov.uk

QUEEN ELIZABETH SCHOLARSHIP TRUST (QEST)

About: A scholarship that funds further study, training and personal development for crafters. Aimed at providing craftsmen and women with the necessary training and experience to further their career.
Organization: The Queen Elizabeth Scholarship Trust.
Fund Value: £1,000–£18,000.
Eligibility Criteria: Applicants need to be able to demonstrate a high level of dedication and skill concerning their craft. Scholarships may not be used to purchase equipment, premises or to set up a business.
Application Process: Applicants are required to fill out an application form, in which they must detail what they will gain from the scholarship and the estimated cost of any training or programmes.

Address: No 1 Buckingham Palace, London SW1E 6HR
Tel: 020 7828 2268
Email: qest@rwha.co.uk
Website: www.qest.org.uk

SENIOR ENTREPRENEUR OF THE YEAR AWARDS

About: A unique award that aims to support and celebrate entrepreneurs over the age of 50. The award consists of three categories: 'Best New Digital Business', 'Best New Product' and 'Best New Service'. In addition, an overal 'Senior Entrepreneur of the Year' is chosen from the three winners.
Organization: PRIME.
Fund Value: £500.
Eligibility Criteria: Applicants must have been over the age of 50 at the time of starting their business. Applicants are required to register with The Prince's Trust initiative.
Application Process: Applicants are required to select which category award they would like to apply for and download the relevant form.
Address: Tavis House, 1–6 Tavistock Square, London WC1H 9NA
Tel: 08458 622023
Email: info@prime.org.uk
Website: www.prime.org.uk

SHELL LIVEWIRE GRAND IDEAS AWARD

About: A scheme targeted at young entrepreneurs looking to create a new business or expand an existing business. This is a monthly scheme that gives applicants the chance to win £1,000 and PR support for their business idea.
Organization: Shell LiveWIRE.
Fund Value: £1,000.

Eligibility Criteria: 16–30 year old UK residents. New or existing businesses that have been in operation for less than 12 months.
Application Process: Applications can be submitted on the website.
Address: Design Works, William Street, Felling, Gateshead NE10 0JP
Tel: 01914 236229
Email: enquirires@shell-livewire.org
Website: www.shell-livewire.org

STARTUP LOANS

About: A national campaign launched in 2011 by the Prime Minister and supported by HM Government. StartUp Britain aims to encourage entrepreneurship and assist new and growing businesses, specifically aimed at young entrepreneurs aged 18–24. Applicants can also expect to receive business support and mentoring.
Organization: StartUp Britain.
Fund Value: Up to £2,500.
Eligibility Criteria: Entrepreneurs aged 18–24.
Application Process: Applicants can register their interest via the website or the company's Facebook page. Loans are regional and applicants will receive a notification when a loan application has become available in their area.

TEENBIZ

About: A unique scheme that awards two students each month with £500 funding, business mentoring and a start-up pack consisting of business cards, a website, office space, logo design and more.
Organization: TeenBiz.
Fund Value: £500.

Eligibility Criteria: Applicants aged between 13–18.

Application Process: A simple online application form is available on the TeenBiz website.

Address: School Speakers, Charle Roberts Office Park, Charles Street, Horbury WF4 5FH

Tel: 01924 277343

Email: info@teenbiz.org.uk

Website: www.teenbiz.org.uk

THE CARPENTER'S CRAFT COMPETITION

About: A national carpentry competition for college and university students studying carpentry, joinery and shopfitting.

Organization: Chris Higley.

Fund Value: £500.

Eligibility Criteria: Students of any age studying carpentry, joinery or shopfitting at any college or learning institute.

Application Process: A downloadable application form is available on the website. A £7.50 entry fee is required for each application.

Address: 35 The Birchwoods, Little Heath Road, Tilehurst, Reading RG31 5UH

Tel: 01189 429468

Website: www.carpenterscraft.co.uk

THE DAVID CANTER MEMORIAL FUND

About: A biennial award scheme that supports UK crafters, awarding them with funding in order to develop themselves and advance professionally. Each award is targeted at a specific field of craft, for example, the 2012 Fund field consisted of ceramics.

Organization: The Devon Guild of Craftsmen.

Fund Value: £500–£1,000.

Eligibility Criteria: Makers who have completed formal training and are working full or part-time in the UK.

Application Process: Applicants can either download an application form or request a postal application form in writing, providing a stamped addressed envelope. The application form should be returned with six colour digital photographs of recent work.

Address: Riverside Mill, Bovey Tracey, Devon TQ13 9AF

Tel: 01626 832223

Email: rachel.mackie@crafts.org.uk

Website: www.crafts.org.uk

THE DISCERNING EYE (DE) DRAWING BURSARY

About: The DE Bursary was established in 2002 and aims to encourage great art and the continuation and development of great artists. Since 2005, the award focuses entirely around drawing and illustration.

Organization: The Discerning Eye.

Fund Value: £1,500 for first place and £150 for each runner up.

Eligibility Criteria: The bursary is awarded for drawing only. Any resident artist in the UK.

Application Process: Applicants are requested to pay a £3 nominal fee. Artists are asked to submit up to three images, along with a written proposal outlining how the bursary will benefit them in their practice.

Email: Contact submission form available on website.

Website: www.discerningeye.org

THE ELEPHANT TRUST

About: The Elephant Trust was established in 1975 in order promote the appreciation of fine art across the UK by providing grants to assist in the completion of projects and exhibitions. The Trust has funded many prolific individuals including Cathy Wilkes and Steve McQueen.

Organization: The Elephant Trust.

Fund Value: Up to £2,000.

Eligibility Criteria: Excludes funding for: arts festivals, group exhibitions, charities organizing community projects, students, education studies, residencies or research, symposia or conferences, publication or catalogues or projects taking place outside the UK.

Application Process: Applications are made by post and require a 300 word proposal, budget proposal, visual material, a CV and a stamped addressed envelope.

Address: 512 Bankside Lofts, 65 Hopton Street, London SE1 9GZ

Tel: 020 7922 1160

Email: ruth@elephanttrust.org.uk

Website: www.elephanttrust.org.uk

THE GOLDSMITHS' CRAFTSMANSHIP AND DESIGN AWARDS

About: The Goldsmith's Craft and Design Council hold these prestigious annual awards to promote and celebrate the craft of silversmithing, jewellery and allied crafts. There are a variety of awards to compete for.

Organization: Goldsmiths' Craft and Design Council.

Fund Value: £1,000–£1,500.

Eligibility Criteria: Applicants must work with precious metals, gemstones

and other allied materials. Work that has been completed in the UK in the 12 months preceding the closing date for applications.

Application Process: Applications fall into three categories: 2D Design, 3D Design and 3D Craft. Applications can be made online.

Address: The Goldsmiths Centre, 42 Britton Street, London EC1M 5AD

Tel: 01233 720067

Email: brian.hill@ craftanddesigncouncil.org.uk

Website: www. craftanddesigncouncil.org.uk

THE MARK TANNER SCULPTURE AWARD

About: An exciting opportunity for emerging sculptors, this award provides £6,000 towards the production of new work and £4,000 towards supporting a solo exhibition.

Organization: Standpoint Gallery.

Fund Value: £10,000.

Eligibility Criteria: Applicants that can demonstrate how this award will benefit their work and career.

Application Process: Application procedures are unclear, however contact details are provided.

Address: 45 Coronet Street, Hoxton, London NH1 6HD

Tel: 020 7739 4921

Email: standpointgallery@btconnect. com

Website: www.standpointlondon. co.uk

THE PITCH

About: Aimed at small business and entrepreneurs across the UK, The Pitch provides winners with an excellent package of prizes and business support including: twelve months of business mentoring, PR support, a twelve month accountancy package, social media training, a bespoke tailored suit, web designing software, a laptop and much more.

Organization: Business Zone and Sift Media.

Fund Value: £50,000 worth of business support.

Eligibility Criteria: Small and start-up businesses across the UK.

Application Process: Applicants may contact The Pitch team for more details.

Address: 6th Floor Bridge House, 48–52 Baldwin Street, Bristol BS1 1QB

Tel: 01179 159600

Email: Pitch@siftmedia.co.uk

Website: www.thepitchuk.com

THE PRINCE'S TRUST

About: A charity that strives to help change the lives of young people across the UK. The charity achieves this by providing advice, support, mentoring and funding grants for disadvantaged 14–25 year olds.

Organization: The Prince's Trust.

Fund Value: Up to £3,000.

Eligibility Criteria: 14–16 year olds not expecting to achieve five GCSEs. 16–25 year olds currently out of education and employment.

Application Process: Applicants will meet with a Prince's Trust Awards Assessor to discuss the grant and submit an application.

Address: 18 Park Square East, London NW1 4LH

Tel: 020 7543 1234

Email: webinfops@princes-trust.org.uk

Website: www.princes-trust.org.uk

THE PROFESSIONAL DEVELOPMENT AWARD

About: An award scheme for individuals professionally practising art, craft, design or any textile-related field.

Organization: The Textile Society.

Fund Value: £1,000.

Eligibility Criteria: Professionals or researchers working in a craft, design or textile-related field.

Application Process: A downloadable application form is available on the website, in which applicants are asked to demonstrate their enthusiasm for their industry and how the bursary will benefit them professionally.

Address: 12 Moorhouse Road, London W2 5DJ

Tel: 020 7923 0331

Email: bursaries@textilesociety.org.uk

Website: www.textilesociety.org.uk

REGIONAL FUNDING SOURCES

East and South East

Breckland Enterprise and Learning Account (BELA)

About: A small grant available to start-up businesses within the Breckland area that demonstrate ambition and growth potential.

Organization: Breckland Council.

Fund Value: £500.

Eligibility Criteria: Businesses must be located within the Breckland area and employ no more than ten people.

Application Process: An application form can be download from the website.

Address: Elizabeth House, Walpole Loke, Dereham NR19 1EE

Tel: 01362 656870

Email: contactus@breckland.gov.uk

Website: www.breckland.gov.uk

Capitalise Business Support

About: Targeted at Sussex, Surrey and Kent-based entrepreneurs: micro and small businesses with the direct intention of promoting positive economic growth within these areas.

Organization: Capitalise Business Support.

Fund Value: £1,000–£7,500.

Eligibility Criteria: Applicants who have been unsuccessful in securing financial assistance from traditional sources. Businesses located in either Sussex, Surrey or Kent. Applicants need to provide a business plan and twelve month cash flow forecast.

Application Process: A downloadable application form is available on the website. Applicants are also required to present a business plan, personal ID, six months' worth of bank statements, a recent utility bill and a copy of a bank decline letter if possible. There are several document templates available on the website to assist in the application process.

Address: Summerfields Business Centre, Bohemia Road, Hastings, East Sussex TN34 1UT

Tel: 08456 018326

Email: info@capitalise.org

Website: www.capitalise.org/index.htm

Creative Industry Finance

About: A joint venture between East London Small Business Centre and Arts Council England: this initiative is aimed at creative businesses, new or established, based either in the Greater London area or in Yorkshire and Humber.

Organization: Arts Council England.

Fund Value: £5,000–£25,000.

Eligibility Criteria: Businesses located within London, Yorkshire or Humber. Applicants must be applying for business ventures or projects involving one of the specified criteria as outlined on the website: these are numerous, but include crafts and design.

Application Process: Applicants are required to set up a user account on the website, followed by filling in an interest form.

Address: 14 Great Peter Street, London SW1P 3NQ

Tel: 08453 006200

Email: cifinance@artscouncil.org.uk

Website: www.creativeindustryfinance.org.uk

Enterprise Fellowship Scheme

About: A funding initiative aimed at entrepreneurs residing in Cambridgeshire. As well as funding, successful applicants will receive business mentoring, specialist training, legal support and advice.

Organization: Anglia Ruskin University.

Fund Value: Up to £35,000.

Eligibility Criteria: Applicants must be residing in the Cambridgeshire area. The scheme is not available to members of staff or undergraduate students at Anglia Ruskin University.

Application Process: Applicants are required to contact Dale Cross via the contact details provided.

Address: East Road, Cambridge, Cambridgeshire CB1 1PT

Tel: 08451 962344

Email: dale.coss@anglia.ac.uk

Website: www.anglia.ac.uk

Enterprise Loan Fund

About: This fund supports the start-up of small businesses within the area of Portsmouth and South East Hampshire.

Organization: Parity Trust.

Fund Value: £2,000–£10,000.
Eligibility Criteria: Applicants must live within the Portsmouth and South East Hampshire region. All applicants need to be able to meet for an initial face-to-face meeting with Parity Trust.
Application Process: Applicants details will only be accepted through a referral process and all applicants will have to provide a business plan, cash flow forecast and a copy of a recent credit check.
Address: East Wing, 1000 Lakeside, North Harbour, Portsmouth PO6 3EN
Tel: 02392 375921
Email: mail@paritytrust.org.uk
Website: www.paritytrust.org.uk

FENS ADVENTURERS RURAL DEVELOPMENT PROGRAMME (FARDP)

About: A funding initiative that targets micro-enterprises located within the rural parishes of Cambridgeshire and the West Norfolk Fens. FARDP's main objectives are to improve sustainable food and farming, rural business development, sustainable rural tourism and enterprising communities.
Organization: Fens Adventurers.
Fund Value: £10,000–£100,000.
Eligibility Criteria: Applicants must be residing in the Cambridgeshire and West Norfolk Fens area. Businesses must have no more than ten employees. Applicants are required to contribute between 20% and 60% of the total funding requested.
Application Process: Interested applicants are invited to contact a member of the FARDP team to discuss the proposal and begin the application process.

Address: Cambridgeshire ACRE, 32 Main Street, Littleport, Ely CB6 1PJ
Tel: 01353 865047
Email: mike.carter@cambsacre.org.uk
Website: www.cambsacre.org.uk

FOUNDATION EAST

About: A foundation that provides business loans for new and existing businesses that have been refused financial funding from traditional sources. Specifically targeted at businesses operating in the East of England.
Organization: Foundation East.
Fund Value: N/A.
Eligibility Criteria: Businesses located in Bedfordshire, Cambridgeshire, Essex, Hertfordshire, Norfolk or Suffolk. Applicants who have been refused financial funding from traditional sources.
Application Process: An electronic application form can be downloaded from the website. Other documents required are cash flow forecasts, three months' worth of bank statements, a full credit report, personal ID and a letter of refusal from a bank, if available.
Address: Saxon House, 7 Hillside Road, Bury St Edmunds, Suffolk IP32 7EA
Tel: 08452 937751
Email: info@foundationeast.org
Website: www.foundationeast.org

LAUNCHPAD@CEME COMPETITION

About: An annual award scheme targeted at young entrepreneurs within the Thames Gateway and surrounding areas. Successful applicants will receive financial assistance, business support and mentoring, along with a variety of other prizes.
Organization: Launchpad@CEME.
Fund Value: Up to £25,000.
Eligibility Criteria: Application is open to anyone located within the Thames Gateway and surrounding areas. Businesses must be in the early stages of trading or just starting up.
Application Process: Applicants are required to submit a full business plan.
Address: Marsh Way, Rainham, Essex RM13 8EU
Tel: 020 8596 5142
Email: launchpad.ceme@oxin.co.uk
Website: www.launchpadceme.co.uk

NORWICH4NEWENTERPRISE PROGRAMME

About: This programme aims to assist unemployed, or soon to be made redundant, individuals who want to start a business within the Norwich, South Norfolk or Broadland areas.
Organization: Norfolk Community Foundation.
Fund Value: £5,000–£20,000.
Eligibility Criteria: Applicants must be residing or intending to locate to the Norwich, South Norfolk or Broadland areas. Eligible applicants are those that are unemployed, or soon to be unemployed, and have been refused funding from traditional sources.
Application Process: A downloadable application form is available on the website, which is to then be returned by post.
Address: St James Mill, Whitefriars, Norwich, NR3 1SH
Tel: 01603 623958
Email: info@norfolkfoundation.com
Website: www.norfolkfoundation.com

NWES ADVANCE LOAN FUND

About: A financial organization that offers a range of funding schemes for various sized businesses throughout the East of England.

Organization: Norfolk and Waveney Enterprise Services (NWES)

Fund Value: Start-up loan: £1,000–£5,000. Business Loan: £5,000–£25,000. Business Development Loan: from £25,000.

Eligibility Criteria: Applicants applying for a start-up loan must have been trading for no more than twelve months. Businesses must be able to demonstrate refusal of funding from traditional sources. Applicants must be residing and operating in the East of England.

Application Process: Interested applicants are invited to contact a member of the NWES team to discuss the borrowing lending scheme further.

Address: Norwich Enterprise Centre, 4B Guildhall Hill, Norwich, Norfolk NR2 1JH

Tel: 08456 099991

Email: info@nwes.org.uk

Website: www.nwes.org.uk

THE FULL CIRCLE LOAN

About: A loan specifically for women living in the Norfolk or Suffolk area who need financial assistance to start a business or develop an existing one. Full Circle also offer express loans for short-term projects, such as craft fairs, trades shows and publicity.

Organization: The Women's Employment, Enterprise and Training Unity (WEETU).

Fund Value: £500–£5,000.

Eligibility Criteria: Members of The Women's Employment, Enterprise and Training Unity (WEETU). Applicants living in Suffolk or Norfolk.

Application Process: Applicants are required to submit an application form along with a business plan and a twelve month cash flow forecast. Upon submission an interview with the Loan Committee will be arranged.

Address: WEETU Ltd, The Royal Business Centre, 25 Bank Plain, Norwich, NR2 4SF

Tel: 01603 283490

Email: Contact submission form available on website.

Website: www.weetu.org

THE JOHN SWEENEY AWARD

About: An annual award celebrating businesses or organizations that have demonstrated environmental responsibility and sustainability within the North Norfolk region – be it reducing energy use or increasing recycling.

Organization: North Norfolk District Council.

Fund Value: £500.

Eligibility Criteria: Applicants must be residing with the North Norfolk district and must provide evidence of environmental responsibility and sustainability.

Application Process: Applicants are invited to contact North Norfolk Council's Sustainability Team for an informal discussion.

Address: Council Offices, Holt Road, Cromer, Norfolk NR27 9EN

Tel: 01263 516271

Email: sustainability@north-norfolk. gov.uk

Website: www.northnorfolk.org

NORTH EAST

BUSINESS ENTERPRISE FUND (BEF)

About: A non-profit organization that assists businesses that have been unsuccessful in securing a loan from a bank or building society. The BEF also provides support and training, as well as monthly meetings once a loan has been approved.

Organization: Business Enterprise Fund (BEF).

Fund Value: £500–£100,000.

Eligibility Criteria: Only available to applicants who have been refused financial funding from traditional sources. Applicants must provide a concise business plan and cash flow forecast.

Application Process: Applicants are required to complete a business plan template, provided by the website, as well as a cash flow template. Applicants are also required to write a personal finance statement prior to submitting the online application form.

Address: Dever House, Vicar Lane, Bradford, West Yorkshire BD1 5AH

Tel: 01274 207217

Email: info@befund.org

Website: www.befund.org

CREATIVE INDUSTRY FINANCE

About: A joint venture between East London Small Business Centre and Arts Council England: this initiative is aimed at creative businesses, new or established, based either in the Greater London area or in Yorkshire and Humber.

Organization: Arts Council England.
Fund Value: £5,000–£25,000
Eligibility Criteria: Businesses located within London, Yorkshire or Humber. Applicants must be applying for business ventures or projects involving one of the specified criteria as outlined on the website: these are numerous, but include crafts and design.
Application Process: Applicants are required to set up a user account on the website, followed by filling in an interest form.
Address: 14 Great Peter Street, London SW1P 3NQ
Tel: 08453 006200
Email: cifinance@artscouncil.org.uk
Website: www.creativeindustryfinance.org.uk

DONBAC BUSINESS LOANS

About: A long-established agency, providing business advice and financial support for start-up businesses or established businesses within the Doncaster area.
Organization: Donbac Ltd.
Fund Value: £1,000–£50,000.
Eligibility Criteria: Applicants located within the Doncaster area.
Application Process: Application forms are downloadable from the website. Documents required along with the application form include: a business plan, twelve months cash flow forecast, personal ID, three months' worth of bank statements and an Experian or Equifax credit report.
Address: Doncaster Business Innovation Centre, Ten Pound Walk, Doncaster DN4 5HX
Tel: 01302 341070

Email: info@donbac.co.uk
Website: www.donbac.co.uk

FINANCE YORKSHIRE

About: Providing loans for new and established businesses within the Yorkshire and Humber region.
Organization: Finance Yorkshire.
Fund Value: £15,000–£150,000.
Eligibility Criteria: Businesses located in, or relocating to, the Yorkshire and Humber region.
Application Process: Applicants are required to briefly summarize their business plan and submit this via the online enquiry form. A Finance Yorkshire advisor should then be in contact within five working days to discuss the application further.
Address: 1 Capitol Court, Capitol Business Park, Dodworth, Barnsley S75 3TZ
Tel: 08456 490000
Email: info@finance-yorkshire.com
Website: www.finance-yorkshire.com

FIVE LAMPS

About: A registered charity that aims to provide support and advice for disadvantaged individuals and families by helping them to achieve their aspirations. The organization also provides financial support for new and established businesses.
Organization: Five Lamps Organization.
Fund Value: £1,000–£20,000.
Eligibility Criteria: Existing businesses who have been trading for a minimum of twelve months. Applicants that have been refused funding from traditional sources.
Application Process: Applications can be made via the website or

by contacting Five Lamps via the telephone number provided.
Address: Eldon Street, Thornaby, Stockton-on-Tees TS17 7DJ
Tel: 01642 608316
Email: info@fivelamps.org.uk
Website: www.fivelamps.org.uk

IGNITE100

About: A programme designed to support start-up businesses located in or relocating to the North East of England. Successful applicants can expect to receive financial funding and business mentoring.
Organization: North East Finance.
Fund Value: £100,000.
Eligibility Criteria: Businesses must be located in or relocating to the North East of England.
Application Process: Applications can be made via the website.
Address: Suite 20, Adamson House, 65 Westgate Road, Newcastle-upon-Tyne NE1 1SG
Email: press@ignite100.com
Website: www.ignite100.com

NORTH EAST MICROLOAN FUND

About: Aims to create new jobs and help to stabilize existing ones within the North East region of England. This is achieved by supporting new and existing micro and small businesses.
Organization: Entrust.
Fund Value: £1,000–£25,000.
Eligibility Criteria: Applicants must provide evidence of having been refused financial assistance from traditional sources. Applicants must be residing in, or have the majority of their business operating in the North East region of England.

Application Process: Applications can be made online and take approximately 30 minutes. A business plan, cash flow forecast and CV are also required.

Address: Portman House, Portland Road, Newcastle upon Tyne NE2 1AQ

Tel: 01912 444000

Email: enquire@entrust.co.uk

Website: www.entrust.co.uk

STREET NORTH EAST

About: A CDFI that supports existing start-up businesses and small and micro businesses that wish to expand. Applicants can also expect support and financial business advice.

Organization: Street North East.

Fund Value: £500–£10,000.

Eligibility Criteria: Applicants residing or working in the North East of England, who have been refused funding from traditional sources. Existing businesses that can demonstrate profitable trade for the preceding six months.

Application Process: Applications, along with a clear business plan and financial forecasts, can be made via the website.

Address: Portman House, Portland Road, Newcastle upon Tyne NE2 1AQ

Tel: 01912 444029

Email: loanenquiries@entrust.co.uk

Website: www.streetnortheast.co.uk

WOMEN'S DEVELOPMENT FUND

About: Any female in Hartlepool and striving to set up a business can apply for this fund, which provides up to £500 worth of advertising and publicity.

Organization: Hartlepool Borough Council.

Fund Value: Up to £500.

Eligibility Criteria: Female applicants living in Hartlepool.

Application Process: Application forms can be requested via the contact details provided on the website.

Address: Brougham Terrace, Hartlepool TS24 8EY

Tel: 01429 867677

Email: info@investinhartlepool.com

Website: www.investinhartlepool.com

YORKSHIRE AND HUMBER FUND

About: This fund is a grant and loan package accessible to start-up or small businesses within the Yorkshire and Humber areas. A grant of up to £5,000 along with a loan of up to £20,000 is repayable over a period of three years.

Organization: Key Fund.

Fund Value: £5,000–£25,000.

Eligibility Criteria: Applicants residing or working in Yorkshire and the Humber region.

Application Process: Applicants are required to contact Key Fund via the telephone number provided to discuss the loan further, before submitting an application form.

Address: 12 Leeds Road, Sheffield S9 3TY

Tel: 08451 401400

Email: info@thekeyfund.co.uk

Website: www.thekeyfund.co.uk

NORTH WEST

LANCASHIRE COMMUNITY FINANCE (LPS)

About: Part of the CDFI, LPS serves individuals or local businesses located in Lancashire who have been refused loans elsewhere.

Organization: Lancashire Community Finance (LPS) Ltd.

Fund Value: From £100.

Eligibility Criteria: LPS will consider loans from anyone within the Lancashire area who has struggled to access funding from traditional sources.

Application Process: The application process can begin with a phone call or by visiting the LPS office and meeting with an advisor.

Address: 4 Fleet Street, Preston PR1 2UT

Tel: 01772 556877

Email: info@lancashirecommunityfinance.co.uk

Website: www.lancashirecommunityfinance.co.uk

LEISURE GRANT FUND

About: This fund aims to assist the personal development of groups, organizations or individual involved in sports or the arts, within the Eden Council area of Cumbria.

Organization: Eden District Council.

Fund Value: Up to £500.

Eligibility Criteria: Applicants must be located within the Eden District Council vicinity.

Application Process: A downloadable application form is available on the website.

Address: Town Hall, Penrith CA11 7QF

Tel: 01768 212473
Email: leisure@eden.gov.uk
Website: www.eden.gov.uk

MANCHESTER ENTERPRISE ZONE

About: This incentive provides businesses that move into the specified areas a discounted business rate for up to five years.
Organization: Manchester City Council.
Fund Value: N/A.
Eligibility Criteria: Applicants and businesses that are locating to the 'zone': Manchester Airport, Wythenshawe Centre or University Hospital South Manchester Foundation Trust.
Application Process: This is a complex initiative and the website advises that all applicants should read through the guidelines and terms and conditions thoroughly before submitting an application. Application forms can be found on the website.
Address: Town Hall, Albert Square, Manchester M60 2LA
Tel: 01612 341103
Email: contact@manchester.gov.uk
Website: www.manchester.gov.uk

NEW ENTERPRISE ALLOWANCE SCHEME (NEA)

About: NEA is a mentoring and finance scheme targeted at individuals that have been claiming Job Seekers Allowance for more than 26 weeks, and who are looking to develop a new business.
Organization: Business Finance Solutions.
Fund Value: Up to £1,000.
Eligibility Criteria: Applicants are required to take part in the NEA mentoring scheme and will need a completed business plan and cash flow forecast. Applicants must be residing in Greater Manchester, Lancashire, Chester or Cumbria. Applicants are required to cease claiming Job Seekers Allowance and be confirmed as eligible by Jobcentre Plus.
Application Process: Applications can be made electronically via an online application form. Several documents are also required, such as photographic ID, address verification, an Experian Credit Report and a business plan.
Address: Lee House, 90 Great Bridgewater Street, Manchester M1 5JW
Tel: 01612 374634
Email: john.cannon@business-finance-solutions.org.uk
Website: www.business-finance-solutions.org.uk

ROSEBUD MICRO

About: Targeted directly at start-up and small businesses within the Lancashire area, Rosebud provides advice and support along with financial assistance. The loan is aimed at businesses that can show potential and, as a result, improve the local economy.
Organization: Lancashire County Council.
Fund Value: £2,000–£10,000.
Eligibility Criteria: Applicants must be located within, or relocating to, the Lancashire Council area.
Application Process: A downloadable application form is available on the website.
Address: PO Box 78, County Hall, Fishergate, Preston PR1 8XJ

Tel: 08450 530000
Email: enquiries@lancashire.gov.uk
Website: www.lancashire.gov.uk

RURAL LANCASHIRE DEVELOPMENT FUND

About: A funding scheme aimed at new or existing businesses with high growth ambitions and based in rural Lancashire. The main objective of the scheme is to support businesses and directly create more jobs for rural areas of the county.
Organization: Lancashire County Council.
Fund Value: £2,000–£10,000.
Eligibility Criteria: Applicants must be located within, or benefitting, the rural areas of Lancashire County.
Application Process: The application process involves completing a proposal form, or contacting the Rural Business Support Team on the telephone number or email address provided.
Address: PO Box 78, County Hall, Fishergate, Preston PR1 8XJ
Tel: 01772 536600
Email: lcdl.rural@lancashire.gov.uk
Website: www.lancashire.gov.uk

SMALL BUSINESS RATE RELIEF

About: Targeted at small businesses within the Bury area, this scheme provides a relief discount of up to 50 per cent on the business rates of properties.
Organization: Bury Metropolitan Borough Council.
Fund Value: N/A.
Eligibility Criteria: Small business properties with a rateable value of up to £18,000. Businesses must not

be already receiving charitable or rural relief.

Application Process: A downloadable application form is available on the website. Alternatively, applicants can contact the business rates office via telephone or email.

Address: Town Hall, Knowsley Street, Bury, Lancashire BL9 0SW

Tel: 01612 535035

Email: businessrates@bury.gov.uk

Website: www.bury.gov.uk

SMALL LOANS FOR BUSINESS

About: Available to applicants residing in Merseyside, Cheshire, Manchester, Lancashire and Cumbria looking to start or expand a business.

Organization: Business Finance Solutions.

Fund Value: £3,000–£50,000.

Eligibility Criteria: Applicants must provide evidence of having been rejected from tradition financial sources, such as a banks or building societies, and a business plan that creates at least one extra job in the area.

Application Process: Applications can be made electronically via an online application form, or by contacting the scheme via the provided contact methods.

Address: Lee House, 90 Great Bridgewater Street, Manchester M1 5JW

Tel: 01612 374021

Email: info@business-finance-solutions.org.uk

Website: www.business-finance-solutions.org.uk

SMALL LOANS FOR BUSINESS FUND

About: Available to applicants residing in Merseyside, looking to start a new business or expand and grow an existing enterprise. Applicants will receive advice and support throughout their venture.

Organization: Merseyside Special Investment Fund (MSIF)

Fund Value: £3,000–£50,000.

Eligibility Criteria: Applicants located in the Merseyside region. Businesses must have fewer than 250 employees.

Application Process: Downloadable application forms are available on the website.

Address: 2nd Floor, 1 Dale Street, Exchange Court, Liverpool L2 2PP

Tel: 01512 364040

Email: info@msif.co.uk

Website: www.msif.co.uk

THE NORTH WEST FUND FOR DIGITAL & CREATIVE

About: An initiative directed at the Digital and Creative sector in the North West of England. This loan initiative is specifically for small and medium-sized enterprises (SMEs) that have the potential to expand.

Organization: North West Business Finance Ltd and AXM Venture Capital.

Fund Value: £50,000–£1,500,000.

Eligibility Criteria: Applicants must be located within, or relocating to, the North West region of England. Businesses must have fewer than 250 employees.

Application Process: To begin the application process, applicants must provide a thorough business plan and complete an online application form.

Address: The Maltings, 98 Wilderspool Causeway, Warrington WA4 6PU

Tel: 01925 418232

Email: Info@axmvc.co.uk

Website: www.thenorthwestfund.co.uk

WOMEN IN BUSINESS LOAN FUND

About: Aimed at assisting female entrepreneurs looking create a business, or running already existing businesses within the North West region.

Organization: Bolton Business Ventures (BBV) Ltd.

Fund Value: Up to 30,000.

Eligibility Criteria: Applicants must be female and located within the North West region. Businesses must have fewer than 250 employees.

Application Process: The first step in this application process is to contact the Loans Fund Manager on the telephone number provided.

Address: 44–46 Lower Bridgeman Street, Bolton BL2 1DG

Tel: 01204 391400

Email: nk@bbvonline.net

Website: www.bbvonline.net

NORTHERN IRELAND

BRIGHTER BELFAST AWARDS

About: An environmentally conscious award scheme that rewards individuals, small businesses and organizations that are benefiting the local environment through the reduction of waste, conservation of natural resources or the reduction of their carbon footprint.

Organization: Belfast City Council.

Fund Value: £500.

Eligibility Criteria: Applicants must be able to demonstrate in what way their project or business helps Belfast's local economy and environment.

Application Process: Applicants are able to download an application form from the website.

Address: Belfast City Hall, Belfast BT1 5GS

Tel: 02890 320202

Email: catcleansing@belfastcity.gov.uk

Website: www.belfastcity.gov.uk

ENTERPRISE NORTHERN IRELAND (ENI)

About: Designed to support new businesses and small businesses throughout Northern Ireland in order to create economic growth.

Organization: Enterprise Northern Ireland (ENI).

Fund Value: Up to £25,000.

Eligibility Criteria: Businesses located in Northern Ireland. Businesses that have been unable to secure financial funding from traditional sources.

Application Process: Applications are to be submitted via post, along with a business plan and a twelve month cash flow forecast. Other documents required include proof of identity, business bank statements (for established businesses) and proof of address.

Address: Aghanloo Industrial Estate, Aghanloo Road, Limavady BT49 0HE

Tel: 02877 763555

Email: loanfund@enterpriseni.com

Website: www.enterpriseni.com

GENERATING RURAL OPPORTUNITIES WITHIN SOUTH ANTRIM

About: Providing finance to organizations across the Antrim, Carrickfergus and Newtownabbey Borough Councils, that can demonstrate that their project will benefit the surrounding rural areas. Grants are available to cover 50 per cent of investment costs – the website does not stipulate a maximum funding amount.

Organization: GROW South Antrim.

Fund Value: N/A.

Eligibility Criteria: Applicants residing within rural areas of Antrim, Carrickfergus or Newtownabbey Borough. Applicants that can demonstrate a that their project will benefit the surrounding rural areas.

Application Process: Applicants are required to submit and expression of interest form in order to be deemed eligible. Successful applicants will then complete and submit an online application form.

Address: Antrim Civic Centre, 50 Stiles Way, Antrim BT41 2UB

Tel: 02894 481311

Email: info@growsouthantrim.com

Website: www.growsouthantrim.com

MICHELIN DEVELOPMENT LOAN FUND

About: Aimed at small to medium-sized enterprises (SEOs) located within Ballymena, the Michelin Development Loan Fund is an attempt to encourage business growth and increase employment in the local area.

Organization: Michelin Development Ltd.

Fund Value: Up to £25,000.

Eligibility Criteria: Applicants must be located within the Ballymena area of County Antrim and employ fewer than 250 people.

Application Process: Applicants are able to fill out an application form via the website.

Address: 190 Raceview Road, Ballymena, County Antrim BT42 4HZ

Tel: 07966 951239

Email: cecil.caldwell@uk.michelin.com

Website: www.michelindevelopment.co.uk

RURAL DEVELOPMENT PARTNERSHIP (RDP) BUSINESS CREATION AND DEVELOPMENT

About: Available to micro-enterprises located in a rural Northern Ireland area.

Organization: Lagan Rural Partnership.

Fund Value: Up to £50,000.

Eligibility Criteria: Applicants located in a rural area and wishing to start up a micro-enterprise or an already existing micro-enterprise with fewer than ten employees.

Application Process: Applicants are able to fill out an application form via the website.
Address: Economic Development Unit, Lisburn City Council, Island Civic Centre, The Island BT27 4RL
Tel: 02892 509419
Email: info@laganruralpartnership.com
Website: www.laganruralpartnership.com

SCOTLAND

ARTS TRUST SCOTLAND

About: Funded by an independent Scottish charitable trust, Arts Trust Scotland is aimed at emerging individuals that require funding for equipment, exhibitions, training and more.
Organization: The Arts Trust Scotland.
Fund Value: £500–£2,000.
Eligibility Criteria: An individual looking to debut in a performance, exhibition or show. Applicants must be working and living in Scotland. The quality of proposal and applicant's potential will be considered.
Application Process: The application process consists of an online application form, available on the website.
Address: 12 Manor Place, Edinburgh EH3 7DD
Tel: 01312 266051
Email: arts.trust@creativescotland.com
Website: www.artstrustscotland.org.uk

BUSINESS STARTUP GRANT

About: Available to new businesses within the West Dunbartonshire area.
Organization: West Dunbartonshire Council.
Fund Value: Up to £500.
Eligibility Criteria: Businesses must have fewer than 250 employees and be located within West Dunbartonshire.
Application Process: Applicants require a business plan and evidence of any start-up expenditure, such as bank statements.
Address: Garshake Road,

Dumbarton G82 3PU
Tel: 01389 738282
Email: contact.centre@west-dunbarton.gov.uk
Website: www.west-dunbarton.gov.uk

CREATIVE SCOTLAND

About: Targeted specifically at the arts, screen and creative industries in Scotland, Creative Scotland offers numerous programmes and opportunities tailored especially to individuals, groups, touring and festivals, young musicians and much more.
Organization: Creative Scotland.
Fund Value: £1,000–£100,000.
Eligibility Criteria: Each investment opportunity has its own eligibility requirements, details of which can be found on the website. Groups and organizations must be made up of no more than 250 individuals. Applicants must be residing within Scotland (unless otherwise stated).
Application Process: Each investment opportunity and funding scheme has different processes of application, for example, some require a 200-word personal statement. There is a FAQs section on the website. Creative Scotland also operate 'Drop In Surgeries' and 'Open Lines' for more detailed discussions and queries.
Address: 249 West George Street, Glasgow, Glasgow City G2 4QE
Tel: 08456 036000
Email: enquiries@creativescotland.com
Website: www.creativescotland.com

DUNDEE VISUAL ARTISTS & CRAFT MAKERS AWARDS

About: A Dundee-based scheme that aims to support visual artists and craft practitioners in their professional development.

Organization: Leisure & Culture Dundee.

Fund Value: Up to £1,500.

Eligibility Criteria: Visual artist eligibility fields are: drawing, painting, sculpture, print making, photography, moving image and filmmaking. Craft maker eligibility fields are: ceramics, jewellery, metalwork, furniture, wood, glass, lettering, musical instruments, textiles and basket-making. Applicants must be living within the Dundee City Council boundary. Funding will not be awarded to applicants still in full-time education.

Application Process: A downloadable application form is available from the website. Applicants must also provide visual images of their most recent, and most relevant, work (no more than six images).

Address: Leisure & Culture Dundee Headquarters, Central Library, The Wellgate, Dundee DD1 1DB

Tel: 01382 431500

Email: susan.keracher@ leisureandculturedundee.com

Website: www.dvaa.info

EAST LOTHIAN INVESTMENTS (ELI) LTD INTEREST FREE LOAN

About: Provides interest-free loans for start-up businesses or already established businesses that have been trading for a minimum of two years.

Organization: East Lothian Council.

Fund Value: Up to £10,000 for start-up businesses. Up to £25,000 for established businesses with two years of trading.

Eligibility Criteria: Businesses must have their head office based in East Lothian and have fewer than 250 employees.

Application Process: Established businesses must be able to provide three months worth of bank statements and two years of P&L or Balance Sheet accounts. A meeting will then be arranged with the Fund Manager.

Address: John Muir House, Brewery Park, Haddington, East Lothian EH41 3HA

Tel: 01620 827282

Email: economicdevelopment@ eastlothian.gov.uk

Website: www.eastlothian.gov.uk

EAST OF SCOTLAND INVESTMENT FUND (ESIF)

About: ESIF provides financial support for start-up, small and medium-sized businesses that can demonstrate strong commercial promise within the East of Scotland. ESIF was built on the success of WSLF.

Organization: East of Scotland Investment Fund Ltd.

Fund Value: Up to £50,000.

Eligibility Criteria: Businesses must be located in the East of Scotland (more detail of specific areas can be found on the website). Businesses must have fewer than 250 employees.

Application Process: A downloadable application form and personal statement form are available on the website.

Address: Kingdom House, Saltire Centre, Glenroathes, Fife KY6 2AQ

Tel: 01738 448323

Email: donna.menzies@eastscotinvest. co.uk

Website: www.eastscotinvest.co.uk

HELENSBURGH AND LOMOND START-UP GRANT

About: The purpose of this grant is to support the creation of new businesses within the Helensburgh and Lomond area of Argyll and Bute.

Organization: Argyll and Bute Council.

Fund Value: Up to £500.

Eligibility Criteria: The business must be based within Helensburgh and Lomond.

Application Process: Applicants need to register with Business Gateway and prepare a business plan and cash flow forecast. Business Gateway will provide an application form and assist in the development of a concise business plan.

Address: Kilmory, Lochgilphead, Argyll PA31 8RT

Tel: 01546 602127

Email: business.grants@argyll-bute. gov.uk.

Website: www.argyll-bute.gov.uk

NEW BUSINESS START-UP GRANT PROGRAMME (NBSG)

About: The priority of the NBSG is to assist in the creation of new businesses within rural areas that suffer from a fragile economy, such as Orkney.

Organization: Business Gateway.

Fund Value: £1,000–£1,500.

Eligibility Criteria: The company must be located in Orkney and the applicant must reside in Orkney. The company must have no more than 50 employees. The business must be

completely new upon application, with no previous trading.

Application Process: Applicants need to register with Business Gateway, who will assist them in writing a business plan and beginning the application process.

Address: 14 Queen Street, Kirkwall, Orkney KW15 1JE

Tel: 01856 886666

Email: business.gateway@orkney.gov.uk

Website: www.orkney.gov.uk

NORTH HIGHLAND REGENERATION FUND (NHRF)

About: Aimed at start-ups and small established businesses. Designed to enable growth and create jobs within the Dounreay area.

Organization: Nuclear Decommissioning Authority

Fund Value: £5,000–£50,000

Eligibility Criteria: Not available to private individuals. Applicants must be able to provide evidence that the fund will create more jobs within the Dounreay area. Businesses must have fewer than 250 employees.

Application Process: A formal discussion with NHRF to establish eligibility, followed by the completion of a formal application form, along with supporting documentation as requested.

Address: North Highland Regeneration Fund, c/o 66 Princes Street, Thurso, Caithness KW14 7DH

Tel: 01847 500103

Email: enquiries@nhrf.co.uk

Website: www.nhrf.co.uk

OPPORTUNITY FUND

About: This funding scheme is designed specifically for newly established and small businesses within the Highlands that have been unsuccessful in receiving funding from other sources. Loans are low-interest and aftercare is provided.

Organization: Highland Opportunity Ltd.

Fund Value: £1,000–£250,000.

Eligibility Criteria: Any business within the Highlands Council area. Businesses must have fewer than 250 employees.

Application Process: A meeting with a Highland Opportunity Business Advisor will be arranged to discuss the business plan in detail. A downloadable application form is available on the website.

Address: 81a Castle Street, Inverness IV2 3EA

Tel: 01463 228340

Email: info@highland-opportunity.com

Website: www.highland-opportunity.com

PRINCE'S SCOTTISH YOUTH BUSINESS TRUST (PSYBT)

About: The Trust aims to encourage young entrepreneurs living in Scotland, and assist them in establishing or expanding a business. As well as funding, this trust provides advice, training, market support, aftercare and much more.

Organization: Prince's Trust.

Fund Value: £1,000–£30,000.

Eligibility Criteria: Applicants must be aged between 18–25 (up to 30 with a disability) and living in Scotland. Businesses must have fewer than 250 employees.

Application Process: The first step is to get in touch with the Trust via the online enquiry form: a member of the team will then be in touch to discuss the application further.

Address: The Prince's Scottish Youth Business Trust, 15 Exchange Place, Glasgow G1 3AN

Tel: 01412 484999

Email: team@psybt.org.uk

Website: www.psybt.org.uk

SMALL BUSINESS BONUS SCHEME (SBBS)

About: This scheme provides relief discount on business properties that have a combined rateable value of £25,000 or less.

Organization: Business Gateway.

Fund Value: N/A.

Eligibility Criteria: SBBS is available to any Scottish business with properties with a value rate of £25,000 or less.

Application Process: Applications are to be made through the applicant's local authorities, downloadable forms are available on the local authority websites.

Address: St Andrew's House, Regent Road, Edinburgh EH1 3DG

Tel: 08457 741741

Email: ceu@scotland.gsi.gov.uk

Website: www.scotland.gov.uk

SMALL BUSINESS LOAN FUND

About: Aimed at creating and assisting small businesses within Glasgow with the intention of creating more jobs and benefiting the local economy.

Organization: Glasgow City Council.

Fund Value: Up to £30,000 for start-up businesses. Up to £50,000 for established businesses.

Eligibility Criteria: Businesses must be based in a commercial premises within Glasgow and have fewer than 250 employees. Applicants must be able to demonstrate how the loan will benefit the economy of Glasgow and prove that funding was not available from elsewhere.

Application Process: Eligibility must be confirmed via Business Gateway or a Business Council Officer. Applicants are required to submit an application form and start-up businesses need to have a thorough business plan. Established businesses must be able to provide their most recent audit documentation.

Address: Business Support Services, Exchange House, 229 George Street, Glasgow G1 1QU

Tel: 01412 877252

Email: Contact submission form available on website.

Website: www.glasgow.gov.uk

SMALL BUSINESS LOAN SCHEME

About: Aimed at aiding in the creation of new businesses, as well as assisting small and medium-sized businesses that are looking to expand. This scheme provides gap funding in the form of interest-free loans.

Organization: Inverclyde Council.

Fund Value: Up to £5,000.

Eligibility Criteria: The business must be located in Inverclyde. Applicants must be able to provide a thorough business plan and businesses must have fewer than 250 employees.

Application Process: Applications can be made via the contact telephone number or email address provided.

Address: Municipal Buildings, Greenock, Inverclyde PA15 1LY

Tel: 01475 715555

Email: eds.enquiries@inverclyde.gov.uk

Website: www.inverclyde.gov.uk

SOUTH OF SCOTLAND LOAN SCHEME

About: This scheme provides loans for small and medium enterprises (SMEs) with the intention of creating economic growth for the local area.

Organization: WRDC (Enterprise Trust) Ltd.

Fund Value: £5,000–£50,000.

Eligibility Criteria: Businesses must have fewer than 250 employees. Available to businesses based in, or relocating to, the Scottish Boarders or Dumfries and Galloway.

Application Process: Applicants need to register with Business Gateway, who will assist them in writing a business plan and beginning the application process.

Address: WRDC Business Centre, 6–8 Queen Street, Newton Stewart, Wigtownshire DG8 6JL

Tel: 01671 404500

Email: enquiries@wrdc.co.uk

Website: www.wrdc.co.uk

THE INCHES CARR TRUST CRAFT AWARD

About: An award for established artists striving to develop their skills and profession. The bursary is awarded annually to applicants who can demonstrate a career of at least five years in their chosen craft.

Organization: The Inches Carr Trust.

Fund Value: £5,000.

Eligibility Criteria: Professional makers working in Scotland, with a career span of at least five years working within their chosen craft.

Application Process: The application form should be submitted along with a brief description of current projects, example photographs or slides and a proposal outlining the applicant's aspirations should the bursary be awarded to them.

Address: 2 Blackett Place, Edinburgh EH9 1RL

Tel: 01316 672906

Email: Contact submission form available on website.

Website: www.inchescarr.org.uk

WEST OF SCOTLAND LOAN FUND (WSLF)

About: WSLF provides financial support for start-up, small and medium-sized businesses within the West of Scotland that can demonstrate strong commercial promise.

Organization: West of Scotland Loan Fund Ltd.

Fund Value: Up to £50,000.

Eligibility Criteria: Businesses must be located within the West of Scotland (more detail of specific areas can be found on the website). Businesses must have fewer than 250 employees.

Application Process: A downloadable application form and personal statement form are available on the website.

Address: London Road Centre, London Road, Kilmarnock KA3 7BU

Tel: 01563 554851

Email: Contact submission form available on website.

Website: www.wslf.co.uk

SOUTH WEST

BRISTOL ENTERPRISE DEVELOPMENT FUND (BEDF)

About: BEDF provide support and financial lending to start-up businesses within the Bristol and South West region, specifically targeting those who have been rejected funding by traditional sources.

Organization: Bristol Enterprise Development Fund.

Fund Value: Up to £15,000.

Eligibility Criteria: Applicants must employ fewer than 25 employees and must be residing and conducting business in the Bristol and South West region.

Application Process: The website recommends reading online guidelines thoroughly prior to submitting the downloadable application form.

Address: The Coach House, 2 Upper York Street, St. Pauls, Bristol BS2 8QN

Tel: 01179 444700

Email: info@bedf.co.uk

Website: www.bedf.co.uk

CHALK AND CHEESE

About: A Local Action Group initiative designed to encourage and support rural businesses within Dorset whose ventures benefit the local economy.

Organization: Local Action Group.

Fund Value: Discretionary.

Eligibility Criteria: Applicants must be residing and operating within Dorset. Proposals and funding requests must be able to evidence their benefit for the local economy, for example: making use of the local resources or providing employment opportunities.

Application Process: Applicants can download registration documents from the Chalk and Cheese website. Applicants can expect to receive application support throughout this process.

Address: Economic Development, Dorset County Council, County Hall, Dorchester DT1 1XJ

Tel: 01305 228699

Email: sarah.e.harbige@dorsetcc.gov.uk

Website: www.chalkandcheese.org

ENTERPRISING WILTSHIRE AWARDS

About: Aimed at encouraging innovation and ambition within Wiltshire by providing a package of business support and financial support for start-up businesses. The competition features nine categories, the winners each receiving a cash prize of £1,000. The overall winner additionally receives £500 and the title of 'The Enterprising Wiltshire Awards Business of the Year'.

Organization: Wessex Chambers.

Fund Value: Up to £1,500.

Eligibility Criteria: Individuals and business must be located within the county of Wiltshire.

Application Process: The application consists of a simple online form.

Address: Pentagon House, 52 Castle Street, Trowbridge, Wiltshire BA14 8AU

Tel: 01225 355553

Email: chris@wessexchambers.org.uk

Website: www.wessexchambers.org.uk

IGNITE CORNWALL

About: Targeted at entrepreneurs and small business in and around the Cornwall region. The prize fund consists of £100,000 worth of cash, services and support, such as business coaching, radio marketing, PR and Social Media support, training in Search Engine Optimization (SEO), Pay Per Click, Web Analytics and more.

Organization: Oxford Innovation.

Fund Value: £100,000.

Eligibility Criteria: Applicants must be residing and operating within Cornwall and the Scilly Isles; start-up businesses or have been trading for no more than twelve months.

Application Process: Interested applicants can register their interest and attend an optional workshop. Applicants are then required to upload a video pitch onto YouTube.

Address: The Old Chapel, Greenbottom, Chacewater, Truro TR4 8QP

Tel: 01872 300116

Email: ideas@ignitecornwall.com

Website: www.ignitecornwall.com

NEW ENTERPRISE COMPETITION (NEC)

About: Provided by the University of Bristol, this enterprise is targeted at staff, students and alumni, who have graduated within five years. The award provides financial support, educational events and business advice.

Organization: Research and Enterprise Development (RED).

Fund Value: Up to £35,000.

Eligibility Criteria: Applicants must be staff, current students or alumni who graduated within five years of the competition start date.

Application Process: An application form can be download from the University of Bristol website.
Address: 3rd Floor Senate House, Tyndall Avenue, Bristol BS8 1TH
Tel: 01179 288676
Email: Red-Office@bristol.ac.uk
Website: www.bris.ac.uk

SOUTH WEST LOANS FUND

About: The South West Loans fund is provided by SWIG and is aimed to assist small and medium sized enterprises (SEOs) to develop, particularly those in disadvantaged areas who have been refused funding elsewhere.
Organization: South West Investment Group Services Ltd (SWIG)
Fund Value: Small businesses up to £50,000. Medium businesses up to £250,000.
Eligibility Criteria: Applicants must be residing in the South West regions and have been refused funding from traditional sources.
Application Process: Applicants are initially required to complete an eligibility form.
Address: Lowena House, Glenthorne Court, Truro Business Park, Threemilestone TR4 9NY
Tel: 01872 223883
Email: info@ southwestinvestmentgroup.co.uk
Website: www. southwestinvestmentgroup.co.uk

SOUTH WEST MICROCREDIT FUND

About: A fund targeted at new and small businesses in the Plymouth, Bristol and Torbay areas. This fund is specifically targeted at disadvantaged areas where businesses have been unable to source all of their required funding.
Organization: South West Investment Group Services Ltd (SWIG).
Fund Value: Up to £7,500.
Eligibility Criteria: Applicants must be located within Plymouth, Bristol or Torbay. An eligibility submission form can be found on the website to further assess eligibility.
Application Process: Applicants are first required to submit an eligibility form via the website; upon confirmation of eligibility, applicants can then complete and submit a formal application form along with a business plan.
Address: Lowena House, Glenthorne Court, Truro Business Park, Threemilestone TR4 9NY
Tel: 01872 223883
Email: info@ southwestinvestmentgroup.co.uk
Website: www. southwestinvestmentgroup.co.uk

START-UP LOANS

About: SWIGs Start-Up Loans scheme is available to 18–24 year olds within the South West region. As well as financial support, applicants will receive business support and mentoring.
Organization: South West Investment Group Services Ltd (SWIG).
Fund Value: £500-£10,000.
Eligibility Criteria: Applicants must be residing in the South West regions stipulated on the company website. Eligible applicants must be between the ages of 18–24.
Application Process: SWIG will provide applicants with an information pack, including an expression of interested form. Applicants are required to return the filled out form, along with a business plan and financial forecasts.
Address: Lowena House, Glenthorne Court, Truro Business Park, Threemilestone TR4 9NY
Tel: 01872 223883
Email: info@ southwestinvestmentgroup.co.uk
Website: www. southwestinvestmentgroup.co.uk

TEWKESBURY GROWING BUSINESS GRANT

About: Aimed at small business that have been trading for twelve months within the borough of Tewkesbury.
Organization: Tewkesbury Borough Council.
Fund Value: Up to £1,000.
Eligibility Criteria: Businesses must be operating within the Tewkesbury Borough Council area. Applicants must employ fewer than 250 people and be able to match funding by a minimum of 50 per cent.
Application Process: An application form can be download from the website.
Address: Council Offices, Gloucester Road, Tewkesbury GL20 5TT
Tel: 01684 272249
Email: katie.power@tewkesbury.gov.uk
Website: www.tewkesbury.gov.uk

WEST CORNWALL BUSINESS GRANT SCHEME

About: Designed to support micro enterprises within the West Cornwall area in order to improve the local economy and quality of life.

REGIONAL FUNDING SOURCES – WALES

Organization: West Cornwall Local Action Group.
Fund Value: From £1,000.
Eligibility Criteria: Businesses must be new or developing, with fewer than ten employees. Applicants must be located within the West Cornwall area.
Application Process: Eligible applicants are asked to contact Claire Leverton via the provided contact details.
Address: Bickford House, South Wheal Crofty, Station Road, Redruth TR15 3QG
Tel: 07528 983335
Email: clare.leverton@ cornwalldevelopmentcompany.co.uk
Website: www.localactioncornwall. info

WALES

BUDDING BUSINESSES GRANT
About: Promoting economic growth in rural areas of Wales, focusing on business fields such as local food, timber, craft and new creative industries. This grant is available for micro-businesses within the rural wards, as stipulated on the website.
Organization: Caerphilly County Borough Council.
Fund Value: Up to £30,000.
Eligibility Criteria: Businesses located in one of the stipulated areas, employing fewer than ten people.
Application Process: To express an interest in this grant, applicants can contact Countryside and Landscape Services via the contact methods provided.
Address: Countryside and Landscape Service, Pontlanfraith House, Pontlanfraith, Blackwood NP12 2YW
Tel: 01443 838632
Email: countryside@caerphilly.gov.uk
Website: www.caerphilly.gov.uk

CAERPHILLY BUSINESS DEVELOPMENT GRANT
About: For new or established businesses located in Caerphilly County Borough. The grant can provide up to 50 per cent of the investment, up to the value of £2,000.
Organization: Caerphilly County Borough Council.
Fund Value: Up to £2,000.
Eligibility Criteria: Businesses located within Caerphilly county borough, employing fewer than 250 people. Businesses that are eligible for the LIF grant scheme will not be considered.
Application Process: New businesses are required to provide a business plan and a twelve month cash flow forecast. Established businesses are required to provide the previous two years of accounts. Application forms are available for download from the website.
Address: Tredomen Business and Technology Centre, Tredomen Business Park, Ystrad Mynach, Hengoed CF82 7FN
Tel: 01443 815588
Email: info@caerphilly.gov.uk
Website: www.caerphilly.gov.uk

CARMARTHENSHIRE LOTTERY LOAN
About: An interest-free loan available to start-up, small and medium established businesses located within Carmarthenshire. The loan prioritizes enterprises that will benefit the local community in some way, such as creating new jobs.
Organization: Carmarthenshire Lottery Society.
Fund Value: £1,000–£7,500.
Eligibility Criteria: Businesses located within Carmarthenshire, employing fewer than 25 people.
Application Process: Application forms are to be submitted via post along with an administration fee of £25.
Address: Loans Administration, PO Box 80, Carmarthen SA33 5YW
Tel: 01267 221071
Email: Contact submission form available on website.
Website: www.carmarthenshirelottery. co.uk/business-loans

197

CONWY SUPPORTING BUSINESS GRANT

About: For new or established businesses located in Conwy County. The grant can be used for marketing purposes, training or equipment.

Organization: Conwy County Borough Council.

Fund Value: £200–£1,000.

Eligibility Criteria: New business applicants that have been trading for at least three months. Applicants must be living and working in Conwy County.

Application Process: Applicants must register to the Welsh Government – Regional Centre Service Programme. Application forms are to be submitted along with cash flow forecasts and most recent financial account data for pre-established businesses. A written recommendation for a CCBC business advisor is also required.

Address: Conwy Business Centre, Llandudno Junction, Conwy LL31 9XX

Tel: 01492 574525

Email: ecodev@conwy.gov.uk

Website: www.conwy.gov.uk

E-COMMERCE GRANT

About: Aimed at providing funding and support for companies looking to create or improve their use of e-commerce. The grant can be used to assist in the purchase of a domain name, design costs for a website and software. The grant will provided up to 50 per cent of the costs, up to the value of £2,000.

Organization: Rhondda Cynon Taf County Borough Council.

Fund Value: Up to £2,000.

Eligibility Criteria: Established businesses located within Rhondda Cynon Taf.

Application Process: An initial expression of interest is to be submitted via the online application form.

Address: The Pavilions, Cambrian Park, Clydach Vale, Tonypandy CF40 2XX

Tel: 01443 425005

Email: customerservices@rctcbc.gov.uk

Website: www.rctcbc.gov.uk

ENTERPRISE BURSARY

About: Providing funding and support for individuals and groups living in Rural Flintshire or Denbighshire. The grant is available for two categories of people: those aged 16–30 and those over 30 who are currently unemployed. Bursaries may cover up to 80 per cent of the funding cost.

Organization: Cadwyn Clwyd.

Fund Value: Up to £2,000.

Eligibility Criteria: Applicants aged 16–30 and unemployed applicants over the age of 30, living in Rural Flintshire or Denbighshire. Businesses with start-up costs of less than £10,000.

Application Process: Applications can be made by registering to the website and downloading and application form.

Address: Llys Clwyd, Lon Parcwr Business Park, Ruthin, Denbighshire LL15 1NJ

Tel: 01824 705802

Email: admin@cadwynclwyd.co.uk

Website: www.cadwynclwyd.co.uk

HEADS OF THE VALLEYS BUSINESS SEED CAPITAL FUND

About: Helping support the costs of setting up a business for residents living in the Heads of the Valleys area. The grant will provide up to 50 per cent of the investment, up to the value of £2,000.

Organization: Blaenau Gwent County Borough Council.

Fund Value: Up to £2,000.

Eligibility Criteria: Both the business and the applicant must be located in the Heads of the Valleys area. At least one founder or director of the businesses must be employed full time. Businesses must not be established prior to the funding application.

Application Process: Applicants are to provide a clear business plan including a twelve month cash flow forecast.

Address: Municipal Offices, Civic Centre, Ebbw Vale NP23 6XB

Tel: 01495 355713

Email: business.services@blaenau-gwent.gov.uk

Website: www.blaenau-gwent.gov.uk

INNOVO

About: A programme designed to provide financial and business support to people under the age of 31 who would like to set up a business or expand and develop an existing one.

Organization: Neath Port Talbot County Borough Council.

Fund Value: Up to £1,000.

Eligibility Criteria: Applicants under the age of 31.

Application Process: Applicants are invited to contact the Sandfields Young Business Centre for further details on how to apply, contact details are available on the website.

Address: The Quays, Brunel Way, Baglan Energy Park, Neath SA11 2GG

Tel: 01639 765695
Email: innov8@npt.gov.uk
Website: www.npt-business.co.uk

INTERNATIONAL OPPORTUNITIES FUND (IOF)

About: An initiative aimed at encouraging artists and crafters in Wales to explore possibilities abroad and raise the profile of Welsh Arts and Crafts.
Organization: Wales Arts International.
Fund Value: Up to £3,000.
Eligibility Criteria: Professional artists and organizations based in Wales. Applicants must have fewer than 250 employees.
Application Process: Applicants can apply to the scheme all year round, and should expect to be contacted within 3 weeks of submitting the online application. Alternatively, applicants can contact an advisor via the telephone number provided.
Tel: 02920 441367
Email: info@wai.org.uk
Website: www.wai.org.uk

LOCAL INVESTMENT FUND (LIF)

About: The LIF grant is available to start-up and small businesses throughout Wales. The grant is restricted to specific counties, details of which can be found on the website. LIF will cover up to 40% of the investment, up to the value of £10,000
Organization: LIF Cymru.
Fund Value: £1,000–£10,000.
Eligibility Criteria: Businesses located in one of the stipulated areas. Businesses employing fewer than 250 people.

Application Process: Applicants must submit an 'expression of interest' form, which is available on the website.
Tel: 03000 603000
Email: businesssupport@wales.gsi.gov.uk
Website: www.business.wales.gov.uk

NEATH PORT TALBOT LOAN FUND

About: Available to new businesses and existing businesses within the Neath Port Talbot region.
Organization: Neath Port Talbot County Borough Council.
Fund Value: £1,000–£10,000.
Eligibility Criteria: Applicants located in, or relocating to, the Neath Port Talbot region, with fewer than 250 employees. Applicants must demonstrate that their business will create or maintain jobs in the local area.
Application Process: Applicants must simply submit an application form, which can be found on the website.
Address: The Quays, Brunel Way, Baglan Energy Park, Neath SA11 2GG
Tel: 01639 686835
Email: Contact submission form available on website.
Website: www.npt-business.co.uk

ROBERT OWEN AND COMMUNITY BANKING FUND (ROCBF)

About: This fund aims to assist in the growth of the economy throughout Mid Wales and the Borders by financially supporting small businesses and start-up enterprises.
Organization: The Robert Owen Community Banking Fund Ltd.
Fund Value: £500–£20,000.

Eligibility Criteria: Businesses and entrepreneurs located throughout Mid Wales and the Borders.
Application Process: To begin the application process, applicants are invited to contact ROCBF via the telephone number provided to discuss the funding further.
Address: Unit H Vastre Industrial Estate, Newtown, Powys SY16 1DZ
Tel: 08453 138458
Email: Contact submission form available on website.
Website: www.rocbf.co.uk

YOUNG ENTREPRENEURS BURSARY

About: A bursary for young entrepreneurs aged 16–24, located in Wales. The priority of this bursary is to encourage growth of economy in Wales through start-up businesses and job creation.
Organization: Jobs Growth Wales.
Fund Value: £6,000.
Eligibility Criteria: Applicants aged 16–24 living in Wales, who are not in education, training or employment. Pre-start businesses.
Application Process: Applicants are required to register to, and receive business advice from, a recognized support advisor. The application form is to be submitted along with a clear business plan.
Tel: 03000 603000
Email: jobsgrowthwales@wales.gsi.gov.uk
Website: www.business.wales.gov.uk

INDEX

INDEX

INDEX

INDEX

INDEX

INDEX

stitch | craft create business

Stitch Craft Create Business is a great source of **FREE** information and advice for anyone interested in learning how to sell their crafts. We blog several times a week with fantastic advice from experts and case studies of other crafters turning their passion into profit.

> **Join the growing number of crafty entrepreneurs profiting from their membership to our Business Club – with 50% off a 12-month subscription for readers of this book!**

Here's what's included in our Business Club package:

THE CRAFT & CREATIVE START-UP KIT

With clear steps, useful links and expert advice from business guru Emma Jones, this PDF ebook is packed with essential knowledge, relevant case studies and top tips for success. **Download your free copy when you join.**

12 MONTHS' ONLINE DIRECTORY ACCESS

Get the listings from this book in a **handy, searchable online format**. Save your favourites to your profile page so you have their details stored whenever you need them, and can access them wherever you are!

25% OFF OUR FLEXIBLE ONLINE TRAINING COURSES

From starting your craft business from scratch to learning how to use your blog to attract new customers, to harnessing the power of social media to grow your brand, we have a wealth of **online courses** that will excite and inspire you, and help make your craft business a success!

STITCH CRAFT CREATE VIP MEMBERSHIP

Get a guaranteed **10% off ALL products** from Stitch Craft Create to help you stock up for your handmade business, as well as free P&P on all orders over £25. Plus speak to us for personalized deals on volume orders!

• 50% discount •

Normally £25 for a 12-month subscription, we're offering readers of *The Craft Seller's Companion* a 50% discount using code CSCBOOK50 at the checkout.

Visit www.stitchcraftcreate.co.uk/business and click on Join Our Business Club to take advantage of this great offer!

EXCLUSIVE PARTNER OFFERS

Over £500 of offers from 18 different top brands – including Staples, Dell, Vistaprint, Natwest, DHL, Paypal and more – on everything from business cards to software, virtual office space to stationery supplies, to really get you up and running.

www.stitchcraftcreate.co.uk/business

A DAVID & CHARLES BOOK
© F&W Media International, Ltd 2013

David & Charles is an imprint of F&W Media
International, Ltd
Brunel House, Forde Close, Newton Abbot,
TQ12 4PU, UK

F&W Media International, Ltd is a subsidiary
of F+W Media, Inc
10151 Carver Road, Suite #200, Blue Ash,
OH 45242, USA

A catalogue record for this book is available
from the British Library.

ISBN-13: 978-1-4463-0310-8 paperback
ISBN-10: 1-4463-0310-1 paperback

Printed in Italy by G. Canale & C. S.p.A. for:
F&W Media International, Ltd
Brunel House, Forde Close, Newton Abbot,
TQ12 4PU, UK

10 9 8 7 6 5 4 3 2 1

Publisher: Alison Myer
Craft Business Manager: Ame Verso
Desk Editor: James Brooks
Design Manager: Sarah Clark
Designer: Jennifer Stanley
Production Manager: Bev Richardson
Directory compiled by Rebecca Bennett
and Abbie Sawyer
Interviews conducted and edited by
Caroline Taggart

For more great craft business advice,
free ebooks and online education visit:
www.stitchcraftcreate.co.uk/business